SAVING THE ARMY

SAVING THE ARMY

The Life of Sir John Pringle

Morrice McCrae

First published in 2014 by
John Donald, an imprint of Birlinn Ltd

West Newington House
10 Newington Road
Edinburgh
EH9 1QS

www.birlinn.co.uk

ISBN: 978 1 906566 75 3

The publishers gratefully acknowledge the support of
the Royal College of Physicians of Edinburgh
and
the Scottish Society of the History of Medicine
towards the publication of this book

British Library Cataloguing-in-Publication Data
A catalogue record for this book is available on request
from the British Library

Typeset in Garamond by
Koinonia, Manchester
Printed and bound in Britain by
Bell and Bain Ltd, Glasgow

Contents

List of Illustrations   vi
Acknowledgements   viii
Maps   ix

Prologue   1

 1 Early Years   7
 2 The Theory of Medicine: Boerhaave and Pringle   20
 3 Physic, Patronage and Philosophy   30
 4 A Commission in the Army   44
 5 Dettingen: Victory and Catastrophe   59
 6 Fontenoy: Defeat and Triumph   74
 7 Rebellion: A Very Different Campaign   86
 8 Fever in Flanders: The End of the War   101
 9 Observations on the Diseases of the Army   113
10 On Treating the Diseases of Armies   122
11 Studies on Putrefaction and Digestion   132
12 The Raids on Rochefort and St Malo   142
13 The Health of the Army in North America, the Caribbean
   and Britain   151
14 Life in London   163
15 Triumph and Frustration   183

Notes   194
Bibliography   204
Index   207

List of Illustrations

1 Sir John Pringle when he was at the height of his international fame in his middle years. (© The Royal Society)

2 Isaac Newton, who published *Philisophae Naturalis Principa Mathematica* in 1687. (Royal College of Physicians of Edinburgh)

3 Archibald Pitcairn, an Edinburgh physician who became professor of medicine at Leiden in 1682. (Royal College of Physicians of Edinburgh)

4 Herman Boerhaave, the professor of medicine at Leiden in the first years of the eighteenth century when Leiden was the most prestigious medical school in Europe. (Royal College of Physicians of Edinburgh)

5 The Earl of Stair, who commanded the British Army in the first British campaign in the War of the Austrian Succession, and chose Pringle as the army's first Physician General. (National Trust for Scotland)

6 The Battle of Dettingen: the area between Aschaffenburg and Dettingen from which the Pragmatic Army escaped entrapment. (Courtesy of *Military History Monthly*)

7 The Battle of Fontenoy: the area of the battle in which the British infantry fought a celebrated attack but in the end the Pragmatic Army was soundly defeated. (Courtesy of *Military History Monthly*)

8 Prince Charles Edward Stuart, who was summoned by Louis XV from Rome to lead a Jacobite rebellion in Britain which ended at the Battle of Culloden in 1746. (© National Trust Images)

9 The Battle of Culloden: a tired, hungry, poorly equipped and badly led Jacobite army was easily destroyed by a larger,

better trained and better led army commanded by the Duke of Cumberland. (Public domain)

10 The title page of *Observations on the Diseases of the Army*, published in 1752 (image from the seventh edition, 1772). (Royal College of Physicians of Edinburgh)

11 Captain James Cook, who discussed with Pringle the plans he was making for the third of his great exploratory voyages in 1776. (© National Maritime Museum, Greenwich, London)

12 King George III: Pringle was a successful physician to members of the royal family for many years. (© National Portrait Gallery, London)

13 Sir John Pringle in his middle years. (Royal College of Physicians of Edinburgh)

14 Board House of Purfleet: in 1772 the Board of Ordnance asked the Royal Society for advice on the installation of lightning conductors on the Royal Navy's powder magazine at Purfleet. (Royal College of Physicians of Edinburgh)

15 Sir John Pringle in his last years. (Royal College of Physicians of Edinburgh)

16 The box in which the ten volumes of Pringle's Medical Annotations were presented to the Royal College of Physicians in 1781. (Royal College of Physicians of Edinburgh)

17 Pringle's Medical Annotations after many years in the Royal College of Physicians of Edinburgh. (Royal College of Physicians of Edinburgh)

18 One of the volumes of the Medical Annotations after all the volumes had been rebound in calf. (Royal College of Physicians of Edinburgh)

19 Pages from the last volume of the Medical Annotations showing evidence of Pringle's final frustration. (Royal College of Physicians of Edinburgh)

20 Memorial of Sir John Pringle's memorial in Westminster Abbey. (Copyright: Dean and Chapter of Westminster)

Acknowledgements

Sir John Pringle was one of the great physicians of the eighteenth century. In his first campaign as the Physician General of the British Army in the War of the Austrian Succession he saw that the number of soldiers dying of disease was very much greater than the number killed in battle. In his second campaign he introduced practices that prevented this horrendous loss of life. His methods were published in his book *Observations on the Diseases of the Army*. Pringle was made physician to the royal family. He was elected president of the Royal Society and was honoured many times. However, very little has been written about his life. I have been very fortunate in having the enthusiastic support of Sir John Pringle's great-great-great-great-great nephew, James Bruce Pringle. He has been an admirable source of information that could not have been found elsewhere.

I have had, as always, the excellent guidance and help of Iain Milne, the librarian of the Royal College of Physicians of Edinburgh. I have also been well served by the libraries of the Royal Society, the Royal Society of Edinburgh, the University of Edinburgh, Westminster Abbey and by the National Library of Scotland. The text has been read by Iain Donaldson, Estella Dukan, Christine Henderson, Jennifer McCrae and Christine Short, who have all provided very useful guidance and comment. I have also been generously supported by the Scottish Society of the History of Medicine and the Royal College of Physicians of Edinburgh.

In the later chapters of the book I have frequently quoted passages from Sir John Pringle's Medical Annotations. When these ten volumes were left to the library of the Royal College of Physicians of Edinburgh in 1781, Sir John made legal provision that they should never be removed from the library and that what he had written in them should never be made public. Recently Professor Walter Nimmo has donated the funds that have made it possible for these restrictions to be legally set aside. This has allowed me to make full and open use of Pringle's Medical Annotations. I am therefore most grateful to Professor Nimmo.

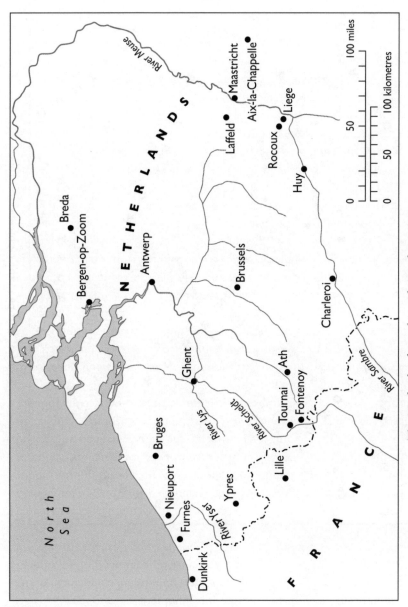

The Netherlands in the eighteenth century

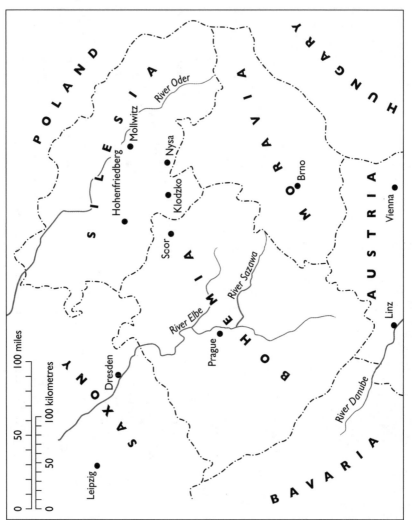

Central Europe in the eighteenth century

Prologue

He himself is subject to his birth
Shakespeare, *Hamlet*, V, iii

The history of John Pringle's family was long, distinguished and turbulent. The first of his ancestors to be noticed was Robert de Hoppryngill.[1] On his return from the last of the Crusades in 1270, the Archbishop of St Andrews awarded him lands in the Scottish Borders and for the next five centuries his descendants played a full part in the history of Scotland. When Alexander III died in 1286 the Hoppryngill family was drawn into the long and bloody struggle to preserve the independence of Scotland. In 1296, Robert's grandson, Elys de Hoppryngill, signed the Ragman Roll, the instrument by which the gentry of Scotland accepted that suzerainty over Scotland had passed to King Edward I of England. Within a few years, resistance to Edward's ambitions had grown again in Scotland. The Hoppryngills served with the Lord of Douglas when he fought at the side of William Wallace at Stirling Bridge in 1297 and beside Robert the Bruce at Bannockburn in 1314. Later, the Hoppryngills were with the Lord of Douglas at the Battles of Halidon Hill in 1333 and Neville's Cross in 1346. When Sir William, Lord of Douglas, was made the Earl of Douglas in 1357, Hoppryngills became his squires; later generations of the family continued to serve the Earls of Douglas for almost a century.

The family's association with the Earls of Douglas ended in 1455 when the 9th Earl broke with King James II and was attainted and his lands were forfeited. The members of the Hoppryngill family remained loyal to the king and for half a century they were prominent at the courts of James IV and James V. They were at James IV's side when the Scottish army was destroyed at Flodden in 1513. Thomas Hoppryngill, the principal trumpeter, sounded the charge and was at the king's side when he died. David Hoppryngill and two of his brothers also died in the battle.

The wars between Scotland and England did not end with Scotland's defeat at Flodden. Some 40 years later, frustrated in his attempt to arrange the marriage of the infant Queen of Scots to his own young son, Henry VIII of England sent an army to lay waste the Scottish Borders and destroy the abbeys of Dryburgh, Jedburgh, Kelso and Melrose.

In all these years from 1286 until 1550 armies from both Scotland and England had marched again and again across the Borders leaving behind a devastated land in which a settled existence was hardly possible. To rebuild a house was futile when it might be ruined again within weeks; to raise crops was pointless as they might be burned before they could be harvested. The Borders became a land in which the people's subsistence depended not on the cultivation of the land but on the possession of cattle that could be hidden away in secret places in the hills. To survive, Border families sent bands of armed and mounted reivers (raiders) to ransack the houses and carry off the cattle of better endowed neighbours on both sides of the border.

From the fifteenth century attempts had been made to enforce some degree of order. Matching sections of the territory on the Scottish side and on the English side of the Border were drawn and labelled as the West, Middle and East Marches and a Warden was appointed to each of the Marches to enforce the law. After the fall of the Earl of Douglas in 1455, his former squire, George Hoppryngill, was appointed Master Ranger of the Tweed Ward in an attempt to bring him back into the service of the king. His great-nephew William was later made a Deputy Warden of the Scottish Middle March[2] and Constable of Cessford Castle. Like so many Wardens and Deputy Wardens of the time, the Pringles often found it expedient to operate on both sides of the law. In 1515, Dand Pringle, William's grandson, as Constable of Cessford Castle, led 400 well-armed horsemen on a raid into England and returned laden with plunder that he could share with the Warden of the Middle March, Sir Andrew Ker of Cessford.[3] The Pringles continued to balance their duties as officers of the law against their need for economic survival until the lawlessness of the Borders gradually declined in the last years of the sixteenth century.

The reassertion of the rule of law in the Borders began in the reign of James VI. When, in 1603, he became both King of Scotland and King of England, the pacification of the Borders was part of his plan to bring his two kingdoms together in peace. As the violence and bloodshed in the Borders subsided, the sons of the gentry were no longer needed as armed men ready to defend their families and their property; those who could not expect to succeed to family lands now looked for employment in more peaceful professions. In 1605, Pringle's great-great-grandfather, Robert

Pringle, became Treasurer Depute for Scotland and Member of Parliament for Roxburghshire.

The Pringle family adapted to the new, more peaceful way of life in the Borders but within a few generations they had become embroiled in a conflict very different from that experienced by their ancestors. In the 1560s, the early leaders of the Reformation in Scotland had been content that, having thrown off the authority of Rome, their Church should continue to be governed by a hierarchy of bishops and to have the king as its head. But by the 1580s a new generation of Church leaders were intent on more fundamental reform. They would not accept the guidance of bishops nor would they have the king as head of their Church. King James saw that to give such independent status to the Kirk would be to allow the creation of a state within the state. As King of Scotland and later as King of Great Britain, he tried peacefully but unsuccessfully to contain the ambition of the Kirk by Acts of Parliament.[4] But his successor, Charles I, was ready to compel the Church in Scotland to make the changes that it had refused to make for his father. First he ordered that the Church of Scotland must use a liturgy in line with that used by the Church of England. In November 1636, he ordered the Privy Council in Scotland to see to it that two copies of a new book of public service, a version of the *Book of Common Prayer* used in England, were acquired by every parish in Scotland and that its liturgy was followed at every church service. This command was resisted. The Scottish people in their thousands joined in signing a National Covenant in which they swore to 'continue in the obedience of the doctrine and discipline of the Kirk, and to defend the same, according to our vocation and power, all the days of our lives'.

In 1639 and again in 1640, the Covenanters raised armies that forced the king to make concessions. But soon the quarrel between king and Covenanters became merged with the civil war that had broken out in England; in 1649, the English Parliament executed the king and created a republican Commonwealth that included Scotland. The Commonwealth lasted for only 11 years. In 1660, the monarchy was restored. When Charles II visited Scotland after his years of exile, he was welcomed in Edinburgh and 'magistrates and citizens alike celebrated this great deliverance'.[5]

But for the Covenanters there was to be no deliverance. Like his father, Charles II claimed the right to rule as the head of a Church in Scotland in 'harmony with the government of the churches of England and Ireland'.[6] All ministers of the Church in Scotland were required to accept the governance of bishops and to conform to the liturgy approved by the king. The majority of the ministers complied and were allowed to continue in their parishes. But over 300, most of them based in the Borders and the south-west of Scotland, remained faithful to the Covenant and found themselves barred from their churches. Many of them continued to preach in the homes of fellow Covenanters or at conventicles held in the open air. Ministers who dared to preach at these meetings were arrested and imprisoned. Nevertheless, conventicles continued to be held and continued to be dispersed by ruthless squadrons of dragoons. The Covenanters armed themselves and formed an army to march on Edinburgh to present to Parliament a petition demanding an end to the persecution that they continued to suffer. When only eight miles from Edinburgh, the Covenanter army was easily defeated; many were shot as they fled; 200 were captured and taken to Edinburgh where 51 were executed. An army of 3,000 foot and 8 troops of cavalry was sent to crush the heart of the Covenanting movement in the Borders and the south-west. Suspects were tortured; those 'proven' to be Covenanters were arrested; many were executed; others were banished to the West Indies. Nevertheless, hundreds of Covenanters continued the struggle. There was a second rising in 1679, but after seven weeks it came to an end when the Covenanters were routed at Bothwell Bridge.

Pringle's forebears had been among the first to sign the National Covenant in 1638. As loyal subjects of the Crown, they had peacefully resisted the persecution of Presbyterianism during the reign of Charles I. During the years of the Commonwealth they had been able to worship in peace. But when Charles II was restored to the throne in May 1660 and the persecution of the Covenanters was resumed, Pringle's great-grand-uncle, Walter Pringle of Greenknowe, was among the first to suffer. He was arrested and imprisoned for a time in Edinburgh Castle. He was arrested again in July 1664 and was fined the vast sum of £3,000. He was released only to be rearrested and confined, first in Edinburgh and later in Elgin. A year later, after paying a second large fine, he was released into house arrest at his home at Greenknowe in the Borders; his confinement there lasted until his death.

Even while Walter Pringle of Greenknowe was in prison, Pringle's forebears continued their support for the National Covenant. The family worshipped at conventicles in the open. They gave refuge to Covenanters being hunted by the forces of the Crown. They provided them with legal help when they were put on trial. Pringle's great-uncle, Walter Pringle of Craigcrook, had graduated in law at Leiden in 1661.[7] In Edinburgh, he became recognised as the most effective of the advocates acting on behalf of the Covenanters. He was suspended from the bar in 1671 but he was restored in time to defend the Covenanters taken prisoner in 1679 at the Battle of Bothwell Bridge and later to appear for the Marquis of Argyll at his trial for treason and perjury. Argyll was executed.

The sympathies of the Pringle family did not go unnoticed. In 1679, the king's brother, James, Duke of York, became High Commissioner in Scotland and, in the three years of his rule, known to history as the 'Killing Times', the persecution of the Covenanters became even more ruthless. Even those who were in sympathy with the Covenanters but had remained unshaken in their loyalty to the Crown became victims. Pringle's uncle, Robert Pringle, thought it wise to take refuge in the Netherlands. But he returned when William of Orange invaded England to lead the Glorious Revolution of 1688. Robert Pringle was with him when he crossed the Channel. When William of Orange became William III of Great Britain, Robert Pringle was made Deputy Secretary of State for Scotland and Secretary of War in the new British government. By then the struggle between Covenanters and the Stuart kings was over.

In 500 years of Scotland's history, Pringle's family had shown courage and efficiency in their efforts to overcome the troubles of the time. They had made powerful alliances and could rely on the support of powerful friends and they had been guided by the principles of their religious faith. John Pringle had inherited a full share of the family's strengths. However, he was born in 1707, the year of the Union of the Scottish and English Parliaments. He lived in Great Britain, a new nation with, for him, strange new ways of living. He served in a British army which had, for him, unfamiliar values. He became a physician looking for something new and more rational at a time when medical practice was still guided by theories that had hardly changed for 2,000 years. He used the qualities that had always served his family well.

ONE

Early Years

Train up a child in the way that he should go and when he is old he will not depart from it.

Proverbs 22:6

By the middle years of the eighteenth century Pringle had become the most distinguished physician in London. He had been made a baronet. He was physician to King George III. He was President of the Royal Society. His achievements had been honoured across Europe.

It might be readily assumed that he was meant for such a life. Born in Scotland's Border country on 10 April 1707, he was a son of Sir John Pringle, 2nd Baronet and 3rd Baron of Stichill and the fourth generation of his family to live in the ancient Stichill House in Roxburghshire.[1] When Pringle's great-great-grandfather Robert Pringle purchased the lands and barony in 1628, the property included the whole parish of Stichill. In 1632, he acquired three more properties in Liddesdale in Roxburghshire; in 1639, he added four more in Berwickshire. In 1667, Pringle's great-grandfather, the first baronet, inherited Newhall in Selkirkshire and later acquired more land in Liddesdale. When Pringle was born, his father owned land in four counties.

The Pringles of Stichill were the senior cadet family of the long-established Pringle clan. The head of the clan, who still used the original name and style, was John de Hoppryngill of that Ilk; he still held the clan's original lands of Hoppryngill and Burnhouse in the Vale of Gala. The other cadet families, the Pringles of Smailholm, of Torwoodlee, of Whytbank, of Greenknowe and of Clifton were all cousins of the Pringles of Stichill. By marriage the Pringles of Stichill were related to an even larger circle of the Scottish nobility. For almost 300 years the Pringles had been allied to the Kers of Cessford, later the Earls of Roxburghe; and for over 200 years, the Pringles of Stichill had close ties with the Earls of Home. In normal times Pringle might have been expected to enjoy a secure, affluent and privileged childhood. But these were not normal times.

In 1695, bad weather and ruined harvests had caused great scarcity across Scotland. The rental incomes of landowners, including Pringle's father, collapsed completely. As bad weather continued in the last years of the century, scarcity worsened into famine. In parts of the country as many as one in four of the population died. The failure of the grain crops was a disaster compounded by a deadly disease among the cattle. Grain had been the country's chief overseas export but cattle had been the chief export to England. The lack of both grain and cattle added further damage to Scotland's already damaged economy; since 1688 England's wars with France had severely disrupted Scotland's access to her trading partners in Europe.

In June 1695, the Scottish Parliament passed an Act launching the Company of Scotland. This was intended as the first step in the creation for Scotland of an overseas trading empire on the model of the trading empire already enjoyed by England. The Act gave the Company powers that included the right to take possession of any 'uninhabited territories'. The Act received royal assent but it did not state where these uninhabited territories were to be found. When it emerged that the intention was to establish a trading colony in the Spanish Americas, King William III was grievously embarrassed and alarmed. The childless King Charles II of Spain was dying and there were two rival claimants to the throne. If the claim of the Archduke of Austria were to be successful, Spain could be expected to remain neutral in France's wars with both William's England and William's Dutch Republic. However, if the chosen candidate were to be the Duke of Anjou, the grandson of Louis XIV of France, the vast Spanish empire would fall into the hands of William's greatest enemy, the King of France. At this critical time William III could not afford to antagonise Spain by allowing his 'other' kingdom of Scotland to seize territory and establish a colony in the Spanish Americas. He therefore made sure that no English capital would be invested in the Company of Scotland.

Nevertheless, when the Company's subscription book was opened in February 1696, Scotland's nobility, landed gentry, merchants and professional men rushed to invest; within two weeks the total issue of £400,000 had been taken up. The Company's expedition to establish a trading colony at Darien on the Isthmus of Panama set sail in July 1698. However, the expedition had been badly planned and ineptly managed. At Darien the climate was very unhealthy for the Scots and the natives had very little interest in what they had brought to sell. Supply ships failed to arrive and, after little over a year, half of the would-be colonists had died of starvation or disease. Even as their miseries increased, the governors of the nearest

English possessions, including Jamaica, had issued an edict sent from London:

> In His Majesty's Name and by command, strictly to command his Majesty's subjects . . . that they do not presume on any pretence whatsoever, to hold any correspondence with the said Scots, nor to give them any assistance of arms, ammunition, provisions or any other necessities either of themselves or by any others for them or by any of their vessels or of the English nation, as they will answer the contempt of His Majesty's command at their utmost peril.[2]

By 1701, the Darien Scheme had failed utterly with the loss of a great part of Scotland's investment capital. Landowners who had already suffered from the repeated destruction of their harvests and the loss of their rental income were again badly affected; many were ruined. By 1707, the experience of the Darien Scheme had confirmed many in Scotland in the belief that the economy of the country could only flourish if Scotland operated, not in conflict with the interests of England, but in full partnership with England under one Parliament.

Attempts to unite Scotland and England under one Parliament had been made in 1667, 1670 and 1690, but there had been little enthusiasm for the idea among the members of the Parliament in Westminster. As Edward Seymour explained in the House of Commons: 'Scotland is a beggar and whoever marries a beggar gets a louse for her portion.' For its part, the Scottish Parliament feared that in a complete union with England there could only be one national Church and that once again episcopal governance and an alien liturgy would be imposed on the Church in Scotland.

However, in 1701, the English Parliament had found good reason to demand the abolition of the Scottish government and the creation of a British Parliament in London. James VII and II had been driven from the throne in 1688 and had fled to exile in France. On James's death in 1701, Louis XIV of France had formally recognised his son James as his legitimate successor to the throne of England, Scotland and Ireland as King James VIII and III. The English Parliament passed an Act of Settlement that laid down that should Princess Anne, the heir to the throne, die without leaving an heir, as now seemed inevitable, the succession would devolve on the next Protestant in line, James VI and I's granddaughter, Sophia, the Electress of Hanover. But no such Act was passed by the Scottish Parliament. This left open the possibility that, on Anne's death, the Scottish Parliament might recall the Catholic James Stuart, now the Pretender James VIII and III, from exile and attempt to restore him to the throne. Such an attempt would be vigorously resisted in Scotland as well as in England and could not succeed without the support of an invading foreign army. Such an invasion was conceivable; war had just broken out between England and France.[3]

By 1702, Queen Anne had succeeded to the throne, but she was over 40, in poor health and the last of her children had died in 1700. The question of who should succeed her in Scotland had become urgent. The Privy Council decided that the answer was the abolition of the Parliament of Scotland. The proposal caused riots in Edinburgh and protests and civil disturbances in many towns across Scotland. The Privy Council ordered the movement of troops to the Border 'to be in readiness in case the ferment should continue to give any further disturbance to the public peace'.[4] The presence of troops on the Border was taken as a signal that, if necessary, the abolition of the Scottish Parliament would be achieved by force. Public protest subsided. In 1705, the House of Commons in England recommended to Queen Anne that commissioners be appointed to negotiate for a union of the parliaments of England and Scotland. On 1 May 1707, three weeks after Pringle was born, the Union with Scotland Act of the English Parliament and the Union with England Act of the Scottish Parliament together made Scotland and England one nation. In London, the day was celebrated by Queen Anne and the former members of the two Parliaments were all 'in the greatest splendour'.[5] In Edinburgh, the guns fired a formal salute from the castle, but in Scotland generally there was little rejoicing.

For decades union with England did nothing to ease Scotland's poverty. In recognition of the damage that had been done by the Darien Scheme, the new Parliament had undertaken to pay reparations of £398,000 ('The Equivalent') to Scotland, but payment was slow in coming. Much worse was the sharp increase in the tax burden on Scotland. In 1711, excise duties were imposed on beer, linen and salt; the cost of salt doubled. In 1713, a malt tax was imposed that would have greatly increased the price of ale, the most popular drink in Scotland at that time. The public protests were so furious that for a time the tax was not enforced, but from 1715 it was enforced in full. The Union had not proved to be the expected miracle cure for Scotland's poverty. For over 20 years Sir John Pringle's tenants had difficulty in scratching subsistence from the land. While Pringle was growing up, his father had land but little money.

Union with England had not only failed to relieve Scotland's poverty, the whole affair had opened up a bitter divide within Scotland. That divide caused the Pringle family a painful conflict of loyalties. At that time political leaders drew their support, not from disciplined party machines, but from groups brought together in alliances based on family loyalties and shared personal interests. Generations of the Pringle family had been close to the Earls of Home.[6] But the Earl of Home of the time had been one of the leading opponents of the Union. As this had been a cause that Pringle's father had refused to join, the relationship had dissolved. The Pringle family had long-standing family ties with the Kers of Cessford now headed, not by an earl, but by a Duke of Roxburghe. Roxburghe had been rewarded for the leading part he had played in achieving the Union for Scotland. Pringle's father had also looked to the Union as the answer to Scotland's poverty. His alliance with Roxburghe had acquired a new and shared political purpose.

Roxburghe was not only an able politician. He was 'a man of good sense improven by so much reading and learning that he was perhaps the best accomplished young man in Europe'[7] before the Union and a member of the Privy Council after it. Already at the age of 27 he had been made a Fellow of the Royal Society; he was a friend of Sir Isaac Newton[8] and other Fellows of the Society. In the eighteenth century no professional or public career could flourish without patronage and the patronage of Roxburghe was always ready to sustain and promote the Pringles of Stichill.

Roxburghe had been one of the leaders of a new political party. At first, the party was no more than a small group of friends and allies of the Marquis of Tweeddale. Tweeddale had been made Chancellor of Scotland on the accession of William III, but, in 1696, he had offended the king by taking part in the promotion of the Darien Scheme and had been dismissed from office. The Marquis of Tweeddale died in 1697, but his group of supporters continued to grow; under the leadership of the Earl of Roxburghe the group had grown into a new political party of some two dozen members. There were at that time two major political parties in Scotland. The Court Party was in effect the servant of the government in London, dedicated to the promotion of government policy in Scotland. The Country Party was the party of opposition, a loose federation of groups each with its own interests and objectives. For a time the new party was regarded as yet another small party of opposition. However in 1704, in a sudden *volte face,* it declared its support for the government and the Union of the Parliaments. In scorn the party was labelled the 'Squadrone Volante' (the Flying Squadron). The name was adopted and, as the Squadrone Volante, the new party continued to flourish. In the election of 1715 both the Court Party and the Country Party lost ground and the Squadrone Volante emerged as a party of influence. In the years that followed the Country Party faded and the Squadrone Volante became Scotland's second party. Although only the second party, it was never without influence and during his early career Pringle could rely on having its patronage.

However, political patronage was not required during Pringle's earliest years. He was educated at home under the careful direction of his father. His tutors taught him what his father considered appropriate for a youngest son who must expect to make his own way in life. In 1722, he sent Pringle to the University of St Andrews where, at St Leonard's College, he would be under the careful eye of his father's cousin, Francis Pringle. The 'able and attractive'[9] Francis Pringle had been a Professor of Philosophy at St Leonard's since 1699; from 1702 he had also been the 'fixed'[10] university Professor of Greek. For some six months, Pringle was happy at St Andrews, but, suddenly, in April 1723, his father died.

Pringle was the youngest of his father's six children and for some years his brothers and sisters had all been living away from Stichill House. Gilbert had married a daughter of Hoppryngill of that Ilk and was living in Edinburgh. Wilfred was practising as an advocate in Edinburgh. His sister Katherine had married William Hamilton of Bangour, the son of the poet. His sister Margaret had married Sir James Hall of Dunglass, the founder of experimental geology. Robert, his oldest brother, had now become the master of all the Stichill lands; six months after his father's death he married and occupied Stichill House. Pringle had been somewhat solitary at Stichill House while his father had been alive. Now that his father had died he felt truly alone.

Pringle was at St Leonard's for five years. In his first year he studied Greek and Latin; in his second year, logic; in his third year, ethics, rhetoric and physics (Aristotle); in his fourth year, physics and pneumatics (Doctrine of the Holy Ghost). He devoted his fifth and last year to the study of the works of Sir Francis Bacon. Then, at the unusually advanced age of 20, in October 1727 he moved to Edinburgh to study medicine.

The great majority of medical practitioners at the time were surgeons who had been taught their craft as apprentices and practised as members of a craft guild. Pringle's great-uncle, James Pringle, a successful surgeon-apothecary in Cupar in Fife, had been trained as a surgeon in Edinburgh according to the syllabus set out in the Seal of Cause of the Incorporation of Surgeons and Barbers of Edinburgh in 1505. Apprentices were required to be literate in Latin, able to read the aphorisms of Hippocrates; they had to acquire practical knowledge of anatomy from the dissection of human cadavers; and they had to serve one of the Masters of the Incorporation for no less than seven years. As apprentices their duties included 'the application of sear clothes to dead bodies, all manual operations and applications about living bodies and the curing of tumours, wounds, ulcers, luxations, fractures and the curing of virolls'.[11]

James Pringle had also trained as an apothecary. During his apprenticeship he was taught the skills involved in the preparation and dispensing of medicines under the supervision of a craft guild, the Incorporation of Surgeons and Barbers in Edinburgh.[12] As a surgeon-apothecary, James Pringle was one of the most valued medical practitioners of the day, particularly welcomed in small towns and rural areas where the local population was too small to provide employment for both a surgeon and an apothecary. However, Pringle did not choose to follow his great-uncle and make his career as a surgeon-apothecary but to follow a cousin, Francis Pringle, and become a physician.

Physicians were few in Scotland. Francis Pringle was one of only a dozen then practising in Edinburgh, the largest and most prosperous town in the country; less than half that number practised in Glasgow; in Aberdeen there had been fewer than 20 physicians in practice during the whole of the previous century. In rural Scotland physicians were almost unknown. By tradition physicians often had part of their practical training as apprentices, but they acquired the greater part of their medical education in the library and the classroom of a university. For many centuries their medical education had been essentially the study of the ancient classical texts of Hippocrates (410–370 BC) and Galen (AD 130–210). The leading university medical schools in Europe also provided instruction in botany, chemistry and anatomy. A physician's licence to practise was, in effect, his medical degree from a respected university.

Scotland's medieval universities, St Andrews (1411), Glasgow (1451) and King's College, Aberdeen (1494), had, at their foundations, been granted the privilege of awarding the degree of Doctor of Medicine. Glasgow did not have a medical school but had the distinction of being the first Scottish university to award a medical degree in 1469. Andrew Garleis was awarded MD *honoris causa*, but very few such degrees were awarded by Glasgow in the next 300 years. St Andrews did not have a medical faculty but made a practice of awarding MD degrees to medical graduates of other prestigious universities or on the recommendation of two or more respected physicians and the payment of a fee. King's College, Aberdeen, was the first university in Britain to make any provision for the teaching of medicine. James IV, the founder of the university had made a grant of lands to endow the appointment of a Mediciner (Professor of Medicine). However, few of those who held the position made any real attempt to teach; those who did, taught medicine only as part of the course of general studies thought appropriate for the education of a gentleman. At King's College the great majority of medical degrees were awarded as a mark of distinction for men who had already made their mark in practice. At the beginning of the eighteenth century neither of Scotland's two Post-Reformation universities, Edinburgh (1503) and Marischal College, Aberdeen (1593) had medical faculties nor had they ever awarded medical degrees.

Until the eighteenth century, Scotland's physicians had studied at the leading university medical schools of Continental Europe (Bologna, Padua, Montpellier and Paris) or more recently at universities in northern Europe (Leiden, Rheims, Angers, Orange and Harderwyck). The first move to have a university medical school in Scotland came with the foundation of the Royal College of Physicians of Edinburgh in 1681. One of the College's earliest objectives was the creation of a medical school at Edinburgh's university.

In 1685, the Royal College of Physicians was able to persuade the university to appoint three of its fellows, Sir Robert Sibbald, Archibald Pitcairn and James Halket, as its first Professors of Medicine. But before a full faculty of medicine could be created the project was brought to an end by the 'Glorious Revolution' of 1688 which deposed the Catholic King James VII and II and set the Protestant King William III on the throne. The new government ordered a very Presbyterian 'visitation' on the university. Sibbald had recently converted to Roman Catholicism, Pitcairn and Halket were both Episcopalian and therefore 'erroneous in doctrine'; all three were found unacceptable and the university was obliged to discard them.

Over the next 20 years various more liberal reforms were introduced and the fortunes of Edinburgh University improved. But still the university did not have a faculty of medicine. Then, in February 1724, a group of young physicians, John Rutherford (Rheims, 1722), Andrew Sinclair (Angers, 1722), Andrew Plummer (Leiden, 1722) and John Innes (Padua, 1722), formally petitioned the Town Council, as the patrons of the university, 'to institute the professing of Medicine in all its branches in the College

[University][13] of Edinburgh'. The four had been elected Fellows of the Royal College of Physicians of Edinburgh only three weeks before. Nevertheless, the College accepted their joint application. In response the Town Council passed an Act stating:

> It would be of great advantage to this College, City and Country that Medicine in all its branches should be professed here by such number of professors of the science as may by themselves promote students to their degrees with as great a solemnity as is done in any other College or University at home or abroad. The council does therefore unanimously appoint Doctors Andrew Sinclair and John Rutherford to be professors of the Theory and Practice of Medicine, Doctors Andrew Plummer and John Innes to be Professors of Medicine and Chemistry in the College of Edinburgh; with full power to all of them to profess and teach Medicine in all its branches, to examine candidates and to do every other thing requisite and necessary to the graduation of doctors of medicine.

In 1720, the Town Council had appointed Alexander Monro to teach at Surgeons' Hall as Professor of Anatomy; the Town Council now invited him to move from Surgeons' Hall to teach at the university. There was also Charles Alston, a Fellow of the College of Physicians, who had been appointed in 1721 by the Town Council as a Professor of Botany to teach apprentice surgeons; he too was appointed to teach at the university. The Principal of the university informed the College of Physicians that there was now 'a sufficient number of professors to make a Faculty of Medicine'. Although only Andrew Plummer had graduated at Leiden, all six of the new professors had studied there for some time. It was the news of the creation of this new Leiden-trained medical faculty that attracted Pringle to study medicine at Edinburgh.

However, in their first years, not all of the professors of the university's new Faculty of Medicine were found to meet the expectations of their students. One student commented that: 'Andrew Sinclair had the easiest and best way of expressing himself in Latin of any man I ever knew. He was the most esteemed of the Professors of Medicine. He made most difficult things in physiology perfectly plain.' However, John Rutherford 'was what we call a dry-man without perspicuity or readiness of gracefulness'. John Innes 'was thought to be a contemptible sort of man by many men of good parts. He obscured what was plain in itself by a multitude of words. He began with

Boerhaave's aphorisms and went through all the external diseases the length of De Morbis Internis.' Andrew Plummer was 'a little black shackling man. He followed Boerhaave in most things. I read along with him [during his lectures] Shaw's translations of Boerhaave's notes which I found to be a mighty good book and in which is to be found the most material things of that College.'[14] This last was the chief cause of the students' disappointment; it seemed to them that their new professors in Edinburgh could tell them nothing of the new medical teaching being developed at Leiden that they could not find out for themselves in Boerhaave's published texts. As Boerhaave had been teaching at Leiden for over 20 years and was already 56 years old, Pringle decided, after only one year at Edinburgh, to go at once to Leiden to study medicine and learn from the master while there was still time.[15]

When Pringle arrived at Leiden, he entered what was for him a very different world. In 1727, Scotland had not yet recovered from the deprivation of the 1690s; its traditional farming methods still produced barely enough for the subsistence of the farmers. Union with England had not yet yielded the increases in trade and commerce that had been expected and the taxes imposed by the government in London continued to increase. Scotland was still a poor country and the size of its population had hardly increased in forty years. Less than ten per cent of Scotland's population lived in towns; Edinburgh with some 22,000 people crowded within its crumbling walls was still by far Scotland's largest town. It was 27 years since anyone had been executed for blasphemy, but Calvinism was still strong and in many communities it was oppressive. Across Scotland differences in religious affiliation persisted and still implied difference in politics. In the north-east and in Edinburgh where the Episcopalian faith had always been strong, there were thousands of loyal Jacobites[16] who still hoped for the return of the Stuart dynasty to the throne.

In Holland (one of the United Provinces of the Netherlands) Pringle found one of the wealthiest and most cosmopolitan countries in Europe. It was a hub of industry and trade and, with over half of its population living in towns, it was the most urbanised country in Europe.[17] Leiden had a population larger than Edinburgh's yet, to the wonder of one visitor from Scotland, it was 'the quietest and cleanest town' he had ever known.[18] And for over a century Scottish students, whether Calvinist, Covenanter or Episcopalian, had come to Leiden to study law or medicine at an internationally renowned university that had enjoyed religious diversity and intellectual freedom for half a century. This was a society in which Pringle quickly came to feel at home. The University of Leiden had been founded in 1575. Only a year before, during the 80-year-long Dutch War of Independence, the people of Leiden had withstood four months of siege by a Spanish army commanded by the merciless Duke of Alva. Leiden had fought on long after every other rebel town had surrendered. As a reward, the leader of the revolt against Spanish domination, William the Silent, Prince of Orange, great-grandfather of the future King William III of Great Britain, offered the people of the town either ten years of freedom from taxation or a university. They chose to have a university. Until then the only university in the Netherlands was at Louvain in the Spanish Netherlands (now Belgium). As a Roman Catholic institution, Louvain had not been open to Protestants, not even to Protestant students from the United Provinces. The new university at Leiden was founded as a Protestant institution, but it was unique amongst all other universities of the time in that students of all religions, including Catholics and Jews, were allowed to study there. As a result, large numbers of students from all parts of the western world flocked to Leiden to study under some of the most famous professors in Europe. By the early decades of the eighteenth century there were some 900 matriculated students at the university and of these over 40 per cent were 'foreign' students. English-speaking students from Scotland, England, Ireland, America and the West Indies came to study theology or law but especially to study medicine. Leiden had displaced Padua as the leading medical school in Europe. [19]

Students who paid the necessary fees and matriculated became full members of the university and enjoyed a number of privileges including open access to the university library and freedom from paying tax on their wine and beer. But only a minority of medical students from Scotland matriculated. Jacobite students, for whom Leiden was still a place of refuge from a hostile government in London, could not allow their names to appear on any public record. To other young gentlemen visiting Leiden briefly as part of a polite education but with no more than a dilettante interest in medicine, membership of the university seemed unnecessary. Of the other Scottish students, few could afford to stay long at Leiden as the cost of living there was very high (over £100 per annum).[20] Most avoided the expense of matriculation at Leiden and, after spending only a limited time there, completed their studies at the less expensive universities at Utrecht, Harderwyck, Rheims, Orange, or Angers.

Nevertheless, there was always a coterie of Scots at Leiden spending their leisure together and, on Sundays, attending divine service together at the

English (i.e. English Language) Church. The minister, the Reverend Thomas Gowan, was unfailing in his frequent visits to the Scottish students at their lodgings; they were probably unaware that one of his duties at Leiden was to inform the government in London of the presence and activities of Jacobite activists and open sympathisers.[21]

However, Pringle's family had openly welcomed Scotland's union with England and were known to be staunchly loyal to the new monarchy. There could be no reason for Pringle to hide from the attentions of government spies. He did not confine himself to the close circle of Scottish students but enjoyed to the full the advantage of being a member of the large multinational and multilingual community at Leiden. He learned to speak Dutch, French and German and became proficient enough to be in demand as a translator, both within the university and between foreign students studying at the university and the local population. But he did not neglect his studies nor did he fail to establish friendships that were to last for many years.

For medical students the academic years at Leiden began in the third week of September. During term time there were public lectures in the university auditorium on Mondays, Tuesdays, Thursdays and Fridays; from seven to eight o'clock, Professor Adrian van Royen lectured on botany; from nine to ten, Professor Herman Boerhaave lectured on clinical medicine; from two until three, Professor David Glaubius lectured on chemistry; and from three to four, Professor Bernhard Albinus lectured on anatomy. These lectures were free and attracted audiences of up to a hundred. At other times convenient to themselves, all four professors held private classes ('colleges') at their homes for which each student paid 13 guilders (£1.50) at the end of the course.

The teaching offered by these four professors could not be equalled at any other school of medicine in Europe, but, of the four, Boerhaave was the most remarkable. On Wednesdays and Saturdays, Boerhaave walked to the small St Caecilia Hospital where he would lead a group of his senior students round all 12 of the hospital's beds and then select one patient for special consideration. He would comment on the patient's symptoms and their significance, demonstrate the signs that had led to his diagnosis and discuss the treatment and his prognosis; throughout the students were encouraged to raise questions and to make their own contributions to the discussion. At the bedside, Boerhaave was teaching medical practice according to the doctrines of Hippocrates and Galen, but at the same time he was attempting to create a theoretical system of medicine that could accommodate the recently discovered knowledge of anatomy and chemistry with the ancient doctrines of Hippocrates and Galen. It was this new approach that Boerhaave gave to teaching medicine that first marked Leiden as the most advanced medical school of the early eighteenth century.

In July 1730, Pringle graduated from Leiden.[22] However, before going home he spent two years visiting the wards of the huge state hospitals in Paris and adding to his experience in the craft of medicine. He then returned to Scotland inspired by the practice and theory of medicine that he had found in Leiden and Paris. At Leiden he had become a close friend of two students, Gerhard van Swieten and Albrecht von Haller. Swieten, who had been born in Leiden, had been Boerhaave's assistant and had published his Aphorisms[23] and his Commentaries;[24] he later became physician to Empress Maria Theresa of Austria. Haller was Swiss; he became a distinguished physician, anatomist and botanist and was later appointed by George II as Professor of Medicine at Gottingen University. Together the three had been the outstanding students at Leiden. All three later became Fellows of the Royal Society some years after leaving Leiden.

Pringle was proud to have studied medicine at Leiden. He admired those who had taught him. He admired Boerhaave but he believed that he was wrong in attempting to create yet another theoretical system to support the ancient theoretical system of Hippocrates and Galen. Pringle was preparing to play his own part in what he recognised as the slow, halting progress of a medical revolution.

TWO

The Theory of Medicine: Boerhaave and Pringle

If a man will begin with certainties, he shall end in doubt; but if he be content to begin with doubts he shall end with certainties.

Francis Bacon, *The Advancement of Learning*, 1605

When Pringle studied medicine at Leiden, nothing was yet known about the true nature of disease. The people of ancient Greece had long believed that health was the gift of their gods. However, Hippocrates (460–377 BC)[1] discounted supernatural powers and the influence of the gods. In his philosophy the human body was entirely of the natural world. He saw the body as a microcosm of the great macrocosm, the universe. He believed that the universe had four essential elements, fire, earth, water and air, and that the body had four related bodily humours, yellow bile, phlegm, blood and black bile. Although naturally present in the body, phlegm and yellow bile were both potentially harmful. When present in excess in the winter months phlegm caused colds and in the summer yellow bile produced diarrhoea and vomiting. Black bile was associated with the late stages of severe illness and contributed to the dark colour of vomitus and excreta. Blood however was a benign humour. It was expelled naturally from the body in menstruation; this suggested to Hippocrates, and later Galen, that bloodletting would be very useful in ridding the body of the harmful quantities of the harmful humours that were causing a patient's illness. Otherwise Hippocratic treatment was expectant. The physicians waited and watched the patient, winning his trust in the healing powers of nature. Whatever was done to help should do no harm. Appropriate attention was given to diet, exercise, sleep and bathing.[2] The physician was not required to give a diagnosis. The talented physician displayed his true skill by offering an accurate prognosis.

In the fourth century BC, Aristotle had modified Hippocratic teaching, giving less emphasis to the season of the year and more to the association of humour with temperament, sanguine (with blood), melancholic (with black bile), phlegmatic (with phlegm) and choleric (with yellow bile). He had dissected a number of different animals and from his studies of embryos developing within eggs he had noted that the first sign of life was the beating of the heart; he concluded that it was the beating heart that gave life to the body and that it was the flow of blood through the intestines that gave sustenance to the body.[3]

In Rome, in the second century AD, Galen (AD 130–200), a physician who had trained in Greece, had modified the concepts of Hippocrates and Aristotle by giving even greater importance to blood-letting. The health of the patient could be restored by removing a quantity of the offending humour by opening a vein to remove up to ten or more ounces of blood. He saw fever as by far the most common cause of death and advocated copious blood-letting as the proper treatment for fever even in its most minor forms. He advocated bloodletting in the treatment of all but the most trivial illness and monthly prophylactic bleeding even when there was no evident threat of illness.

Galen also gave some attention to the study of anatomy. As dissection of the human body was forbidden in Rome in the second century, he had dissected a number of species of animals. Whenever possible he had chosen the Barbary ape, the animal that was thought to most resemble man. From his dissections he concluded that in the human body there were three essential major organs. He claimed that the brain was the seat of the rational faculties; the heart was the seat of the passions and the source of the arteries that carried life to the body; the liver was the seat of the appetites and desires and the source of the veins that carried nutrition to the body.

As his anatomical studies had not been carried out on human bodies, the conclusions that Galen had drawn were little more than speculation. A number of his concepts were entirely mystical. He believed that animal life was made possible by *pneuma*, the life breath of the cosmos. Within the body the *pneuma* was modified by the three major organs, becoming in the heart the vital spirit that gave life to the body, in the liver the nutritive spirit that supported nutrition and in the brain the animal spirit that sustained sensation and movement. Galen was confident that he had explained everything. He wrote:

I have done as much for medicine as Trajan did for the Roman Empire when he built bridges and roads through Italy. It is I, and I alone, who have revealed the true path of medicine. It must be admitted that

Hippocrates already staked out this path. He prepared the way but I have made it passable.[4]

After the fall of the Roman Empire in the fifth century AD, much of the scholarship of ancient Greece and Rome was either lost or neglected. However, the texts of many of the major works on medicine, mathematics and astronomy survived in Arabia. From the seventh century, as the Muslim empire swept westward from the Arab peninsula past Gibraltar to the Atlantic coast and then north into Spain, the ancient medical texts that had survived in Arabia were carried along with it. For some 600 years, in libraries from Baghdad to Cordoba, they were translated into Arabic and new concepts were added.[5]

It was not until the twelfth century that the medical texts began to find their way back into southern Europe. Southern Europe had begun to recover from the disorder that had followed the fall of Rome and was enjoying a period of modest prosperity. Scholarship revived and Christian scholars were allowed access to the libraries of Muslim Spain. They began the task of retranslating the texts from Arabic into Latin. Although the translated texts were few and precious, a number found their way into Christian Europe. By the end of the fourteenth century, manuscript copies of the original works of the Persian physician Avicenna (980–1037) had been translated into Gaelic and were in the hands of the physicians at the court of the Lord of the Isles in the Scottish Hebrides.[6]

However, this early period of renaissance was short lived. Soon after the rediscovery of the medical and other texts, Europe was devastated by the Great Plague (Black Death). By 1350 it had reached Scotland. The Scottish chronicler John of Fordun wrote:

In the year 1350 there was that year in the kingdom of Scotland so great a pestilence and plague among men as, from the beginning of the world even unto modern times, had never been heard of by man, nor is it found in books, for the enlightenment of those who come after. For to such a pitch did the plague wreak its cruel spite, that nearly a third of mankind were thereby made to pay the debt of nature. Moreover by God's will, this evil led to a strange and unwonted kind of death insomuch that the flesh of the sick was somehow puffed out and swollen and they dragged out their earthly life for barely two days.[7]

Europe did not recover from the catastrophe for many years. However, when the Italian Renaissance began in the fifteenth century, humanist scholars explored the libraries in Spain and North Africa and produced Latin versions of hundreds of Arab texts. But many of the Arab texts that they recovered were unreliable translations of the original Roman works. This prompted later scholars to search for the original Greek texts that were thought to have survived in Byzantium. By the end of the fifteenth century, translated versions of the works of Hippocrates, Aristotle and Galen were in the possession of universities across Europe. When, in the 1450s, the printing press and movable type were invented, copies of the ancient texts ceased to be treasured rarities. By 1500, hundreds of translations of the classical texts were being published across Europe.

On their recovery after so many centuries, the works of Hippocrates, Aristotle and Galen were accorded the veneration of holy writ. The study of medicine became the study of the translated classical texts and the practice of medicine was confidently based on the ancient theory of the bodily humours. For many years it was this theoretical framework that supported medical practice while its all-purpose convenience served to inhibit new thinking. In 1605, Francis Bacon, wrote:

> Medicine is a science which hath been more professed than laboured and yet more laboured than advanced; the labour having been in my judgement rather in a circle than in progression.[8]

However, the dictates of Aristotle, Hippocrates, and Galen had been challenged. In 1527, Paracelsus (Theophrastus Bombast von Hohenheim) (1495–1541), Professor of Medicine at Basel, had publicly burned his collection of the works of Galen. This dramatic rejection of the classical concept of medicine won him an enthusiastic following, but the concept of medicine based on alchemy that he offered in its place was as mystical as the system that he aimed to replace. By 1541, when he died, his more extravagant claims were already discredited. Nevertheless, his ideas inspired others in succeeding generations to join in a search for a more rational system of medicine based on an understanding of chemistry. But while chemistry continued to be little more than alchemy, little of substance was achieved.

The study of anatomy offered much better prospects of progress. The Romans had considered the violation of bodies by dissection socially and morally unacceptable. However, in the years of the Renaissance these strictures had eased and the study of human anatomy had begun to flourish.

In 1537, Vesalius (Andries van Wesel) (1514–1564), Professor of Surgery and Anatomy at Padua, had begun to perform his public dissections of human cadavers in a completely new way. Until then the teaching of anatomy had aimed only to demonstrate the truth and relevance of the claims that Galen had made from his animal dissections. The Professor of Anatomy would read a commentary taken from the relevant passages of Galen's text while an assistant (often a surgeon) carried out the dissection; a second assistant would use a pointer to indicate the part of the body being described by the professor exactly as it was described in Galen's text.[9] Vesalius, however, carried out the dissections himself and discussed his findings directly with his students. He was able to demonstrate that Galen had made errors in applying his findings in his animal dissections to his descriptions of the human body. Vesalius wrote: 'I myself cannot wonder enough at my own stupidity and too great trust in the writings of Galen and other anatomists.'[10] In 1543, he published his *De Humani Corporis Fabrica,* an anatomical atlas of the human body, beautifully drawn by a pupil of Titian, Jan Stephan van Calcar. These depictions of the bones, muscles and tendons and the demonstration of their probable function as levers, pulleys and ropes together with the pumping action of the heart promoted the idea that the human body could be regarded as a machine.

The idea that a new model was required for the human body received further encouragement after William Harvey (1578–1657) published his *Exercitatio Anatomica de Motu Cordis et Sanguinis in Animalibus* (An Anatomical Essay on the Motion of the Heart and Blood in Animals). Harvey had first noted that the volume of blood leaving the heart every hour was greater by far than the total volume of blood in the body. Such a great volume of blood leaving the heart could not possibly be consumed so completely or so rapidly replaced by new blood as Galen had described. He studied the blood vessels of the cadaver's limbs and demonstrated that both arteries and veins were present and that the valves in the veins would only allow blood to pass inwards back to the heart, while the blood in the arteries passed outwards to the body and limbs. He concluded that the blood was carried through the body in a continuing flow outwards from the heart through the arteries and back to the heart through the veins. Galen had also written that before leaving the heart's left ventricle the blood received air and other useful substances from a small quantity of blood delivered from the lungs to the heart's right ventricle. Since there was no clear way in which the air could be conveyed from the right to the left side of the heart,

Galen had insisted that it must be passed through hidden pores in the wall separating the left and right ventricles.

Harvey interpreted his anatomical dissections not in accordance with Galen's teaching but as he found them himself. He showed that the blood was circulated from the left side of heart to the periphery of the body and returned to the right side of the the heart; from there circulation was continued carrying the blood to the lungs and then back to the left side of the heart.

In 1687, the developments in the understanding of the human body and in the practice of medicine were surpassed by advances in astronomy. Aristotle had long held that the earth was at the centre of the universe and that the celestial bodies were carried in perfect circles round it, embedded in ethereal crystal spheres like jewels set in crystal orbs. This concept had been challenged by the Egyptian astronomer Ptolemy (AD 90–168) and the Polish mathematician and astronomer Copernicus (Nicolaus Kopernikus 1473–1543). The concepts of these astronomers were promoted by little more than the elegance of the idea. The first concepts in astronomy to be put forward on the basis of observations were those of the Italian physicist and mathematician Galileo (1564–1642). He had made a telescope by inserting spectacle maker's lenses into a hollow tube. He saw stars as he had never seen them before, 'in numbers ten times exceeding the old and familiar stars'.[11] 'He saw moons orbiting Jupiter'.[12] He concluded that Aristotle's notion that the arrangement of the celestial bodies was perfect and unchanging was wrong. But Galileo believed that without a means to measure the motion of the planets and stars it would always be impossible to determine the changing positions and the relationships of the heavenly bodies with each other.

Within a few years, Isaac Newton (1642–1727) had achieved what had been thought to be impossible. Between 1664 and 1666, he developed a new form of mathematics (calculus) that made it possible to measure the variation in properties such as velocities that change not in a series of finite measurable steps but in a continuum of infinitesimal differences.[13] Calculus made it possible for him to describe the course of each planet in its orbit.

Newton measured the course and duration of the orbits of Jupiter's four satellites and was able to show that the planets were indeed 'heavy' towards one another, drawn by the force of gravity.[14] From this he was able to create a mathematical model of the movements of the planets and their relationships with each other, his system of celestial mechanics, his 'System of the

World'. When he published his work in *Philisophiae Naturalis Principia Mathematica* in 1687 it seemed that he had achieved the impossible.

Many now assumed that the mathematical modelling technique (the Newtonian Style)[15] that Newton had used to explain the movements of heavenly bodies could produce the answer to everything. In Edinburgh, the Newtonian Style was used successfully in creating the actuarial basis of the ground-breaking insurance scheme of the Scottish Ministers' Widows Fund.[16] On the other hand, as a boy of 16, Pringle's friend the Edinburgh mathematician Colin Maclaurin (1698–1746) had tried unsuccessfully to use the Newtonian Style in an attempt to solve an ethical problem, in his *De Viribus Mentium Bonipetis* (On the Good-Seeking Forces of the Mind).[17] Newton's achievement had been welcomed as the greatest in the history of natural philosophy but whether the technique he had used could be applied to medicine was uncertain. The question was answered by the Scottish physician Archibald Pitcairn (1652–1713).

Since Newton's friendship with Pitcairn has rarely been noticed and since it was important at a critical time in Pringle's career, it deserves some explanation. Several years before Newton published his *Principia*, news of his achievement had already reached Scotland. James Gregory, Professor of Mathematics at St Andrews, had been corresponding with Newton since 1668. Defeated by a problem in analytical geometry, Gregory had written to Newton for assistance. In return Newton had taken the opportunity to ask for Gregory's help in designing a reflecting microscope.[18] They had continued to write to each other for several years. James Gregory became Professor of Mathematics at Edinburgh in 1674. He died in 1675, and after his death it was arranged for the papers relating to their long and learned correspondence to be edited jointly by Gregory's nephew David Gregory and David's friend Archibald Pitcairn.

David Gregory had studied mathematics at Edinburgh from 1674 until 1679. He had then gone to study mathematics and medicine at Leiden. Archibald Pitcairn had matriculated at Edinburgh University in 1668 to study divinity but later moved to Paris to study law. On his return to Edinburgh in 1674, Pitcairn attended Professor James Gregory's classes on mathematics; it was at these classes that he established his friendship with David Gregory. In 1675, Pitcairn returned to Paris, this time to study medicine. He graduated at Rheims in August 1680 and five years after his return to Scotland he was appointed Professor of Medicine at Edinburgh University. When, in 1683, David Gregory returned from Leiden to become Professor of Mathematics at Edinburgh University, he and Archibald Pitcairn resumed their correspondence with Newton.

When Newton published his *Principia* in July 1687, he sent a copy to Gregory and Pitcairn in Edinburgh. Gregory immediately began his commentary on it, his *Notae in Newtoni Principiae* (Notes on Newton's *Principia*). Pitcairn produced his own commentary, *Solutio Problematis de Historicis* (A Solution to Ancient Problems). Gregory and Pitcairn became, for a time, the most influential Newtonians in Britain.

However, the careers of Gregory and Pitcairn were halted by the Glorious Revolution that brought the Protestant William of Orange to the throne of Great Britain in 1688. When William III negotiated with the Scottish Parliament the terms on which he would be accepted as their king, it was agreed that Catholics and Episcopalians would be barred from holding public office in Scotland. What followed was a purge not only of the small number of Catholics but also the much larger number of Episcopalians in Scotland. Both Gregory and Pitcairn were Episcopalians and neither had made any secret of their Jacobite sympathies. Gregory was not dismissed from the Chair of Mathematics, but by 1691 his position had become so precarious that he left Edinburgh for London. There he was warmly welcomed by Newton who secured his election to the Royal Society and his appointment as Professor of Astronomy at Oxford. Pitcairn, who had been conspicuously loud in his support for the Jacobite cause, was dismissed from the Chair of Medicine at Edinburgh.

Pitcairn's growing reputation as a physician attracted attention and on 28 November 1691 he was appointed Professor of Theoretical Medicine at Leiden University. On his way to Holland he went to spend a few days with Newton in Cambridge. Newton was already unwell. He had been writing a paper, *De Natura Acidorum* (On the Nature of Acids) but had been unable to finish it. Pitcairn completed it for him; the last sections are in Pitcairn's handwriting.

While in Cambridge, Pitcairn discussed with Newton the relevance that the technique he had used so successfully in his studies of the movement of the planets might have to the study of medicine. It became clear that it was most unlikely to be of any value. In his inaugural lecture at Leiden, Pitcairn told his audience that the great questions in medicine could be solved, not by the higher mathematics of calculus and the sophistication of Newtonianism, but by everyday mathematical analysis and applied physics. While the search for the ultimate causes of life and the workings of the human body was of the greatest interest to philosophers, it was irrelevant in the practice of medicine. He urged his students to accept that 'their knowledge of things should be confined to the relations they have to one another, the laws and properties of powers'.[19] In the autumn of 1693, Pitcairn left Leiden to return to Cambridge where Newton was now in the depths of a severe clinical depression. He remained in Cambridge until Newton began to show signs of recovery. By then Pitcairn was no longer Professor of Medicine at Leiden. As he had chosen not to inform the University of Leiden of the reason for his absence and had been unable to give a firm date for his return, he was dismissed from his Chair.

One of the students who had been influenced by Pitcairn's lecture at Leiden was the young Herman Boerhaave (1668–1738). Born in a village near Leiden, he had studied theology and had taken a degree in philosophy before he began to study medicine in 1689. He read the Greek and Latin texts of Hippocrates and Galen, studied the works of Vesalius and other modern anatomists, attended public dissections and dissected the bodies of animals and became skilled in chemistry and botany. After taking his medical degree in 1693, he practised as a physician and gave public lectures on chemistry. He proved to be an excellent teacher. In 1701, he was appointed a lecturer in medicine at the University of Leiden; in 1709, he was made Professor of Botany and Medicine; in 1714, he was made Rector of the University and Professor of the Practice of Medicine; in 1718, he was made Professor of Chemistry. His reputation attracted students from every part of Europe. In 1728, he was elected to the French Academy of Scientists and in 1730, he was made a Fellow of the Royal Society of London. His book, *Institutiones Medicae* (The Institutes of Medicine), first published in 1702, later ran to ten editions and was translated into five languages.

In his inaugural addresses on his appointment as a lecturer at the university in Leiden in 1701 and again on his appointment as professor in 1709, Boerhaave followed Pitcairn in making a clear distinction between the practical skills of clinical medicine and the theory of medicine. On clinical medicine, he accepted without question the principles of Hippocrates. On the theory of medicine, Boerhaave sought to strengthen the ancient contributions of Aristotle and Galen by adding new thoughts derived from his own observations. He saw that, as the blood passed from the aorta into tubular vessels of smaller and smaller calibre, the smallest vessels eventually became visible only as fibres, fibres that eventually became matted together to form all the solid parts of the body. These smallest tubular fibres he could not see but he believed that they became joined with similar fine tubules that carried the exhausted blood back towards the heart. He saw the body as a hydraulic model of fluids and tubes. It was a mechanical system

which followed the line of the biomechanics that had been discussed by
Giovani Borelli (1608–1679) and Lorenzo Bellini (1641–1707) in Pisa. It
was a model that must be subject to the laws of mathematics and physics.
Boerhaave assured his audience that:

> Those who calculate the forces of bodies according to their mass, form
> and velocity, found by direct observation are called mechanists. By the
> practical results of their science they have gained the esteem of right
> thinking men in such a measure that one will not easily find another
> science which might equally enjoy universal applause . . . Mechanics
> are of the utmost importance for medicine.[20]

When Pringle became a student at Leiden, he was prepared by his years of
study of philosophy, particularly the work of Francis Bacon, to disagree with
Boerhaave. Boerhaave's first years of study had been on speculative philosophy, not natural philosophy, and on theology on which the ancient written
authority was Scripture. Pringle believed that Boerhaave's new model of the
body based on very incomplete observations could not be used to replace
the ancient ideas of the ancient medical masters. It was based not on facts
but on his own speculations. His model did not satisfy Francis Bacon's
demand for observation, inductive reasoning and experiment in establishing
a fact. Pringle believed that Boerhaave was wrong in attempting to improve
Aristotle's and Galen's theoretical models of the working of the body by the
construction of yet another theoretical model. He agreed with Pitcairn that
the practice of medicine could best be improved by observing and studying
the 'relations that things have to one another'. Throughout his career, Pringle
followed Boerhaave in separating the everyday practice of medicine from
the search for a new understanding of medicine. He continued to treat his
patients according to the ancient theoretical notions of Hippocrates and
Galen; the theories had been used for centuries and nothing better had been
invented. But in looking for something new he followed the advice given by
Francis Bacon in his *The Advancement of Learning* in 1605. Pringle established facts scientifically by observation, inductive reasoning and experiment.

THREE

Physic, Patronage and Philosophy

Throw physic to the dogs; I'll none of it.
Shakespeare, *Macbeth*, V, iii

Pringle returned to Scotland in the summer of 1732. He had enjoyed the freedom and intellectual excitement of Leiden and the experience of life in Paris. Now he found himself at home again in a country that had suffered troubles that had begun before the Union with England and had continued in the years that followed.

The great majority of the people of Scotland lived and worked on the land.[1] The wild and destructive wind and rain in the 1690s had caused long-lasting damage to the unsheltered stretches of earth on which they worked for their subsistence. Many had died from famine; many others had emigrated to Ulster to survive. In these years, the population of Scotland was reduced by some 15 per cent.[2] For those who had struggled to restore their land to its normal worth, the only help they had received had been from those who owned the land they cultivated and from the charity of their Church.

Scotland's other industries continued to operate in the towns and villages across the country but they had suffered from the Union with England in 1707. The competition with England had destroyed Scotland's woollen trades. New duties had been levied on linen, brewing, paper making and salt. Most of the revenue from these taxes was used in Scotland to meet the cost of its own routine civil administration, but the duties had been imposed by the new Parliament in London and for that reason they were greatly resented. In 1725, a new malt tax that added three pence to the cost of a barrel of beer provoked riots in many towns in Scotland. In Glasgow the distur-bance was so severe that troops were called in to supress it; when eight of the protestors were killed, the Provost commanded the troops to withdraw. The disturbance settled but the city's magistrates were later arrested and taken to Edinburgh for trial. They were found not guilty and returned to Glasgow to a triumphant welcome. But across Scotland the failure of the Union with England to relieve the country's poverty continued to cause bitterness and disappointment.

Scotland's Jacobites were yet another constant cause of uncertainty and disquiet. There were many Jacobites living in the north-eastern counties, there were numbers of Jacobite clans in the Highlands and there were some Jacobite families scattered almost everywhere in Scotland. The Jacobites all found it offensive that James VII and II had been forced from the throne in 1688; some would fight for his return to power; some had a long established personal loyalty that would make them fight for him if that loyalty was called on; some had a sentimental loyalty to him and would welcome his return if that could be achieved peacefully. But how many Jacobites there were and how they might respond if an attempt were to be made to restore him was quite unknown.

In the planning of the Union of the Parliaments of England and Scotland, great care had been given to the question of how Scotland was to be represented in the new single Parliament. After months of debate and disagreement the Anglo-Scottish parliamentary commissioners had reached an agreement. To the 513 members of the English House of Commons, 45 members were added from the Scottish counties, each with an electorate of 2,600, and 15 from the Scottish burghs, each with an electorate of 1,500.[3] This decision reduced the number of parliamentary constituencies in Scotland by two-thirds while keeping the Scottish electorate at only 0.2 per cent of the Scottish population, a much smaller proportion of the population than in constituencies in England and Ireland. Sixteen of Scotland's nobles, ten per cent of the total number, were to be elected to sit in the House of Lords. A new minister, a Secretary of State for Scotland, was added to the Cabinet. However, the Jacobite Rebellion in 1715 had indicated that closer control of Scotland was required. The office of Secretary of State for Scotland was abolished and the management of Scotland was put in the hands, not of a formally appointed minister, but of someone personally trusted by the head of the government. When, in 1721, Walpole became First Lord of The Treasury, in effect Britain's first prime minister, he chose Lord Islay. Islay's task was first to maintain the loyalty of the Scottish Members of Parliament to the Hanoverian government in London. Members who had been useful could be rewarded by a commission in the army or an appointment in the East India Company for their sons; other personal favours could be granted by whatever means was appropriate. Islay's other task was to ensure that every position of public importance or social influence in Scotland was given to the candidate most useful to the Hanoverian government in London and to Scotland. Apart from a gap from 1742 to 1746, Islay was to serve both the government and Scotland until his death in 1761.

From the beginning, Lord Islay had impressive sources of patronage. He was able to build up a formidable empire of clients. Two-thirds of the judges promoted to the Court of Succession soon owed their positions to his influence and those appointed as sheriffs were little more than a list of the sons, sons-in-law and allies of Lord Islay's clients.[4] He paid great attention to senior appointments being made in the universities and the Church. In 1727, he founded the Board of Trustees for Fisheries, Manufactures and Improvements in Scotland to benefit the country's economy. King George II described him as Viceroy in Scotland.[5] Within a short time he had created a degree of stability in Scotland that assisted many in making improvements that were of benefit to the country.

The Royal College of Physicians of Edinburgh was one of the first bodies to receive his assistance. In 1681, at its first meeting, the College had voted to provide a service for the care of the sick poor. In 1705, when it acquired its first Hall in Fountain Close, the College decided that the sick poor should be seen there on Monday, Wednesday and Friday afternoons. In 1729, the College founded a new 'Physicians Hospital or Infirmary for the Sick Poor' but soon discovered that, although the funds available to found it were adequate, they were insufficient to maintain it. This unforeseen problem was relieved by Edinburgh's Lord Provost, George Drummond.

Since the Union in 1707, Drummond had been Accountant-General of the Excise, Commissioner of the Excise and a member of the Board of Customs. In 1725, he had rescued Edinburgh from bankruptcy and became the city's Lord Provost.[6] While holding all of these offices he was also reporting regularly to the government in London on the state of affairs in Scotland. In 1729, he received acknowledgement of that support. Lord Islay ensured that the Town Council and the Bank of Scotland provided the funds necessary for the maintenance of the new teaching hospital.

Although Scotland was still a poor country, ten years of Lord Islay's careful management had created opportunities for new ideas. In 1731, the Society for the Improvement of Medical Knowledge had been created by Pringle's friend Colin Maclaurin, the Professor of Mathematics at Edinburgh.[7] When Pringle returned to Edinburgh, the Society began to publish *Medical Essays and Observations*, the first medical journal to be produced in Britain.[8] Unfortunately Pringle left no written record of the part he played in its planning. It was written not in Latin but in English. It was published quarterly in Edinburgh and was also printed and distributed in Glasgow, London, Paris, Amsterdam and Newcastle. In its first issue it promised:

> to give some account of the diseases that shall be observed most frequently in this city and neighbouring places and of their changes and successions. We judge it proper to begin our observations at some intermediate period betwixt the two grand classes of epidemic distempers, the vernal and the autumnal. Our medical year therefore shall commence at the summer solstice, when the spring diseases are generally worn out and before the declination of the sun has brought on the product of the autumn.[9]

At that time, few if any of the journal's readers would have doubted that the weather played a major part in the causation of disease. The early pages of the first edition of the journal were given over to a Meteorological Register that listed twice-daily readings of barometric pressure, temperature, humidity, wind direction, rainfall and weather (clear, cloudy, rain, hail or snow). This was accompanied by a note of all the diseases known to have occurred in Edinburgh in the course of the year from May 1731 until April 1732.

The most frequently reported ailments were 'swelling of the face and salivary glands' (mumps), ophthalmia (conjunctivitis), toothache, rheumatism, ague, bastard smallpox (chickenpox), gentle cholera (diarrhoea), pleurisy, pleuripneumony (pneumonia), slow fever (typhus), quinsy, kinkcough (whooping cough), erysipelas, lumbago, rheumatism and tertian ague (malaria).

Medical Essays and Observations offered an account of the treatments used by Edinburgh physicians at that time. The management of illness was still based on the ancient theory of the four bodily humours. The treatment of the less serious illnesses was based on the belief that the proper balance of the bodily humours could be restored by a few simple 'evacuations'. A gentle cholera, for example, usually passed off in two or three days, but, when necessary, it was 'cured by a few doses of rhubarb'. Children suffering mumps, chickenpox and or whooping cough were, in most cases, 'easily cured by a purgative or two'; however, when there was an 'attendant fever at least a single bleeding' was administered. Toothache, ophthalmia, or rheumatism were 'seldom accompanied by so acute a fever or such violent symptoms as to require large evacuations. A few doses of cathartics completed the cure.'

In general, ailments caused little anxiety unless they were accompanied by fever. Fever was then a mysterious and malignant disease; at that time, no other disease caused so many deaths. When the patient was fevered, truly heroic treatments were thought not only justified but imperative. Bleeding the patient was the first essential. The bleeding was performed by opening a vein, usually in the arm, and draining off a pint or more of the patient's blood. Although ordered by a physician, the procedure was often carried out by a surgeon (or a barber surgeon, the nature of whose skill was advertised by the red and white, blood and bandage, insignia on the barber's pole at the entrance to his shop). Physicians could also assist in ridding the body of harmful humours by applying hot metal or glass cups (vesictories) to raise large fluid blisters on the skin of the patient's torso; by prescribing ipecacuanha root or mustard seeds to make the patient vomit; by administering rhubarb purges or turpentine clysters (enemas) to evacuate the bowels; or by giving doses of guaiacol, camphor, or alcohol to cause profuse sweating.

As the clinical reports published in *Medical Essays and Observations* show, these various measures were the staples of treatment in Edinburgh in the early eighteenth century. In 1737, the city suffered a brief but disturbing epidemic of quinsy (suppurative tonsillitis) in which every case was accompanied by fever. *Medical Essays and Observations* reported that all were successfully treated by 'plentiful bleeding and blistering in the beginning and plentiful sweating after letting blood'.

However, bleeding was less successful during a sudden increase in the severity of the tertian ague that had been endemic in Edinburgh for many years. *Medical Essays and Observations* recorded that:

> This disease did not form into regular paroxysms and perfect inter-missions but appeared more in the shape of a remitting fever. During the remissions the pulse was much sunk but as the sweat came on the pulse became fuller and stronger. When the sweat did not break out the patients became delirious and some continued quite dire for some days.

Some were cured of this disease after two or three paroxysms by a vomit or two, but in others the disease lasted much longer. Bleeding was not found of use; vomiting and blistering were thought to have a better response.

This classical form of treatment was even less successful during an epidemic of a mysterious 'slow fever' in 1731.

It was attended with a violent pain of the head, a small but quick pulse, ravings and watchfulness. Several in advanced age died of it but of the younger sort many passed worms by stool and recovered. This fever abated in January but in the next month it became more frequent and hazardous than before. The headache was more violent the ravings more constant and the watchfulness more obstinate. To these bad symptoms were added tremulous motions and sometimes symptomatic bleeding at the nose. These fevers when allowed their course some days without interruption were most obstinate to remedy and carried off several young men; but in the first days, bleeding and vomiting and afterwards blistering did good service and prevented or abated some of the worst symptoms.

It was now recognised that such heroic treatments could be dangerous. *Medical Essays and Observations* recorded the unfortunate course of a number of cases of pneumonia presenting first as pleurisy:

The patients, during the whole disease could never bear to lie on the affected side; but a thick, difficult and painful breathing, a heat and oppression in the breast from the beginning gave good reason to suspect that a pleuripneumony was joined to it. Perhaps also in some cases the stomach was slightly inflamed for many of them who laboured under it had a frequent and strong reaching to vomit and even bore the operation of a gentle vomit more than these throws. The pulse was generally quick and low but very changeable and sometimes intermitting; the urine in small quantity and of pale colour; the thirst great and the tongue foul and parched. Upon the first bleeding the pain was somewhat allayed, the pulse grew fuller and stronger and the breathing easier; but the return of the former complaints soon required a second and then a third bleeding which however often sunk the pulse so much that it was difficult afterwards to raise it to a moderate strength unless vesictories were instantly applied which frequently was of great use and sometimes brought on a sweat. If this was free and plentiful it carried off the disease; but if partial and short the patients struggled on with pain, inquietude and agony till their strength was quite spent.

It had been accepted for many years that such heroic treatments, used when the patient seemed to be in danger of death, were unreliable and often failed completely. Physicians were uneasy that their treatments were derived from a model of disease that had been created not on the basis of observation and experience but by the exercise of 'pure reason'. In *Medical Essays and Observations* in 1733, John Drummond, a former president of the Royal College of Physicians of Edinburgh, wrote that 'the greatest masters of reasoning have proved the most unsuccessful interpreters of nature by neglecting to consult nature itself and overlooking the most obvious phenomena. Aristotle, with all the advantages of a great genius and most uncommon opportunities of improving physic, made no better use of these than some abstract notions and certain fictitious elements to account for the appearances of nature.'

The editors of *Medical Essays and Observations* aimed to promote a search for new rational forms of treatment. Its essays were, for the most part, reports of notable cases presented to extend, even at second hand, the personal clinical experience of medical practitioners and to inspire them to escape from the dogmas of the ancient classical texts. Even more revolutionary was the journal's attempt to promote the advance of medical science and practice by publishing the findings of properly conducted trials, experiments and investigations. From the beginning there were physicians and surgeons ready to take advantage of the journal's new venture.

Charles Douglas, a physician practising in Fife, described a new treatment for cholera that he had first tried successfully on himself. His earlier experience had led him to believe that the accepted practice of treating patients with cholera by the administration of bleedings, vomits, purges and sweats was 'adding oil to the flame'. In his trial of an alternative treatment he had the patient 'drink heartily of warm water three or four times'. Much of this the patient would immediately throw up, but thereafter the patient was encouraged to drink copiously of a concoction of toasted oat bread diluted to 'the colour of weak coffee'. Other than a pill of one grain of opium, the patient received no other form of treatment. Douglas was able to report that he had treated a series of cases of cholera in this way, all with great success. It would now be recognised that, although his technique was perhaps naive, Douglas was correct in principle; unfortunately, the vital importance of the replacement of fluids was neglected for another hundred years and cholera continued to be treated ineffectively and dangerously by bleeding well into the middle years of the nineteenth century.

As we have seen, it had long been believed that health and the onset of illness were strongly, even critically, influenced by the season of the year and changes in the weather. That belief was put to the test in a multi-centre investigation organised by Alexander Monro, the Professor of Anatomy at Edinburgh, and carried out by Patrick Ker, one of his medical students. From May 1731 until June 1736, the prevalence of disease and meteorological conditions were recorded in Edinburgh, Plymouth, Rippon and Nuremberg. The results were published in full in *Medical Essays and Observations* in 1742. The 50 pages of data were not subjected to the statistical analysis that would now be expected. However, the results did clearly indicate that a relationship did exist between the onset of certain diseases and the season of year.

In 1733, an essay lauding the special 'virtues and use of the mineral water near Moffat', written by a successful surgeon practising in Moffat, was published in *Medical Essays and Observations*. But the same issue contained a report on 'Experiments on the Medicinal Water of Moffat' conducted by Andrew Plummer, Professor of Medicine and Chemistry at Edinburgh University. His analysis of the water had failed to discover in it any substance peculiar to Moffat or indeed any rare or previously unknown substance; he reported 'that the principles contained in this medicinal water are very subtle and volatile sulphur, some particles of copper and common salt'.

Each issue of *Medical Essays and Observations* included such reports challenging established ideas and, in some cases, providing good evidence for change. The journal did not limit its contribution to the search for a new evidence-based medicine to the contents of its own pages. Each volume contained a list of all the new medical books published in that year; a list of the books promised and about to be published; a list of the medical societies formed for the improvement of physic; and a section giving a brief account of the most remarkable improvements and discoveries in medical science and practice made during the year. Edinburgh had begun to challenge the principles on which medicine had been established for centuries.

Soon after his return to Edinburgh in 1732, Pringle began his own first contribution to the improvement in medical practice. In these early years of the eighteenth century, physicians, reluctant to subject their patients to bleeding and purging or disappointed with the results of such measures, or even to impress their patients with their special personal expertise, often prescribed one or other of a myriad of substances that tradition, mythology, imagination and imposture had put forward over the centuries as cures for man's many ills. An apothecary almost anywhere in Britain might stock as many as 2,500 different items of animal, vegetable and mineral materia medica. Some were herbal preparations known to be effective as laxatives, emetics, diuretics or sedatives, but the majority were pretentious preparations, each with its own supposed action and its own dubious justification.

From the sixteenth century, a number of pharmacopoeias, listing the substances recommended for use in the treatment of the sick, had been published in Italy, Germany, France and the Netherlands. The London College of Physicians had produced six editions of a pharmacopoeia, the *Pharmacopoeia Londinensis*, between 1618 and 1721. In 1724, the authority of the *London Pharmacopoeia* changed; the edition published that year carried a proclamation by King George giving royal approval to its use in 'England, the dominion of Wales and the town of Berwick upon Tweed'.

In Scotland in 1680, a group of Edinburgh physicians had begun to prepare their own pharmacopoeia of useful drugs. In 1682, the task was passed to a committee of the Royal College of Physicians of Edinburgh. The committee struggled to find an agreed version that could go forward for publication. In his *Memoirs*, Sir Robert Sibbald, the greatly respected founder of the College, attributed the long delay to 'malice and faction'. Malice there may have been, but it was the growing disenchantment with the classical medicine of Aristotle and Galen that was at the heart of the matter. Sir Robert Sibbald insisted on the inclusion of all the remedies that had been part of the 'simple method of physic' that he had been taught in Paris in 1661; Sir Archibald Stevenson, the President of the College, was equally insistent that medicaments based on nothing more than imagination and tradition should be discarded. It was not until 1699 that a hard-won consensus was achieved and the *Pharmacopoeia Collegii Regii Medicorum Edinburgensis* (The Dispensatory of the Royal College of Physicians of Edinburgh) was published. A further edition of the *Edinburgh Pharmacopoeia* followed and, by 1724, the *Edinburgh Pharmacopoeia* had acquired the authority in Scotland that had been given earlier that year to the *London Pharmacopoeia* in England.

On Pringle's return to Edinburgh in 1732, although not yet a Fellow or even a licentiate of the Royal College of Physicians, he expressed his strong objection to the continued listing in the *Edinburgh Pharmacopoeia* of many of the ancient remedies that had been championed by Sir Robert Sibbald in 1682. In 1733, he was invited to join in the production of the third edition of the *Edinburgh Pharmacopoeia*. When it was published in 1735, a number of the more revolting substances had been removed, notably *cranium hominis violenta morte extincti* (skull of a man who has died a violent death), *secundia humana* (human placenta) and *stercus humanum* (human faeces). However, the format was still much as it had been in the first two earlier editions.

Part 1 was a list of the 'simples,' the substances from which all the approved medicaments were derived; the list was subdivided into vegetable, animal and mineral sources. In all, 520 vegetable sources were listed. Of these a dozen – alcohol, aloes, camphor, cannabis, coffee, digitalis, hellebore, ipecacuhana, magdrigora, opium, senna and rhubarb –are still recognised as having pharmacological properties. But the list was still made up principally by large numbers of herbs, fungi and resins whose medicinal properties were, and still are, obscure.

The 50 animal substances listed still included human material – blood, urine, milk, skull and powdered human mummy. Apes, beetles, bulls, crabs, dogs, elephants, millipedes, scorpions, snakes, stags and wolves were all still listed as sources of medicinal material. The 70 minerals recommended included gold, silver, copper, lead, mercury, crystal, sulphur, pearl, lapis lazuli, petroleum, bismuth, borax and talcum. Unicorn horn (described here as an earth) was also included as a mineral.

Part 2 presented the *Medicamenta*, the full list of distillates, decoctions, elixirs, infusions, pills, powders, tinctures, syrups and confections in which the various 'simples' could be made up and administered to the patient. Part 3 listed chemical medicines (*Medicamenta Chemica*) made from vegetable, animal and mineral sources.

In 1733, Pringle's aim was to ensure that no medicament was recommended in the *Pharmacopoeia* unless there was clear evidence of its worth. In the 1756 edition it was proudly announced that 'all those medicines that had been retained unchanged through superstition, credulity or established custom had been banished'.[10] But Pringle was still not content. He was now practising in London and he had become a Fellow of the Royal College of Physicians of London. The London College was conservative and seldom felt it necessary to revise and update its pharmacopoeia. Pringle therefore made further efforts to improve the quality of the treatment of disease in Britain by continuing the upgrading of the *Edinburgh Pharmacopoeia* which was already the most influential and most widely used pharmacopoeia in Britain. In his usual brisk style he wrote to the President of the College of Physicians of Edinburgh:

> As to the arrangement of the compound medicines, all I can say at this time is that I am not satisfied with our present form. We make a division, but only give a title to the last part of it *viz* the *Medicamenta*

Chemica. Now if it should be asked by what name we call the *Medica-menta* preceding this class we should be at a loss what to answer. Galen knew nothing of distillations and I fancy very little of our tinctures and elixirs which all come under this anonymous class of medicines. And indeed I cannot see that with any propriety we can separate those processes from chemistry.[11]

At this time, Pringle's objectives were to have the format of the *Pharmacopoeia* made more convenient, the nomenclature made more modern and the contents made more 'scientific'. He also held that the contents of each section should be arranged alphabetically. But above all he insisted that the list of approved drugs should be kept under constant review. In 1764, he wrote again to the President:

> With regard to the list of simples, if I remember right, I wrote my opinion of it to Dr Hope [chairman of the Pharmacopoeia committee] in 1756 and likewise at that time transmitted to him such a catalogue as what I believe was more conformed to modern practice than what stood in the pharmacopoeia in which I observed there was a such a multitude of simples which were either never called for by physicians or so seldom that for the most part they must be found in a spoilt condition. I was therefore clear in my opinion that our list should be much abbreviated and by way of specimen I took the liberty of offering a new one drawn up accordingly.[12]

The President's response was to invite Pringle to revise the *Pharmacopoeia* in time for the publication of its sixth edition, due in 1774.

Pringle's revision secured a number of major changes. In Part 1, the number of 'simples' was reduced from 590 to 240 and the name 'simples' was changed to the more appropriate 'Material Medica'. Human material was banished completely; the number of other animal sources was reduced from over fifty in 1735 to less than ten (millipedes, beetles, spiders and other insects) in 1774. Vegetable sources were reduced from 521 to 165; and new effective substances were added, including cinchona (quinine) for the treatment of malaria, colchium for the treatment of gout, and aconite, a diuretic and diaphoretic. In Part 2 infusions, distillates, elixirs powders and the 'chemical medicines' were all listed together in alphabetical order and under a new title, 'Preparations and Compositions'. There was therefore no Part 3.

The College now ruled that in future editions of its pharmacopoeia no medicine would be approved unless formally attested by the College or by some other recognised authority. The College also undertook to 'effect a complete reform of the language of material medica on general scientific principles and to abandon a language that had formerly been so barbarous and heterogeneous'.[13] This latter change was not welcomed by a number of the senior Fellows of the College who complained that they were now 'obliged to have recourse to their junior apprentices for an explanation of the technical language of the day'.[14] However, as a result of the reforms begun and continued by Pringle, the *Edinburgh Pharmacopoeia* continued to be the most widely used pharmacopoeia in Britain until 1864 when the Pharmacopoeias of Edinburgh, London and Dublin were replaced by a new *British Pharmacopoeia*.[15]

However, for Pringle these achievements were far in the future. In 1733, he was now 25 years old but had not yet succeeded in establishing himself in practice. He could expect to become Fellow of the Royal College of Physicians of Edinburgh in the next year or two and would then have responsibilities for the College's dispensary for the sick poor. Since it was founded in 1682, the Fellows of the College had given their services free and the cost of the drugs was met by the fines imposed on Fellows who had failed to attend college meetings.[16] In 1727, the College had launched a public subscription for the building and the maintenance of an infirmary for the sick poor.[17] The scheme had been hugely successful and, in August 1729, the infirmary was able to admit its first patients. After some time of uncertainty and debate, it was agreed that all the Fellows of the College would be included as attending physicians. Pringle would receive no payment for his attendance at the dispensary or at the infirmary. However, he attended patients in their homes and, as was the way at that time, he made himself available for consultation at a popular tavern or at a coffee house. But in this open medical market he faced strong competition. Edinburgh's new medical school was producing increasing numbers of graduates. There was even more competition from surgeon apothecaries, from apothecaries practising illegally as physicians and from quacks. He could hope for success in a quite different form of practice, consultation by mail. At Leiden, Boerhaave had carried on a successful practice by correspondence; some years later at Edinburgh the famous William Cullen had such a large practice by mail that he had his friend James Watt design a machine to make copies of his letters. Practitioners uncertain of their diagnosis or having failed in their treatment would write giving the principal features of the case and ask for the physician's opinion. In time it had become not unusual for patients themselves to write to Cullen for advice; the fees were often very generous. But Pringle had not reached the eminence of Boerhaave or Cullen. He needed to find a source of income. For the first time, he was to have the benefit of political patronage.

In the autumn of 1733, William Scott, the Professor of Ethics at Edinburgh University, was over 60 years old, in poor health and hoping to find a young philosopher to share his teaching duties. In 1695, he had been appointed as the most junior of the five regents teaching philosophy at Edinburgh.[18] When the old system of regenting[19] was abolished at Edinburgh in 1708, Scott had been made Professor of Greek, a subject then taught as essential for the study of philosophy. When William Law, who held the more senior and more prestigious Chair of Ethics and Moral Philosophy, died in 1729, Scott, as the most senior of the former regents, had been automatically promoted to succeed to him. However, Scott had been teaching Greek for over 20 years and he had found his new duties exacting. John Lees[20] had deputised for him on occasions, but as he got older he felt in need of a permanent, formally appointed, assistant.

The Duke of Roxburghe was no longer Secretary of State for Scotland but he was still leader of the Squadrone Volante, a party constant in its support for the Hanoverian regime and its government in London. Members of the Pringle family already owed their senior appointments in the legal world to the Squadrone Volante.[21] Now Pringle was quietly put forward for the new post of assistant to the Professor of Ethics. The necessary political negotiations were not put on paper but were the subject of conversations in Edinburgh and London.[22] There was no difficulty. Pringle was a suitably qualified candidate. He had been a pupil of the distinguished philosopher Professor Francis Pringle. Scott was agreeable and he formally petitioned the Senate of the university to make the appointment. The Senate not only accepted the proposal but increased the status of the post that was to be offered to Pringle. It was not to be 'merely an interim appointment'.[23] The teaching of philosophy at Edinburgh was to be reorganised. Pringle and Scott were to be joint Professors, not only of Ethics, but also of Moral Philosophy. And Pringle's appointment was made on the understanding that he would succeed to the chair when Scott could no longer continue. As William Scott had been, for some years, somewhat 'perfunctory' in carrying out his duties,[24] the Senate laid down new directives. The professor (in effect Pringle) was to lecture on Moral Philosophy between the hours of ten and eleven on five days each week from 1 November till 1 May. His

Monday lectures were to be on 'the truth of the Christian religion'. Before his appointment was confirmed, Pringle was required to 'deliver a discourse in the Common Hall on Ethics and Moral Philosophy'. His discourse was 'highly approved by all the learned audience'.

Pringle was an excellent lecturer. His students admired his command of Latin and the clarity of his presentation. But the subject matter of his lectures came as a surprise. One of his students[25] commented that he would have learned nothing of moral philosophy had he not owned a copy of Von Pufendorf's *The Whole Duty of Man According to the Law of Nature*.[26] In his Monday lectures Pringle confined his attention to natural theology, a subject that allowed him to avoid any reference to divine revelation. All his lectures on philosophy were said to be 'altogether practical'. He made no mention of Aristotle or the great philosophers of the classical world. Instead he discussed the works and ideas of Francis Bacon, Isaac Newton, John Locke and the developing field of experimental philosophy. It became evident that what Pringle taught owed more to his years as a medical student at Leiden than to his years as a student of philosophy at St Andrews. Certainly it seemed to his colleagues at the university that he had 'no taste for philosophy'.[27] Nevertheless, Pringle continued to teach philosophy, as he understood it, for eight years.

FOUR

A Commission in the Army

My sentiments are and always will be to make war with all the generosity and humanity possible.

Field Marshal the Earl of Stair, 1743[1]

By 1740 Scotland was at last enjoying the economic benefits of the Union of Parliaments. Scotland now had free access to trade with what had been English colonies and her ships could sail under the protection of the Royal Navy. In the years between 1707 and 1731 Glasgow's tobacco merchants' annual imports of tobacco from America had already increased from £1.5 million to £5.6 million, causing a serious fall in the market shares of Bristol and Whitehaven.[2] Scottish aristocrats, major landowners and their merchants engaged in the grain trade had benefited from changes in export bounty; shipments had doubled in the years between 1707 and 1722 and then had continued to increase. From 1727 the Scottish linen trade had the support of the Board of Trustees for Fisheries and Manufactures and production had doubled in the next 25 years. By 1740 the profits from these three commercial activities had already secured a major improvement in Scotland's finances.

Scotland was changing. The Scottish Parliament was gone, but the ruling bodies of the Scottish Church, the law and the universities were still north of the Border. The government in London was content to leave Scotland to rule itself under the careful eye of Lord Islay. In Edinburgh, Lord Islay had seen to the creation of a new Royal Bank of Scotland, a Whig bank to rival the Bank of Scotland which was believed to have Jacobite sympathies. There were many Jacobites in Edinburgh but they lived at peace with their neighbours who were content to have George II as their king. For most of the people of Edinburgh there was probably greater immediate interest in their three new newspapers, the two new magazines and the new theatre. Portrait painters such as William Aikman (1682–1731) and Allan Ramsay (1713–1784) and writers including James Thomson (1700–1748), Tobias

Smollett (1721–1771) and James Macpherson (1736–1796) still went to London to find patronage. But the philosophers, historians and scientists, David Hume (1711–1776), William Robertson (1721–1793), Adam Smith (1723–1790), William Cullen (1710–1790) and Lord Kames (1697–1782), who were soon to put Scotland at the heart of the intellectual and cultural vitality in Europe, were already at work in Edinburgh.

By 1742 Pringle had achieved a respected place in the life of Edinburgh. His closest friends were remarkable men. Colin Maclaurin (1697–1746) was a mathematician who had published works on algebra and geometry and had been made a Fellow of the Royal Society in 1721; in 1722, he was made Professor of Mathematics at Edinburgh on the recommendation of his friend Sir Isaac Newton. James Maitland (1718–1789) later, as Earl of Lauderdale, became one of Scotland's representative peers in Parliament. James Clerk (1712–1782), later Sir James Clerk of Penicuik, was an architect and town planner. James Mitchell (1709–1783) was the son of the minister of the High Kirk of St Giles in Edinburgh. He became Under Secretary of State for Scotland. Later, as Sir James Mitchell, he was for many years British envoy to Prussia; shortly before his death he was made a Field Marshal of the Prussian army.

Pringle was a member of the Rankenian Club in Edinburgh. The *Scots Magazine* wrote in May 1771 that it was 'well known that the Rankenians were highly instrumental in disseminating through Scotland freedom of thought, boldness of disquisition, liberality of sentiment, accuracy of reasoning, correctness of taste and attention of composition; and that the exalted rank which Scotsmen hold to present in the Republic of Letters is owing to the manner of and spirit begun by that Society'. William Wishart (Principal of Edinburgh University), John Stevenson (Professor of Logic at Edinburgh), George Turnbull (Professor of Moral Philosophy at Marischal College, Aberdeen), Sir Alexander Dick (President of the Royal College of Physicians of Edinburgh), Alexander Boswell (a Lord of Session) and his friend Colin Maclaurin were all among Pringle's fellow members.[3]

Pringle had reason to be content in Edinburgh. However, his classes at the university had not attracted a great number of fee-paying students; as a professor at Edinburgh his total income amounted to, at best, £100 a year.[4] He had been a Fellow of the Royal College of Physicians of Edinburgh for seven years. He had played his part in the College of Physicians' charitable provision for the sick poor; he had taught medical students at the Edinburgh Royal Infirmary; he had made major contributions to the upgrading of the College of Physicians' *Pharmacopoeia* and to the early success of *Medical*

Essays and Observations. But he had not been successful in building up a practice of paying patients. At the age of 34 he was still financially dependent on his older brother. It was something that had made him uneasy for much of his life.

Suddenly, in February 1742, came the news that Britain was to send an army to the war in Europe. For Pringle the raising of a new army opened up the prospect of more lucrative employment. Already, four of his close relatives had chosen to make their careers as officers in the British army.[5] Pringle decided that he too would 'go abroad with the army',[6] not as a combatant but as a physician.

The War of the Austrian Succession had begun in Europe in 1740, but in the many years since coming to power, Robert Walpole, the First Lord of the Treasury, and in effect Britain's first prime minister, had avoided the great expense of wars, especially wars from which Britain had little to gain. Since 1739, Britain had been at war with Spain in the West Indies (War of Jenkins' Ear) and in that war the issue was the disputed access to trade with Spanish colonies and the acquisition of valuable overseas assets. Walpole had been reluctant to go to war but, although troops were to be used, it was essentially a sea war in which the British navy was likely to win. However, in 1740, Walpole had refused to send British troops to fight in a new war in Europe in which Britain's interests and objectives were obscure. It would require the assembling of a new army, a small army that was unlikely to be successful in achieving anything of great advantage to Britain. But, on 11 February 1742, Walpole, who had been in office for 20 difficult years, had lost his majority in Parliament and had been forced to resign. King George's ambitious and convivial friend the Secretary of State, Lord Carteret, became the most influential minister in the new administration. Together, King George II and Lord Carteret were determined, for reasons of their own,[7] that Britain should commit an army to a war that had already been disrupting Europe for almost two years.

Pringle was aware that the British army offered very few places of employment for physicians. The medical care of the troops was, in general, the responsibility of the individual regiments. Every regiment in the army had its own surgeon; as there were two to four battalions in each regiment, each surgeon was responsible for the care of from 1,000 to 2,700 men.[8] Almost every regimental surgeon had been trained in his craft in some form of apprenticeship, often as a surgeon's mate in the army. His commission was with the regiment; like other commissions in the army it could be obtained either by purchase or by patronage. Once appointed he could expect to serve in the same regiment throughout his career in the army. The surgeon wore the uniform of the regiment and was responsible to the colonel of the regiment for the operation and administration of the regiment's infirmary.

He was assisted by one, or perhaps two, surgeon's mates appointed by the regiment, and his hospital orderlies were drawn from among the soldiers of the regiment. His nurses were chosen from the strictly limited number of soldiers' wives on campaign with the regiment; at that time, 4 per cent of all the wives of the men of each regiment were chosen by lot to accompany the regiment on campaign. It had been customary for every regiment to have its own self-sufficient infirmary capable of caring for some 40 casualties and sick at any one time. However, at the end of the seventeenth century, when Britain became involved in major wars in Europe, it was found that the intake of casualties left little room in these Regimental Infirmaries for the sick. Often the sick had to be left to the care of local doctors and to the charity of the local people. General Hospitals (that is, hospitals to support the Regimental Infirmaries and to serve other unattached army personnel) of 600 beds were formed to take the sick and wounded that the Regimental Infirmaries could not accommodate. Most often sited at or near the headquarters of the army, these new General Hospitals were not, as in civilian life, permanent buildings on fixed sites; in the army medical service the word 'hospital' referred to the personnel and equipment of a hospital that could be set up wherever it was needed, in a large house or some other suitable structure commandeered for the purpose. As General Hospitals were only required in time of war they were normally disbanded, and their medical personnel stood down on half pay, when the war came to an end.

The army's medical services were directed by a Physician-General and a Surgeon-General at Whitehall in London. Physicians-General were Fellows of the Royal College of Physicians of London, chosen on the strength of their eminence as physicians in civilian practice; it was unusual for a Physician-General to have personal experience of the medical care of an army in wartime. Surgeons-General had usually been trained as surgeon's mates and had gone on to distinguish themselves during many years of active service as surgeons in the army. Once appointed, the Physician-General and the Surgeon-General could, if they wished, hold their appointments for life. For their part-time services they received £1 a day and, except in times of war, their responsibilities were very few. In wartime they became directly responsible for the staffing and supervision of the General Hospitals and for advising on the management of the Regimental Infirmaries.[9]

In 1742, only one General Hospital was to go with the army to Flanders. As was then normal, it was to be staffed by one physician, one surgeon, one apothecary, four surgeon's mates, two apothecary's mates and one matron. The medical staff had no responsibility for the performance and discipline of the rank and file personnel serving in the General Hospitals. As the ward-masters, nurses, orderlies, cooks and clerks were all seconded for hospital duty by their regiments they were all under the command of a regimental officer appointed as Hospital Director.

The staff surgeons of the General Hospitals were chosen by the Surgeon-General on the basis of the expertise that they had shown in civilian practice; a few were chosen from among the best of the regimental surgeons. The staff physicians were recruited by the Physician-General and were, without exception, civilians with no training or previous experience in army medicine. They were required to be graduates of Oxford or Cambridge and Licentiates or Fellows of the Royal College of Physicians of London. They were paid 20 shillings a day, twice as much as the surgeons.

For Pringle an appointment as an army physician would provide a salary near to double his total income in Edinburgh. However, he was not a graduate of Oxford or Cambridge; nor was he a Licentiate or Fellow of the Royal College of Physicians of London. It was also very unlikely that he could attract the particular attention of the Physician-General, Dr Charles Peters, a London physician to whom he was completely unknown. Pringle could, once again, only look to his family's loyalty to the Squadrone Volante and the power of political patronage.

It was widely assumed that George II, an experienced soldier, would take command of the army being sent into Europe. It was also assumed that he would take with him as his second-in-command one or other of his two most senior officers in the army, Field Marshal the Duke of Argyll and Field Marshal the Earl of Stair. Either would be in a position to secure for Pringle a commission as a physician in the army. However, the Duke of Argyll and his brother, Lord Islay, were leaders of the Argathelian party, the party that had managed Scotland on behalf of Walpole's administration from 1725. Walpole's fall from power in 1742 had greatly weakened their position. It seemed probable that, even if the Duke of Argyll still had the power to do so, it was unlikely that he would be ready to grant a favour requested by the Squadrone Volante.

The Squadrone Volante was now in the ascendency. The Duke of Roxburghe had died in 1741. The 2nd Marquess of Tweeddale, the son of the founder of the party, was now the leader of the Squadrone Volante and in the new administration in 1742, he had become Secretary of State for Scotland. Tweeddale's family and Pringle's family were related by marriage.[10] It was perhaps even more important that the new Under Secretary for Scotland was Pringle's close friend Andrew Mitchell. From the office of the Secretary for Scotland in Whitehall in London, Andrew Mitchell acted as Pringle's agent in securing him a commission as a physician in the army.

It seemed probable that Lord Stair would be sympathetic to Pringle's case. His family and Pringle's family had been allies in the past and they knew each other well. Lord Stair was the son[11] of a distinguished Scottish lawyer, James Dalrymple. Together James Dalrymple and Pringle's great-uncle, Walter Pringle, had been the advocates who courageously but unsuccessfully defended the Marquess of Argyll at his trial for treason in 1681. In 1685, when the persecution of the Covenanters was at its height, members of both the Dalrymple and the Pringle families had been forced to leave Scotland and to take refuge under the protection of Prince William of Orange in the Netherlands. Three years later, after the Glorious Revolution of 1688, John Dalrymple had returned to Scotland where he had been chosen as one of the three Scottish commissioners sent to London to offer the crown of Scotland to William of Orange. The new King William III had made him Viscount Stair and one of his two Secretaries of State.[12]

When, after four years, the new King William III returned to the Netherlands to resume command of his army in his war with France, he gave Viscount Stair's 19-year-old son John Dalrymple a commission in one of the British regiments serving in the Dutch army. On the outbreak of the War of the Spanish Succession in 1701, the young John Dalrymple returned to the army. He served under the Duke of Marlborough, at the Battles of Blenheim, Ramillies and Oudenarde. At the Battle of Malplaquet he was one of Marlborough's Major Generals. In 1710, at the age of 37 (and now after his father's death, the 2nd Earl of Stair) he was promoted to Lieutenant General and appointed a Knight of the Thistle.

For almost ten years Lord Stair had been one of Marlborough's most reliable commanders and in that time he became Marlborough's friend, confidante and confidential envoy.[13] In London, Marlborough was admired as one of Europe's greatest generals, but politically he was deeply distrusted. In the revolution of 1688 he had abandoned his loyalty to James VII and II to help William of Orange to take the British throne. In 1710, there was further cause to distrust him. There were many in government and in Parliament who were convinced that the Battle of Malplaquet, which had cost an unprecedented number of lives, had been unnecessary and had been fought only for Marlborough's glory. Marlborough had a small but powerful team ready to defend him, the queen, his wife Sarah, a close friend of the queen, and Sidney Godolphin, the First Lord of the Treasury. However, Marlborough could not be protected from his critics indefinitely. In the election in 1710 Godolphin was driven from office. In December 1711, Marlborough was dismissed as Captain-General of the Army. Although it was known that Lord Stair had been actively involved in Marlborough's clandestine political manoeuvrings to prolong the war, he was allowed to retire from the army on half pay and to take his seat in the House of Lords. In 1742, King George recalled him to the army and made him a Field Marshal.

At the beginning of February 1742, Andrew Mitchell approached Lord Stair with a request for a commission for Pringle as a physician in the army. By the middle of April, neither Andrew Mitchell nor Pringle had received any direct response from Lord Stair. But there was some news. It came in a letter that the Earl of Loudoun, one of Lord Stair's four aides de camp, had written to his mother in Edinburgh. Loudoun informed his mother that before embarking for Flanders with the first detachment of the army, Lord Stair had left him an instruction that 'if there were to be a second embarkation'[14] he was to act in Lord Stair's name and have Pringle appointed as a physician to the army. When the Dowager Countess of Loudoun passed on this news, a delighted Pringle wrote to Mitchell of how much he was 'obliged by Lord Stair's kindness in what is likely to be a critical part of my life'. But for weeks Pringle heard no more. On 17 June, he wrote to Andrew Mitchell:

> In my last letter I expressed my doubts of the success of my scheme for going abroad from the notion we had here that the King or the Duke of Argyll was to command the army. But now we are made to believe that Lord Stair is to be head of the army and that the artillery and the horse are embarking. I should have resumed my hopes had it not been for the silence of my friends, having heard nothing from Lord Stair nor has Lord Loudoun wrote anything of the affair. I was expecting every post to hear that I was named or some other person. I desire therefore, my dear Mitchell, you will speedily take me out of this state of uncertainty and let me know what is to become of me for I can settle to nothing till that important point is settled.

However, the silence continued until 3 July when he heard, very unofficially, from Andrew Mitchell that he was to receive a commission as a physician to the army on a salary of 10 shillings a day. He immediately applied for leave from his duties at Edinburgh University. When leave was granted, he wrote to Andrew Mitchell:

As my Lord Stair's nomination is honourable I have no anxiety about the profits and, as I am not to untie myself here [from Edinburgh University] my fortune can never suffer. I have been a pensioner these eleven years and my enlargement, as it is beyond expectations, gives me more pleasure than I believed I should have had this side of Eternity. The concern you show for my interest and your expressing your dissatisfaction with the progress is a new proof of your kindness. Make my compliments to Lord Loudoun and let me know if on getting my warrant if I should come to London or repair immediately to the Hague in the event of my having no letter from Lord Stair.

After a further month there had still been no letter or other communication from Lord Stair. Without any instruction to do so, Pringle now made his own way to Lord Stair's headquarters at the Hague. His arrival there was not expected. He found the staff at army headquarters even less informed about his appointment than he was himself. His reception by the staff was at first 'civil but cool', but eased somewhat when Lord Loudoun sent a number of letters of introduction.

However, there was still no indication of how Pringle was to be employed. As there were reports that the garrison at Ghent was 'very sickly', Pringle thought that he might be sent there to help but he was to be disappointed. For weeks after Lord Stair had returned to his headquarters, Pringle found him 'ominously silent' about his future employment.[15]

While he waited, Pringle renewed friendships that he had made at university in Leiden. He spent some time with Gerhard van Swieten, soon to be appointed Austria's Chief Physician and Director of the Imperial Library, and Jan Ingen Housz, the physiologist and clinician who was later to become personal physician to the Empress Maria Theresa of Austria.[16] He began his correspondence with the botanist and anatomist Albrecht von Haller, who had recently been made a professor at the new University of Göttingen.[17]

Pringle visited and was warmly welcomed by his Hope cousins in Amsterdam where Isaac Hope was the owner of one of the most successful trading houses in Europe. He persuaded Colin Maclaurin and his other

General and staff officers appointed to serve in Flanders for the year 1742

	Salary per day	£	s	d
Field Marshal	Earl of Stair	10		
Lieutenant Generals	Honywood	4		
	Earl of Dunmore	4		
	Sir James Campbell	4		
Major Generals	Howard	2		
	Cope	2		
	Ligonier	2		
	Hawley	2		
	Earl of Albemarle	2		
Brigadier Generals	Cornwallis	1	10	
	Earl of Rothes	1	10	
	Earl of Effingham	1	10	
	Onslow	1	10	
	Pultney	1	10	
	Hushe	1	10	
	Ponsonby	1	10	
	Frampton	1	10	
Quartermaster General	Colonel Bland		10	
Secretary	William Adair		10	
Deputy Judge Advocate	Thomas Cokayne		10	
Physician	Doctor Pringle		10	
Chaplain	Guideon Murray		6	8 |[18]

friends to visit him from Edinburgh and made a point of introducing these very interesting and stimulating young men to Lord Stair. Lord Stair was intrigued by Colin Maclaurin's scheme for opening up of a Northwest Passage between the Atlantic and Pacific Oceans. Isaac Hope explained to Lord Stair the need for the protection of Britain's overseas trade from the privateers operating in the Channel; Lord Stair arranged for Isaac Hope to meet the relevant government minister, the Secretary of State, Lord Carteret.[18]

Pringle also continued to make himself useful to his patrons in London, the leaders of the Squadrone Volante. He provided his friend Andrew Mitchell, the Under Secretary for Scotland, with up-to-date reports of the strength and distribution of French forces in Germany; with news of the movements of the Austrian generals Prince Charles of Lorraine and

Count Khevenhüller; with his assessment of the training and equipment of the Hanoverian army; and maps of the expected theatre of war that he had specially commissioned from Mercator of Amsterdam, the leading mapmaker of the time.

At the same time Pringle did what he could to prepare himself to be of service to Lord Stair himself. Lord Stair had learned his soldiering under Marlborough. In 1704, he had been with Marlborough when he had led the British army on a march of 500 miles from Flanders to Bavaria and victory over a larger French army at Blenheim. In great part the success of this historic campaign was due to the attention that Marlborough had given to the care of his troops. He had insisted that, in order to march and fight, his soldiers must be properly fed on bread, beef and beer. He had seen to the efficient distribution of the men's rations; he concerned himself with the state of their boots and their feet; he had attended to these important matters that had always been seen as the responsibility of the army's most junior officers; to his troops he became known as 'Corporal John'. Pringle thought it probable that in the coming campaign Lord Stair would wish to apply, or even improve on, the measures that his great mentor, Marlborough, had used to maintain the health and strength of his troops.

Pringle read Xenophon's account of the sufferings of the Greek army when exposed to extreme cold, Pliny on the distemper that afflicted the Roman army in a long campaign in Germany and Plutarch on the thousands of deaths from lack of provisions suffered by Demetrius's army in India. He reviewed the range of medical services provided in the other armies involved in the war. Since 1705, France had maintained a complement of 200 physicians and surgeons to serve the army in the field; all those employed were examined by specialist boards to make sure of their competence; 50 advisory physicians were appointed to ensure the quality of medical practice in the hospitals; 138 surgeons to provide immediate care in the field; four surgeons-major to inspect military forts and camps, and four medical inspectors-general were appointed to oversee the whole system.[19] In all, 85 military hospitals had recently been built or improved in fortified towns across France.

At the other extreme, in Prussia in every campaign each army commander had been left to make his own arrangements for the provision of medical and surgical services for his troops. In 1705, only 6 of the 35 regiments of the Prussian army employed surgeons. Surgical services were generally delegated to the barber-surgeons who had been employed to shave the officers; in the

Prussian army the status of the barber-surgeons was only slightly above
that of the drummers. By the 1740s, some improvements had been made.
A Surgeon-General had been appointed in 1716 and a Physician-General
in 1724; and the king had issued an instruction that the competence of
physicians and surgeons should be examined before they were appointed
(a regulation that was seldom enforced). Prussia's first military hospital
was established in Berlin in 1725. But, in 1726, a new regulation forbade
any medical attention being given to the wounded until the battle was
over.[20] Pringle meant to make it clear to Lord Stair that, although he had
never served in an army at war and had no personal experience of military
medicine, he had made every effort to compensate for that deficiency by
careful study of the experience and medical services of the British and the
other armies.

To make it clear that he had made a close study of all of Lord Stair's
many campaigns, he presented him with a set of maps that he had specially
commissioned from Mercator of Amsterdam. They highlighted every
strategic march, every battlefield and every besieged fortified town that
marked the progress of Stair's military career.

Pringle meant to show that he was prepared for Lord Stair's coming
campaign. Lord Stair could look forward to a campaign of six months in
which an army could expect to lose half of its strength from desertion and
disease. In any war in eighteenth-century Europe, it was to be expected that
disease would kill many more than the battle with the enemy.[21] If Lord Stair
aimed to reduce this massive waste, he required expert medical advice. The
appropriate advice could not be provided by the Physician-General or the
Surgeon-General in Whitehall. The expertise of the Physician-General, Dr
Peters, was in civil private practice. The Surgeon-General Mr John Pawlett
had been a surgeon's mate at Blenheim and later surgeon to the Horse
Guards but had never been called on to pay attention to the prevention of
the diseases that killed so many soldiers in every army.

However, Pringle had advantages. He had lived and travelled in Europe
for over four years and was fluent in Dutch, German and French, all useful
attributes when serving in a multinational allied army in northern Europe.
He had already made his mark in Edinburgh as an innovating physician
and in the weeks since his arrival in the Low Countries he had shown his
readiness to accommodate himself to the needs of the army. These considerations might persuade Lord Stair to employ him. But the delay suggested
the possibility that Lord Stair had been reluctant to respond to a request
from a political party in London to which he owed nothing. Or it may

have been that, having taken no part in the political life of Britain for 30 years, Lord Stair was uncertain of his standing with the new administration headed by the Secretary of State, Lord Carteret. If so, his fears were unfounded.

When Lord Carteret visited Lord Stair's headquarters at the Hague on 5 October 1742, the meeting was entirely agreeable. Lord Stair presented Pringle with a commission as Physician-General to the Army and, at the same time, appointed him as his personal physician. Pringle, who had hoped only be made a physician at the army's General Hospital was surprised and delighted. He was also surprised and delighted that he was to receive, not 10 shillings a day as a physician on the staff of a General Hospital, but a salary of 20 shillings a day as Physician-General to the Army and 10 shillings a day as Physician to the Commander-in-Chief; and when his services were not required by the army he would be retained for life on half pay of 15 shillings a day. He was at last financially independent of his family.

As Physician-General to the Army, he was naturally allowed some discretion in deciding how he should be most usefully employed.

The persons appointed to the General Hospital in Flanders 1742

Position	Name	Salary per day
Hospital Director	John Ellis	25 shillings
Physician	Alexander Sandilands	20 shillings
Master Surgeon	Robert Adair	10 shillings
Apothecary	William Ores	10 shillings
Surgeon's Mates	John How, Robert Wynn	5 shillings
	John Adair, George Ketling	
Apothecary's Mates	Robert Kerr William Eyre	5 shillings
Matron	C. Murray	2 shillings 6 pence

During the campaign he would be obliged to be with Lord Stair at the headquarters of the army but he decided that, while the army was in winter quarters at Ghent, he would share Sandilands' duties at the army's General Hospital. This was an arrangement that was agreeable to Sandilands since it allowed him time to attend to his private patients; it was of course understood that Pringle would also see private patients from the local population and would continue to be consulted privately by the officers of senior rank in the army.

Pringle found himself in a strange environment with new and unfamiliar problems. He made every effort to learn from all those around him whatever there was to learn and at the same time establish sound professional relationships with them. On 2 February 1743, four months after his appointment as Physician-General, he wrote to Andrew Mitchell giving an account of what had been achieved.

He reported that he had been on good terms with Lord Stair although there had been times when 'being with him gives me more pain than can be compensated with all the honour and profit of being the only physician here' at headquarters. He stood well with all three Lieutenant Generals and five Major Generals. He had fewer contacts with more junior officers but they had treated him with civility, a civility that he attributed to the care that they saw him take of their men. He had been particularly concerned over his relationship with Dr Sandilands who had been somewhat upset by his arrival at Ghent, not as his assistant but as his superior officer. However, he had been careful not to offend Sandilands' dignity. He had been careful to call him in consultation when Lord Stair's son had been dangerously ill with smallpox.

In the months he had already spent in Flanders Pringle had seen something of the life of an army. A number of the officers were of aristocratic families, but the majority were young gentlemen who could afford to purchase a commission. It seemed clear to Pringle that the officers identified more with their opposite numbers in the enemy army than with the men they commanded. They knew that if captured they would be treated with courtesy; they could expect to be exchanged for prisoners of the same rank in the enemy army or returned at the end of the summer when the fighting stopped. War for the officers was an honourable occupation that could bring further honour.

Life for the ordinary soldiers was very different. It seemed to Pringle that they were a commodity necessary for the conduct of war. Many would die in battle. But many more would be lost through desertion and disease during a campaign in which it was unusual for any distinction to be made between the deserters and the diseased. Nevertheless, during their first weeks in Flanders they seemed content with their lot. Pringle found that they 'were well cared for and enjoyed high spirits'. Most had reason to celebrate. Every regiment had a useful number of seasoned men; a few of them had joined up for glory and excitement, others had been attracted by the prospect of loot and plunder, but in time the army had become their way of life. However, the majority of the men were new recruits, driven to enlist by poverty and hunger. At that time, half the population of Britain lived at subsistence level[22] and in hard times scarcity became acute want. Famine was then the most effective of recruiting sergeants. Recruits were only required to be at least 5 feet 5 inches tall, without obvious physical deformity, with no hernias, not subject to fits and able to write their names. The bread, cheese, meat and beer provided by the army made a better diet than most of the men had ever known. The bounty of £4 that they received on enlistment and thereafter a regular pay of sixpence a day gave them more money in their pockets than they had ever had. They had to learn discipline and they had to be trained for combat. But in their free time they could leave aside their scarlet coats in favour of a standard loose white shirt and relax with their friends. Many were accompanied by their wives; drinking and dancing were the favourite forms of entertainment.

However, as always when new armies came together, sickness increased as many of the recruits became 'acclimatised' not only to a new environment but also to the diseases that were already endemic in the regiments that they had joined. Almost as soon as the British troops landed in Flanders the itch (scabies) had become so common among the men that their officers believed that either the salt provisions at sea or the change of air must have been responsible. Pringle, however, was in no doubt that 'it was solely owing to the contagion of a few, who having the distemper before embarkation communicated it to their companions on board the ships or in the barracks'.[23] Scabies continued to plague the army throughout the war; the damage to the skin caused by scratching was always among the most common disorders requiring treatment in the army's Regimental Infirmaries. Smallpox continued to be at least as common in the army as in the civilian population. Venereal disease was as rife as it was in every army.

In the summer of 1742, fever (malaria) had become a major problem among the men; the officers were much less likely to be affected. At Ghent, where three battalions of the First Foot Guards were stationed, Pringle noticed that the incidence was high in the two companies that were lodged in billets in the low-lying parts of the town 'in the ground floors of houses without drains in rooms so damp that the men could scarce keep their belts from moulding'; at the same time the eight companies of the same regiment lodged in the higher part of the town 'in barracks, having drains and free air and quite dry' enjoyed perfect health. On noting the differences in the incidence of fever in all the regiments stationed at Ghent, Pringle concluded that regiments 'suffered much less in proportion' to the height of their billets above sea level. At Bruges, in the most low-lying part of Flanders, the incidence of this fever began in June, reached a peak in August and continued until November; overall the incidence was three times higher there than at Ghent and a greater proportion of its victims died. In sharp contrast, at Grammont, in one of the highest parts of Flanders, a regiment of dragoons billeted in private houses remained completely healthy during the nine months it was there. The treatments normally applied in similar cases of fever in Britain proved to be inadequate in Flanders; in Flanders many of the fevers degenerated into continuous fevers (typhus) as the remissions became shorter and less frequent; at this stage the disease was often fatal.

Almost as common as fever was the flux (diarrhoea), in some cases developing into bloody dysentery. It seemed to Pringle that in the causation of this illness it was not the height above sea level that was important but the height above ground level. He observed that 'such as lay in the upper stories were much more healthy than those who were below in the ground floors which were very damp'. It was later recognised that these diseases resulted from poor drainage and contamination by faecal material.

In November, the epidemics of fever and of flux came to an end and the winter disorders began, colds, coughs, rheumatic pains and 'inflammations of the lungs', all of which, Pringle believed, were to be expected among soldiers, 'unused to cold quarters and unprovided with clothes suited to the country and the season, at this time particularly sharp'.

Much more alarming for Pringle was a further outbreak in hospital of the continuous fever (typhus), 'slow in its course and attended with a sunk pulse and a constant stupor. The 'novelty and danger more than the number seized, made this distemper considerable'; the great majority of the patients died. In December, of the 442 men admitted to the General Hospital at Ghent, 82 had died of this continuous fever. Many more had been treated in their Regimental Infirmaries and an unknown number had died there. Thereafter the incidence of sickness continued to increase.

For months the British army had suffered greatly from disease but it had achieved very little. When it arrived from England in the spring of 1742, the army had settled with its headquarters at Ghent but with other units stationed at Breda, Bruges, Courtrai and Oudenarde. In October 1742, the 16,000 troops that Lord Stair had brought from Britain were joined by 16,000 Hanoverian troops and, as Lord Carteret negotiated alliances with the other anti-Bourbon allies, the new Pragmatic Army grew to a force of 52,000. But the armies had waited while British, Hanoverian, Dutch and Austrian generals puzzled over where they were to be sent and how they were to be used.

FIVE

Dettingen: Victory and Catastrophe

Think what thousands fell in vain
Wasted with disease and anguish
Not in glorious battle slain.

Traditional[1]

On 16 January 1743, the British army began to move out of winter quarters in Flanders and into its first campaign in the war in Europe. It was a war being fought by the Bourbons of France and Spain, the Hapsburgs of Austria, the Hohenzollerns of Prussia and the Wittelsbachs of Bavaria. It was a war to determine the balance of power in Europe.

The occasion of the war was the death on 20 October 1740 of Charles VI, Holy Roman Emperor of the German Nation and Archduke of Austria. In 1713, when his daughter, Maria Theresa, was only four years old, he had secured the agreement of the ruling houses of Europe to his Pragmatic Sanction. This was a decree that on his death all his Hapsburg possessions should pass unchallenged and intact to his daughter: he conceded that, as a woman, Maria Theresa could not succeed to the elective office of Emperor of the Holy Roman Empire, an office that his family had held for over two centuries. In 1713, Britain, France, Spain, Prussia, Russia and the United Provinces had all agreed to the terms of his decree,[2] but 27 years later, when Charles VI died, it was less than certain that the heads of the major European nations would still honour that agreement. In 1740, Austria was the heart of his daughter's Hapsburg inheritance, but Austria's provinces, variously acquired by conquest or marriage, lay as an archipelago scattered across Europe from Flanders to Italy. Each one had its own culture, customs and language and since they had been acquired they had always been difficult to administer. Now, they had also become difficult to defend. Austria had become overstretched both financially and militarily by years of war with her Ottoman neighbours to the east. Maria Theresa wrote that she found herself 'without money, without credit, without an army, without experience'. A number of the ruling houses of Europe were ready to set aside the guarantees that they had given to abide by the Pragmatic Sanction and to take advantage of Austria's, and Maria Theresa's weakness.

The conflict that followed was acted out in three separate theatres of war. The northern theatre was in the Low Countries, extending across the Austrian Netherlands and the Dutch Republic. The central theatre centred on Prague on the River Elbe and included Bohemia, Silesia and Moravia. The southern theatre lay south of the Alps across the north of Italy.

The first nation to breach the Pragmatic Sanction was Prussia. On 16 December 1740, Frederick II of Prussia led his armies across his southern border to seize Silesia, the most industrialised and the richest of Austria's provinces. Austria had been unprepared for the attack; the army that was hastily gathered to oppose it was outnumbered and soon heavily defeated. Frederick's seizure of Silesia had been quick and complete. His success stirred the ambitions of King Charles Albert of Bavaria to take Bohemia; by taking Bohemia he would not only acquire one of Austria's major provinces he would also acquire Bohemia's crucial vote in having himself elected as the new Holy Roman Emperor. And Elisabeth Farnese, the Bourbon Queen Consort of Spain, meant to take advantage of Austria's weakness and send an army to acquire territories in northern Italy for her son.

Louis XV, the Bourbon King of France, had one of the largest kingdoms in Europe and one of the largest armies. He had no ambition to expand territorially but he was ambitious to become the dominant power in Europe and bring to an end the long-standing eminence of the Austrian Hapsburgs. This he planned to achieve by sending armies to support the assaults on Austria planned by Charles Albert of Bavaria and Elisabeth Farnese of Spain.

However, support for Austria was gathering in the north. Britain, Hanover, the Dutch Republic, the Austrian Netherlands, Saxony and Russia came together to uphold the provisions of the Pragmatic Sanction. The scene was now set for war. The northern allies began to plan a Pragmatic Army to enforce the terms of the Pragmatic Sanction. The Dutch Republic, the Austrian Netherlands and Saxony promised to send equal numbers of troops; as Elector of Hanover, George II committed Hanoverian troops to the army. Britain undertook to pay George II's Hanoverian troops and to hire Hessian and Danish troops to join them. Britain also provided finance to strengthen Austria's armies in the south. But Walpole's administration in London refused to commit a British army to the coming war.

However, in February 1742, when Walpole lost his majority in Parliament and was forced to resign, the new administration in Britain decided to send an army and to lead the Pragmatic Army in the north. But much had changed since then. Austria had recovered her strength and the armies of Prussia, Bavaria and France had all been driven back. Frederick of Prussia still held only the northern part of Silesia. Charles Albert of Bavaria had invaded Bohemia and had been elected Holy Roman Emperor; but he had been unable to hold Bohemia. It seemed that Louis XV of France had failed to shift the balance of power in Europe and make the Bourbons the dominant power in Europe.

When Pringle joined the army in Flanders, the original causes of the war had all been resisted and were no longer relevant. However, in Britain the new Secretary of State, Lord Carteret, meant to secure Europe against any further attempt by Louis XV to upset the balance of power. He was confident that this could be achieved, preferably by diplomacy but, if necessary, by force. King George II was intent on continuing the conflict as the leader of the Pragmatic Army in the north, but his objectives had not been made clear.

In January 1743, the army moved out of Flanders to begin its march into Germany. The weather was extremely cold. There was deep snow on the ground as the army marched 125 miles to Aix-la-Chapelle, 20 miles beyond the German border.[3] Fortunately, each night the troops were billeted in warm houses and they were well supplied with food and drink. As the army marched south, the health of the troops rapidly improved. From Aix-la-Chapelle on 2 February, Pringle reported to Andrew Mitchell that 'our men have kept their health on the march and are better than in the barracks. They have likewise been extremely regular, obedient and quiet in all their actions and abstaining from any outrage what so ever.'[4]

However, not every section of the army had been so fortunate. Part of the cavalry had been left behind for a time at Brussels and there they were exposed to an unfamiliar disease that had been sweeping across Europe. Pringle called this strange new disease 'influenza'.

While at Aix-la-Chapelle, Pringle could look back on his time in Flanders with some satisfaction. He had been made Physician-General to the Army and personal physician to Lord Stair, appointments more prestigious than he could possibly have expected. His appointments had surprised and disconcerted the other members of Lord Stair's staff but after a period of some awkwardness they had accepted him. Thereafter, he 'had continued to live without the least quarrel or animosity with any person.'[5] Everything had been far beyond his expectations. He had been on good terms with Lord Stair and all the senior staff officers. He had had less day to

day contact with the regimental officers but they had been ready to consult
him privately when they were unwell and his private practice among the
local population had also flourished. In a letter to Andrew Mitchell he
wrote:

> Practice crowded in on me more in the last month than I expected
> or desired. If anything pleased me it was finding how much more
> easily I could please strangers than my own countrymen. I mean that
> although my temper of manners was unluckily unsuitable to my own
> there were people with whom they tallied.

There had been some early difficulty in his relationship with Dr Sandilands,
the physician who had been upset when Pringle was appointed Physician-
General. However, a few days before leaving Ghent, Pringle had invited
Sandilands to his lodgings; they had passed a pleasant evening together and
had parted on good terms.

While at Aix-la-Chapelle Pringle began to look to the future. In a letter to
Andrew Mitchell, he wrote that he had:

> given great application to studying the garrison diseases and have wrote
> all my observations. I have not yet had time to put anything in order
> proper to be seen by others but if you think it can be of service to me
> in my further fortune to communicate what I know to the curious and
> considerable of our profession through you I shall endeavour to do it
> the best I can. If I can see a campaign through and keep my health I
> flatter myself I may have a work useful to the public.

As that campaign progressed, Pringle continued to record his observations on the health and wellbeing of the British troops.[6] But throughout the
campaign in 1743, he also continued to send confidential reports on the state
and progress of the army to Andrew Mitchell at the office of the Secretary
for Scotland at Whitehall in London. When signing these letters Pringle
frequently used the pseudonym 'J. A. Frazer'. There was good reason for his
caution. In his letters he was expressing his disapproval of the confusion at
army headquarters and the failure of the army commanders to produce any
coherent plan for the coming campaign; he was concerned that the weeks
of idleness might impair the health of the troops. The letters were carried
to London by couriers employed by army headquarters and there was a
constant danger that they might be opened.

The Pragmatic Army was at Aix-la-Chapelle, fully assembled and ready to move, but where it was to be sent was still unknown. For Pringle this was something that he 'could not begin to guess at'. It was not until the middle of April that King George directed that the allied army (16,000 British, 16,000 Hanoverian, 6,000 Hessian and 20,000 Austrian troops) should march 300 miles south to Aschaffenburg in Bavaria. The king's purpose was not revealed, but it was clear that the march would bring the army into contact with the large French army stationed south of Aschaffenburg at Strasbourg.

Before leaving Aix-la-Chapelle in April, Pringle made some remarkable preparations for the long march and the battle that would inevitably follow. To Mitchell in London he reported:

> I am advised by Sir John Ligonier to write to the director of the French hospitals for an account of their diseases and at the same time promising them all our information. He does not doubt of their correspondence. I mentioned it to Lord Stair and he was of the same opinion. I propose by the same advice and authority to demand of the Protomedicus [Chief Physician] at Vienna a history of the Austrian garrison and camp diseases which will not only satisfy my curiosity on the way but be of service to ourselves when exposed to the same hardships.

This exchange of letters led to Pringle's proposal to Lord Stair that he should seek an agreement with the Duke of Noailles, the commander of the French army, that the hospitals of both sides in the campaign should be kept immune from attack, that the staff of military hospitals should not be made prisoners of war and that all military hospitals should be prepared to take care of the sick and wounded of both sides in the conflict.[7] Lord Stair agreed to convey Pringle's proposal to the Duke of Noailles. In his letter, Lord Stair assured the duke that his 'sentiments are and always will be to make war with all the generosity and humanity possible'. The Duke of Noailles accepted Pringle's proposal in an equally courteous letter.

From Aix-la-Chapelle the army marched 160 miles to Hoechst near Frankfurt, arriving there on 17 May. The troops then endured another period of idleness. Pringle was becoming more and more anxious about the health of the men. For the troops, the campaign was short periods of exhausting marches separated by longer periods of boredom. They faced a risk of death by disease that was far greater than the risk of death in battle.[8] The battles were likely to be very few. In the wars in Europe in the first half of the eighteenth century, battles never came as often as once a month. Battles could be easily avoided. Armies always marched in column, and the columns were often some miles long. To position an army in battle formation in a long line facing the enemy took much longer than it took an army to march off from the proposed field of combat. In this way a cautious commander who wished to avoid battle could always impose his will on a more belligerent opponent. Battles were joined only when both commanders were confident of victory as the risks of engagement were high. Defeat could mean the loss of the bulk of a commander's troops, his artillery, his baggage train, his strategic position and perhaps even the war. In the course of the war in Europe, the only general who always chose battle was Frederick II of Prussia.[9] More typical of that time was France's general, Maurice de Saxe, who achieved his ends by skilful tactical manoeuvres that threatened and effectively dominated his opponents so successfully that he had no need to commit his troops to battle.

Even when opposing commanders had chosen to fight, the manoeuvring continued as they moved their troops to occupy any available high ground or to conceal their presence and strength from the enemy in depressions in the ground or behind woods or even behind other sections of their own armies. A battle rarely lasted for as long as half a day; but the marching and manoeuvring before the battle could last for weeks and during those weeks armies continued to lose large but uncertain numbers by disease.

Pringle was now commenting in his letters to Andrew Mitchell on the lack of attention to the care of the troops. Throughout the eighteenth century the infantry made up three-quarters of the British army. During all the weeks or months of manoeuvring the infantryman's feet were his only mode of transport and he was ill-equipped for such prolonged and often difficult marching. His uniform, intended primarily to distinguish friend from foe, was designed neither for comfort nor efficiency. It consisted of a knee-length wideskirted scarlet coat, faced and cuffed in the colour of his regiment and turned and buttoned back at the tail; a long-flapped waistcoat; scarlet breeches covered to thigh length by white or grey canvas gaiters; buckled black shoes; and the whole topped off by a black tricorne hat and a leather stock at the neck to keep the soldier's head upright and facing the front. From his belt hung his cartridge pouch of 24 rounds. On his left hip, attached to a waist-belt, was a 16-inch-long bayonet of fluted steel. A grey canvas haversack carried two shirts, two pairs of stockings, a pair of breeches, a pair of shoes, brushes, blacking and pipe-clay and enough bread for six days. On his shoulder he carried a Black Bess musket weighing over 11 pounds and, on his back he carried over 60 pounds of equipment. As he trudged along, his shoes often failed to protect his feet and the lashing together of his heavily gaitered thighs could cause irritation and bleeding. On the march he had no overcoat to protect him from the weather. When he slept, he had no blanket and, unless he was lucky enough to find a more comfortable billet, he had to lie only on straw. Supply services were unreliable and on a long march they often failed completely, leaving the infantryman forced to forage for himself. The cavalry were rather better off. They had war cloaks to protect them from the weather and their greater mobility gave them some advantage in searching for tolerable quarters and in foraging for food.[10]

During the march to Hoechst the troops had been generally well; only 20 men had died from sickness. Lord Stair was very reluctant to take the army further up the River Main and for five weeks the army remained encamped at Hoechst. The troops were housed in tents in groups of five or six men who formed their own small mess, sharing their rations and the cost of any food that they could buy from the local people. When they slept, they shared any blankets that they had. Pringle noted that although 'the days were warm, the nights were still cold and condensed the vapours. Interchanges of hot and cold, joined to the moisture inseparable from tents, could not but affect the health of men unused to the field and accordingly many were seized with inflammatory diseases.'[11] A Flying Hospital[12] was opened at Nied, a small village near the camp, and in the following weeks it admitted 500 patients suffering from coughs, pleurisy, pneumonia, rheumatic pains, fevers and fluxes. A much greater number were treated in their Regimental Infirmary.

Early in June, instructions were received from King George that the army was to continue its advance along the north bank of the River Main to Aschaffenburg in the Archbishopric of Mainz. On 17 June, the army encamped on an open site on the north side of the river at the small village of Klein Ostheim on the western outskirts of Aschaffenburg. The condition of the army had become desperate. After an arduous march of 200 miles the allied troops had been bivouacked at Aschaffenburg without tents, and exposed to heavy rain. There were many sick. After marching from Strasbourg, the Duke of Noailles had sent a detachment of his army downstream to block the passage of the boats carrying the allied army's supplies from Flanders to Aschaffenburg by way of the Rhine and the Main. The allied army had been without bread or other food supplies for over a week. Discipline had broken down; pillaging bands of men were scouring the countryside in search of food; the local peasantry had driven their cattle away to prevent the troops from seizing them.

Only now did it become clear that King George's aim in bringing the allied army to Aschaffenburg was to make his power felt in the election of a new Archbishop of Mainz. As Elector of Hanover, King George II had an obvious and commanding interest in which of the candidates was chosen as the Archbishop was also Elector of Mainz and had a vote. However, it was not until 19 June that King George arrived to take personal command of the army. He was accompanied by his second son William, Duke of Cumberland, his Secretary of State, Lord Carteret, and a very large retinue, all carried in a great column of coaches accompanied by 25 squadrons of British and Hanoverian cavalry. However, after their arrival, King George and his party immediately left again for Mainz, some 50 miles away, to attend the election of the new Archbishop of Mainz. The army waited at Aschaffenburg, its misery increasing.

Meanwhile the Duke of Noailles had taken a position on the high ground on the south side of the river overlooking the allied Pragmatic Army encamped below in the valley on the north side of the river. The generals on either side did not rush into battle but each took time to study the strength and disposition of his enemy. When King George returned to his army, it was already clear that the advantage now lay overwhelmingly with Noailles. Noailles had an army of over 70,000 men, well-supplied and in good health, in a commanding position on high ground. King George had an enfeebled army of fewer than 50,000 men, enclosed in a narrow valley overlooked by high ground on both sides of the River Main. King George blamed Lord Stair for the state of the army and the difficulties of its position. He consulted his Hanoverian generals and decided to abandon Aschaffenberg and withdraw his army downstream on the road running along the north side of the River Main.

Anticipating this move, Noailles had planned to trap the allied army within the narrow valley as it attempted to withdraw. On 26 June, he sent his nephew, the Duke of Grammont, and 23,000 men 3 miles downstream to Dettingen to block the western exit from the valley. During the night at Dettingen, Grammont crossed to the north side of the river over a bridge of boats and took up a strong defensive position, blocking the road from behind the protection of an area of bog created by small tributaries as they flowed across the road into the river.

As expected, in the evening of 26 June, the allied army moved out of

Aschaffenburg and marched during the night towards Dettingen. As the allies left Aschaffenburg, Noailles sent the main body of his infantry to occupy the town, effectively blocking the eastern exit from the valley. King George discovered that his army had been trapped early in the morning of 27 June when scouts at the head of his retreating column reported Grammont's presence at Dettingen. The king decided to fight his way out of the trap through Dettingen. First he had to form his army from columns into lines of battle, the British troops forming the front line, with the Austrians behind them and the Hanoverian troops in the rear line. Few of his 50,000 troops had experience of battle and the manoeuvre took more than three hours to complete. During that time, the French artillery, ranged along the high ground on the south side of the valley, bombarded the allied army's column caught immobile on the road below. Pringle, lodged in Lord Carteret's coach, had his first experience of battle. He survived without injury.

After the formation of the allied army's battle line had been completed it was Grammont's troops who seized the initiative and moved to the attack. Their move was inexplicable and led to disaster for the Duke of Noailles. They had been ordered to remain as the defence against the Pragmatic Army's escape and a vital part of their defence had been the bog and broken ground lying to their front. By moving forward into the attack the boggy ground ceased to be to their advantage and became a hazard that made it impossible for them to maintain their order and discipline as they advanced. With their ranks broken and confused, they were unable to withstand the well-directed fire of the British infantry and the onslaughts of the British cavalry that followed. They broke and ran; in trying to escape many of them were drowned in the river.

There were hundreds of casualties on both sides. One British regimental surgeon wrote:

It is impossible to describe the variety of wounds from cannon shot, small arms, sword and bayonets. My first intention in dressing wounds was to stop bleeding, which I did by stitching the vessels, dry dressings, bandage, etc. Having no assistant I avoided amputations as much as possible although the necessity obliged me in some cases. The night passed amidst the groans of the dying and the complaints of those who survived them. Slight wounds were dressed with Balsam Traumatic. Drought is the most universal complaint from all the wounded and surgeons would do better in filling their chests with proper liquors for this purpose than stuffing them with apothecaries' drugs; shrubs and water answer this intention.[13]

When the battle at Dettingen had clearly been won, and ignoring the vigorous protests of Lord Stair, King George chose not to pursue the enemy but to withdraw his hungry army as quickly as possible to a supply depot 20 miles downstream at Hanau where some provisions were still available. In his hasty withdrawal, many of his army's sick and wounded had to be left behind. Fortunately the Duke of Noailles honoured the agreement that Pringle had proposed in April and they were well cared for at the French military hospitals by both their own regimental surgeons and French army surgeons. The regimental surgeon already quoted above wrote:

> The day after the battle I was sent to the French camp in order to visit the wounded of our army. Their surgeons went around the hospital with a tub of brandy and a syringe with which they washed out the wounds, dressing with dry lint dipped in brandy and covering with a 'digestive' [a styptic ointment of yellow basilicon, black basilicon, balsam and turpentine]. Our men say the French bleed often and cut much.[14]

British army surgeons came to admire the efficiency of the French field hospitals. In British armies each regiment made its own arrangements for the care of its wounded. In the French army regimental hospitals were brought together into a single unit close to the scene of the battle where they could perform their duty 'with more exactness and dispatch'. The French hospitals were also better equipped and more generously staffed. The medical arrangements in the Hanoverian army were also much admired:

> Their dressings are very neat drawn lint; wounds cleaned with fine sponge soaked in warm water and brandy. Their hospital medicines are carried on a large wagon divided into many partitions so that any particular medicine may be easily got at, the whole easily packed and unpacked. One of their physicians visits the kitchen daily and examines the provisions.[15]

Pringle was not on the battlefield at Dettingen to see for himself the success of his scheme for the care of the wounded. He had gone with the retreating army to Hanau. The wounded men had spent the night after the battle in the open with no shelter from the rain; next day, when the army set up camp at Hanau, the troops had tents but no straw and again they had to sleep on the cold wet ground. Within days there was a brisk outbreak of dysentery which Pringle attributed to the cold and wet weather and the inadequacy of the shelter provided for the troops. The outbreak continued and within weeks half of the men had been affected. A hospital specially established 20 miles away at Fechenheim admitted 3,386 sick and wounded and 640 of them died; of the 291 wives and children admitted almost 50 per cent died.

At Hanau, Pringle began to understand that exposure to bad weather was not the only or even the chief cause of the outbreak of dysentery. He noted that 'those who were affected first were those who lay wet at Dettingen'.[16] However, the troops who became ill later had not been exposed to the cold and wet at Dettingen. Pringle concluded that they must have been made ill 'by infection'. He also noted that a detachment of troops that had been sent from Ostend as escort for the king's baggage had not been affected by the outbreak of dysentery. They had reached Hanau two days before the battle and had set up camp half a mile from the site occupied by the army and 'by this separation from the line [army] they were also removed from the contagion of the privies and having pitched close to the river they had the benefit of a constant stream of fresh air'. The germ theory was not generally accepted until late in the next century, but Pringle already had a clear concept of the principles involved.

In August, the incidence of dysentery reached a second peak. Pringle wrote that the heat was 'so great that the humours, already disposed, were further prepared to receive the infection'. At the hospital at Fechenheim 'the air became so vitiated that not only the other patients but the apothecaries, nurses and others employed in the hospital with most of the inhabitants of the place were infected'. Several weeks later, he wrote that after the army left Hanau in October 'the dysentery so sensibly abated that the change could only be ascribed to leaving the infectious privies, the foul straw and the filth of a long encampment'.

However, at the height of the epidemic of dysentery, a number of the patients had gone on to suffer a second complicating fever that very often proved fatal. This virulent disease presented with high fever, a petechial rash (spots of bleeding into the skin), severe headache and delirium. The disease (typhus) was as dangerous to the staff of the hospitals as it was to their patients; at Fechenheim, of the 14 hospital mates, 5 had died. Two more large hospitals, at Osthofen and Bechtheim, were taken over for the care of the sick and the wounded; the patients in these hospitals were not overcrowded and none of them had contracted the virulent complicating fever until the end of October. It was then ordered that the patients from all three hospitals should be carried together by river barge to a hospital some 80 miles to the north at Neuwied on the Rhine. Half of the patients died on the journey; of the 1,467 admitted to Neuwied, 397 died. During the voyage, some of the patients had used a bundle of old tents as bedding. The tents were later bought by a firm of tradesmen; of the 23 tradesmen, 17 died of the fever. Pringle decided to call this virulent disease 'hospital fever'.

It was Pringle's experience during his first military campaign that inspired him to find a way to prevent the great loss of life from disease suffered by the British army during its campaigns. However, at the end of his first campaign with the army there could be no certainty that he would be employed in a second.

In Britain, the Battle of Dettingen was celebrated as a triumph. Handel composed a *Dettingen Te Deum* and an anthem, *The King Shall Rejoice*. George II had reason to rejoice. His presence at Aschaffenburg had helped to guarantee the security of Hanover and, thanks to the fortunate blunder by the Duke of Grammont's troops, he had escaped being made a prisoner of war. Under his command in battle, the Pragmatic Army had suffered 2,294 dead and wounded (British, 823; Hanoverian, 493: Austrian, 978), while the enemy had suffered well over 8,000 dead and wounded.

However, there was much resentment in Britain that, in sending the army to Aschaffenburg, King George had served the interests of Hanover with little reference to the interests of Britain. In Britain, it became doubtful which sentiment was greater, anti-Gallicanism or anti-Hanoverianism.[17] Lord Carteret, who had conspicuously failed to restrain the king's actions, found his position in Parliament undermined. In October 1744, he withdrew from the House of Commons and took his seat in the House of Lords as Earl of Granville; on 27 November he resigned from the government.

Pringle's patron, Lord Stair, had already resigned but for quite different reasons. He had been appointed Commander-in-Chief of the British army and had been given overall command of the allied army. Yet King George had ordered the advance into the valley at Aschaffenburg against his advice. The king had later prevented him from completing the victory at Dettingen by pursuing and destroying the French army. Above all, Lord Stair and all his British officers felt deeply humiliated that whenever they had some difference with officers of the Hanoverian army the king had taken the

Hanoverians' part. In a letter to Lord Carteret he explained that he wished to give up his command of the army as 'in general he had not been consulted either on military operations or on details of the army'.[18] On 3 September he resigned as Commander-in-Chief of the British army and was succeeded by the 70-year-old George Wade.

Pringle had reported his own highly critical views on the conduct of the campaign. In a letter sent from Hanau ten days after the battle, he promised to send Mitchell his comments in full under a number of headings: 'Bread Contract – Forage and Magazines – Hesitation at Aix-la-Chapelle – Generals – Lord Stair's grand plan unsupported – repassing the Main – Express Orders.'

Some days later Pringle sent the promised letter containing a full and detailed report of all the failures and errors that he had listed. By chance he sent it in a package in which he also sent a letter addressed to the University of Edinburgh requesting an extension of leave from his Chair. Before forwarding the letter to the university, Mitchell read it and was alarmed to find that, in a postscript, Pringle had set out a summary of all the adverse comments on the campaign in Germany that he had made in the reports that he had sent to Mitchell during the campaign. Mitchell destroyed the letter to the university and sent in its place a carefully written letter applying for leave on Pringle's behalf. He later explained in a letter to Pringle that:

> I found in the postscript things said with regard to the situation of our army at Aschaffenburg that I did not think advisable to put it in their power to quote you as an authority for facts that at first sight may seem to reflect on the conduct of your best friend [Lord Stair]. For the question still remains how came the army there? And if the blame is to be laid elsewhere it is equally improper for you to appear as evidence when you are not called as it would have been for you to have charged at the head of a regiment on the day of the battle. I have of late witnessed so much indiscretion by people by publishing complete or abstracts of letters in the newspapers that I had a suspicion that the postscript of your letter might have appeared there which I imagine would not be agreeable to you.

Pringle's letter was destroyed but later references to it in his letters strongly suggest that, among other matters and the errors of other people, Pringle had claimed that Lord Stair had been at fault in carrying out King George's instruction to take the army into the dangerously enclosed valley at Aschaffenburg.

At the same time, Pringle was himself the subject of criticism. As we have seen, after the Battle of Dettingen a number of British sick and wounded had been left behind at Aschaffenburg in the care of the French. When this became known in Britain, it was widely condemned and many held that, as Physician General, Pringle had failed in his duty. Dr Samuel Johnson was particularly severe in his judgement of Pringle; he complained that '. . . we pleased ourselves with a victory at Dettingen where we left our wounded men to the care of our enemies'. For many years Johnson continued to detest Pringle. During their tour of Scotland in 1773, Samuel Johnson and James Boswell were invited to visit Boswell's father, Lord Auchinleck, who was one of Pringle's oldest and closest friends. Before introducing Johnson to his father, Boswell begged Johnson 'to avoid three topics as to which they differed very widely, Whiggism, Presbyterianism and Sir John Pringle'.[19]

Johnson's fierce censure and dislike of Pringle can hardly be justified. The French army had a well-equipped and well-staffed hospital close to the scene of the battle and the Duke of Noailles had given his word that the wounded of both armies would be well cared for. Had the British wounded been carried over 20 miles to Hanau without proper support and exposed to the cold and rain on open army wagons, many of them would have died. However, those who had benefited most dramatically were the seriously wounded who had been taken prisoner. Had it not been for Pringle's humane initiative they would have been left to die or deliberately slaughtered as had usually been the fate of severely wounded prisoners of war in all armies in all wars.

All those who had been at Dettingen and had been caught up in the aftermath of the battle agreed that Pringle's arrangement had been a quite extraordinary success. On 28 July his concept was formally adopted in the Cartel of Frankfurt as 'a treaty and agreement for the sick, wounded and prisoners of war'. Article 37 stated that 'physicians, apothecaries, directors and other officers serving in the hospitals shall not be liable to be made prisoners of war'; Article 41 that 'care shall be taken of the wounded on both sides; their medicines and food shall be paid for and all the costs shall be returned on both sides; that it shall be allowed to send them surgeons and their servants with passports from their generals'; Article 42 that 'the sick on both sides will not be made prisoners; that they may remain with safety in their hospitals, where each of the belligerent and auxiliary parties shall be free to leave them a guard which shall be sent back, the same as the sick under the passports of the generals by the shortest way without being molested or stopped'. The principles of the Cartel of Frankfurt were to form the basis of the First Geneva Convention in 1864.

However, the care of the casualties of battle was not the British army's major problem. On the day before the battle at Dettingen, 500 men were admitted to the army's General Hospital suffering from the bloody flux (dysentery). More cases were admitted in the following days to the General Hospital which had become overcrowded by the wounded of the battle. There was an outbreak of 'continuous fever' (typhus). When the army slowly returned to its base in Flanders, almost half of the men had become victims of the fever.[20] How many were treated and died in their Regimental Infirmaries was not recorded. Almost 5,000 had been admitted to a local hospital and of these some 1,500 had died. This appalling carnage by disease suffered by the army received little or no public attention. There was great satisfaction that the army had suffered only some 229 deaths on the battlefield; it had long been accepted that, during any campaign, it was inevitable that the British army would suffer an uncounted loss by desertion and disease.

In 1742, Pringle had expected to be employed by the army only until the end of the campaign to enforce the provisions of the Pragmatic Sanction. However, three months after the Battle of Dettingen, by the Treaty of Worms, Britain, Austria and the King of Sardinia formed a new alliance. Its principal objective was to break the alliance of Louis XV of France and Charles Albert of Bavaria. As the treaty made it clear that the war was to continue, Pringle could be confident that he would serve further campaigns as a physician to the army. In March 1744, and much to his surprise, he was appointed to the new office of Physician-General to His Majesty's Forces Overseas. He had not forgotten the appalling number of deaths suffered in the weeks and months after the battle at Dettingen and was determined that such a catastrophe should never occur again.

SIX

Fontenoy: Defeat and Triumph

If I can see a campaign near and keep my health I may have a work useful to the public.

John Pringle, letter to Andrew Mitchell, 1742

The battle at Dettingen was celebrated in London, but Pringle saw the campaign as a disaster. His greatest concern was the epidemic that had broken out among the troops as the exhausted British army withdrew after the battle to its base in the north. The epidemic had continued for months and thousands had died. Pringle meant to ensure that such a catastrophe would not be repeated during the British army's next campaign.

That campaign was imminent. The shock of defeat at the Battle of Dettingen had not dulled Louis XV's ambition to make Bourbon France the dominant power in Europe. However, the battle had redefined his perception of the war and had reshaped his strategy. He now saw Britain rather than Hapsburg Austria as his principal enemy. From the beginning of the war, Britain had been a skilful opponent in the field of diplomacy. At Dettingen, Britain had proved to be a dangerous enemy on the field of battle. But above all, Britain, with her unequalled financial resources, had emerged as the generous paymaster of the armies of France's enemies in Europe.

Louis XV now understood that if he was to dominate Europe it was essential that the power and influence of Britain should be crushed. In October 1743, his Minister of Marine, Count Maurepas, proposed an invasion of England to remove George II from the British throne and to put a client monarch in his place. The ideal client was ready at hand, James Francis Edward Stuart, the son of the exiled James VII and II and now the Pretender to the throne that his father had lost. Louis XV had already acknowledged him as James VIII and III. And even half a century after James VII and II had been driven from the throne of Britain there were many in both Scotland and England who still cherished a lingering loyalty to the Stuart dynasty. In

Britain the government was still haunted by the fear of a rebellion to restore a Stuart to the throne supported by a French invasion.

In 1688, when James VII and II fled to France, he had been generously received by Louis XIV. At the Château de Saint-Germain-en-Laye he had been installed and maintained in the dignity and style of a royal court. In the years that followed there had been many plots to restore him to his throne but they could never be kept secret and all of them had failed. Nevertheless, British governments had continued to seize every opportunity to undermine his royal status in Europe. In the Treaty of Ryswick that ended the Nine Years' War[1] in 1697, the British government had secured an undertaking from Louis XIV that he would deny 'all aid, direct or indirect, financial or military to the enemies of King William III without any exception'.[2] Although he was not named in the treaty, James Stuart was the enemy that the British administration had in mind. In 1701, James VII and II died and his son James Francis Edward Stuart became the Pretender to the throne. The plots continued and Jacobite rebellions were mounted in Britain in 1708, 1715 and 1719. All failed and the reduction of the House of Stuart continued. In negotiating the treaty that marked the end of the War of the Spanish Succession[3] in 1713 the British government had taken the opportunity to put further pressure on the exiled James Francis Edward Stuart, still recognised in France as the legitimate king of Great Britain. Britain insisted that, at Saint-Germain-en-Laye, 12 miles north-west of Paris, the Pretender James Francis Edward Stuart was too close to the Channel coast and much too near to the resources and services that he might use to make a landing in England. The Pretender was moved first to Avignon and then to Rome. In 1744, he was still in Rome and for almost 30 years Louis XV had shown little interest in his hopes and ambitions. He had been made to dispose of his fleet of privateers; he had been obliged to part with all the regiments of his Irish Brigade; his establishment had been deprived of the status and dignity of a royal court. But now, suddenly, Louis XV planned to install him as James VIII and III of Great Britain in place of George II.

In November 1743, Louis XV began his planning of the invasion of England. He decided that the Pretender's son, the 23-year-old Prince Charles Edward Stuart, should be made the figurehead of the Jacobite rising that he believed would break out across Britain on the landing of the French army on the coast of England. But he should not be involved until the landing in England had been accomplished. Success seemed assured. Britain was defenceless. Her only army was in Flanders. Louis XV was confident that

without the financial and military support of Britain, the alliance against
him in Europe would be unable to continue the war. In December, he
informed the Bourbon King Philip V of Spain 'of a project I have formed in
the greatest secrecy for destroying in one blow at its foundations the league
of enemies of the House of Bourbon'.[4] Prince Charles Edward Stuart first
heard of the proposed invasion in January 1744. He immediately made his
way to Paris where he was made to wait.

It was planned that an army commanded by Count Maurice de Saxe
would be transported in a fleet of transports from Dunkirk to the Essex
coast at Maldon. However, reports of the French activities had reached
Britain and, when the invasion set out on 6 March, it was halted by the
British Channel Fleet. As the British and French fleets confronted each
other some eight miles apart off the coast of Kent a violent storm blew up. It
severely damaged all but one of the British ships, but the French expedition
was totally destroyed. Its escort warships were disabled and scattered, the
transport ships were swept aground and the equipment and provisions that
had been so carefully and so expensively assembled at Dunkirk were totally
destroyed. Louis XV abandoned the project and all intention of making any
further attempt to invade England.

Prince Charles Edward Stuart was distraught. He wrote to his father's
representative at the French Court that if Louis would not help him further,
he would hire a fishing boat and sail to Scotland where he was sure that his
faithful Highlanders would rally to him. 'I would rather die at the head of
these brave men than languish in exile and dependence.'[5]

However, Louis XV was no longer interested in the restoration of the
Stuart dynasty. He had failed in his attempt to put an end to Britain's
part in the war in Europe by unseating her government, but he was confident that he could destroy Britain's only army, now conveniently within
reach in the Austrian Netherlands. On 15 March 1744, Louis XV formally
declared war on Britain. At France's border with the Austrian Netherlands,
he assembled an army of 87,000 which he aimed to command himself;
as he had no experience as a soldier he made Maurice de Saxe a Marshal
of France and appointed him as his second-in-command. On 17 May,
he began an assault on the line of fortresses guarding the border of the
Austrian Netherlands. He divided his army into two corps. The larger
corps of 50,000 men, he moved across the border to besiege the fortress
at Menin that blocked access to the Scheldt estuary, the centre of the
Austrian province's commerce. A second corps of 37,000 men, commanded
by Marshal de Saxe, he moved forward to the north-west to provide the

corps besieging Menin with a covering screen against possible attack by the Pragmatic Army.[6]

Meanwhile the main body of the anti-Bourbon Pragmatic Army was drawn up in the area between Brussels and Ghent, 100 miles from the French border. Its most forward part was formed by the British and Hanoverian armies. Pringle estimated that by the end of the Dettingen campaign of 1743 the British army had lost, by sickness alone, some 25 per cent of its strength. However, following the arrival from Britain of new recruits to the depleted regiments, new squadrons of dragoons and ten new battalions of infantry, the army was now larger by upwards of 10,000 men than it had been at the end of the campaign in 1743. With the Hanoverian troops, it made up a body of 38,000 men. A small Austrian contingent of only 7,000 men was stationed further from the border with France and behind the main body of British and Hanoverian troops.

At the border the line of fortresses was manned by inexperienced and poorly motivated Dutch troops. In 1744, the Dutch Republic was not formally at war with France and its troops were present only because of a Barrier Treaty of 1713 that required the Dutch to provide garrisons for the fortresses if at any time the Austrian Netherlands should come under attack. Their commander Prince Maurice of Nassau was understandably reluctant to commit his force to battle with a much larger and more experienced French army. The result was predictable. The first trenches for the siege of the fortress at Menin were dug on 29 May; the garrison surrendered on 5 June. The resistance offered by the other fortresses was equally ineffectual. By 29 June, the fortresses at Ypres, Knocke and Furnes were all in French hands.

Then suddenly, on 30 June, the French advance ended. To the south a large Austrian army had moved to occupy Alsace. A German-speaking province, once part of the Holy Roman Empire, Alsace had been French for less than a hundred years and its people were not averse to coming once again under Austrian rule. Louis XV, again accompanied by the Duke of Noailles, marched a corps of 50,000 troops over 250 miles to the defence of Alsace, leaving Marshal de Saxe in Flanders with instructions to hold what had been gained but to make no attempt to advance further.

The Commander-in-Chief of the British army was now Field Marshal Wade, and as the commander of its leading component, he was in overall command of the Pragmatic Army in Flanders. As a more junior commander he had a distinguished career but as a general he was much less effective and had acquired the reputation of being 'ill-disposed to offensive action'. In

1724, he had been sent by the British government to prepare a report on the provisions necessary for the military control of the Highlands of Scotland. Thereafter, he had been appointed Commander-in-Chief of His Majesty's Forces, Castles and Barracks in North Britain and had spent 12 years establishing barracks at Ruthven, Fort George and Fort Augustus and building some 250 miles of roads. In 1743, on the basis of his seniority in the army, he had been promoted to Field Marshal and appointed successor to Lord Stair as Commander-in-Chief of the British Army and overall commander of the Pragmatic Army in Flanders. In 1744, he was in command of an army in the field for the first time in 20 years. It soon became clear that he was still ill-disposed to offensive action.

After Louis XV had withdrawn the French army from Flanders to march to the relief of Alsace, Wade moved the Pragmatic Army forward unopposed across the River Scheldt and into France to take up a position near Lille at Anstaing. But in the months until the end of the campaigning season of 1744, he made no attempt even to retake the poorly manned and armed border fortresses. In the south-west corner of the Austrian Netherlands, Marshal de Saxe was left in peace with ample time to perfect the military skills and discipline of his army.

Pringle had used these inactive months of the campaigning season to achieve a number of reforms in the army's medical services He issued new instructions to every regiment in the army. In Flanders in 1742 and 1743 he had noted that the incidence of sickness was high in regiments billeted or encamped on low ground, especially where the ground was wet and poorly drained. The incidence of sickness was also high in regiments encamped closely together in places where they were sheltered from every breeze. He ordered that during the campaign every quartermaster should mark out the site on which his regiment was to be camped even for one night. The quartermaster was to be accompanied by a sergeant and at least one man, each carrying a spade or an axe, to dig latrines on the site in advance of the arrival of the troops and to act as a sanitary squad thereafter. On the march the surgeons of the regiments were 'to carry their medicine chests and instruments upon their horses which are to march at the head of each corps with the men's tents'.[7] A specially designated wagon for the sick was to go at the rear of the regiment; any sick men who were to be carried in it to a General Hospital were to be accompanied by a sergeant with the appropriate certificates signed by an officer and the regimental surgeon.

However, the admission of sick and wounded to a General Hospital was to be restricted. Pringle ordered that during the campaign the sick and wounded were to be cared for in their Regimental Infirmaries; only when it was clearly essential should they be referred to a General Hospital. When being treated at their own Regimental Infirmaries, the sick and wounded would be spared a journey to a General Hospital during which, in the past, as many as 50 per cent had died. Regimental Infirmaries were almost always housed in makeshift structures with haphazard but effective ventilation; they carried proportionately smaller patient loads than the General Hospitals; and they were less likely to become overcrowded. As a result the risk of infection in Regimental Infirmaries would be relatively low.

Pringle ordered that during major battles the wounded were to be collected at carefully positioned ambulance stations and from there carried to the nearest Regimental Infirmary, not necessarily the infirmary of the regiment to which the soldier belonged. It was at the Regimental Infirmaries that all routine major surgery was to be carried out; only the most difficult cases were to be transferred, properly escorted and in an appropriate vehicle, to the nearest General Hospital.

The number of General Hospitals to be with the British army on campaign was increased to three; the number of physicians was increased to eight and the number of surgeons to nine. A General Hospital was no longer to be 'fixed' close to army headquarters. General Hospitals were to be appropriately equipped teams that could be readily moved with the army in the field and set up in any suitable building constructed, legally acquired, or commandeered for the purpose. As there were now to be three General Hospitals, one would be stationed as a base hospital at a site some way from the scene of battle. The others would each be sited at a short but relatively safe distance from the scene of the action. When either of these two hospitals was in danger of becoming overcrowded, arrangements were to be made to carry the excess, again with the appropriate care and support, to the base General Hospital.[8] As General Hospitals were now to be positioned near to the action there would no longer be a need for 'Flying Hospitals', the small bodies of staff and equipment that in the past had been sent out from a single General Hospital to treat casualties at the site of the battle.

It had been the practice to close the General Hospitals when the army went into winter quarters at the end of the campaign season. Pringle ordered that in future one base General Hospital would remain open throughout the year; the other General Hospitals would be closed and the staff deployed wherever they were required.

Pringle also issued instructions for the future management of the General Hospitals. They must be well ventilated. Overcrowding was to be avoided.

Every man was to have his own space; an area of 36 square feet was set as the minimum for each patient. The common practice of lodging two or more patients in one bed was forbidden. Hospital Directors were required to give particular attention to the maintenance of discipline. Pringle believed that it was the appalling lack of discipline that had been responsible for the poor performance and the low morale that had degraded the army's General Hospital throughout the Dettingen campaign in 1743. Throughout that campaign drunkenness had been rife among the hospital nurses, surgeon's mates and ward orderlies and it had become accepted practice for the nurses to sell alcohol to the patients. And it had been equally common for the nurses and orderlies to rob the patients of their few belongings. Pringle held the Director of Hospitals, John Ellis, responsible for the lack of discipline and the poor standard of care. He was discharged. Pringle also discouraged the secondment of private soldiers to serve as nurses in the Regimental Infirmaries; he proposed that, in their place, the regiments should recruit and train a full complement of soldiers' wives.

When, in October 1744, the army withdrew from Lille and retired into winter quarters, Pringle was able to report that the army was much healthier than it had been at that the end of the campaign of 1743. The incidence of dysentery had been low and it had not been revived by the wet weather. Fever had been chiefly confined to recruits and the new regiments which had been in camp for the first time. The General Hospital at Ghent had remained open throughout the year and Dr Sandilands had continued as its senior physician; until the end of campaign season, 1,698 patients were admitted with a mortality of 11 per cent. In April, Pringle had opened a second General Hospital at Brussels with Dr Wintringham as senior physician; it had admitted 1,259 patients with a mortality of 7 per cent. In August he opened a third General Hospital at Tournai with Dr Maxwell as its senior physician; 778 patients were admitted with a mortality of 19 per cent. Pringle was satisfied that when the troops returned to winter quarters at the end of 1744, they were not only clearly fit and well, 'they carried with them few seeds of disease'.

When the army went into winter quarters, Pringle closed the General Hospitals at Ghent and Tournai and ordered that the regimental surgeons at these two garrisons should take care of the sick in their own barracks. Their senior physicians, Dr Wintringham and Dr Maxwell, were to be available as consultants to whom the regimental surgeons could refer for assistance and advice. Pringle later recorded that although the General Hospitals at

Ghent and Tournai had been closed to save money, it had 'answered another purpose which was that of preventing infection, the usual consequence of keeping great numbers of sick together'.[9]

When the 1744 campaigning season ended in Flanders, the French army commanded by Louis XV and the Duke of Noailles was still embroiled in the multinational war in Germany. Early in August, Prussia had re-entered the war and marched into the Austrian province of Bohemia. The Austrian army had therefore been forced to abandon the invasion of Alsace and withdraw to defend Bohemia. In the second week of August, Louis XV became desperately ill with smallpox[10] and for a time French military activity in Flanders was at a standstill. Nevertheless, the war continued to rumble on in central Europe and northern Italy. Austria fought with partial success to drive Frederick of Prussia from Silesia; Spanish forces attempted but failed to force their way through Piedmont and seize Austrian territories in Lombardy; the Emperor Charles VII had raised an imperial army to end Frederick of Prussia's occupation of Bohemia. However, by January 1745, all the armies engaged in central Europe and Italy were more than ready to cease hostilities and retire into winter quarters. The army commanded by Louis XV and the Duke of Noailles returned to Flanders

Britain had taken little part in the complex war in central Europe. The British Treasury had provided Austria with a subsidy of £150,000, but the British army had remained quietly in Flanders. It was widely thought in Britain that, throughout 1744, the performance of the nation's diplomats and army commanders had been woeful, even laughable. Lord Carteret's over-ambitious diplomatic manoeuvring had failed miserably; in January 1745, the Duke of Newcastle took his place as Secretary of State. Field Marshal Wade had quarrelled with his allies, the commanders of the Austrian and Dutch armies, and his failure to take advantage of the sudden weakness of his French opponent by retaking the border fortresses had been lamentable; he was replaced as Commander-in-Chief of the British Army in Flanders by Sir John Ligonier.

In April 1745, the winter over and the campaigning season about to begin, the Duke of Cumberland arrived from England to take overall command of the now 43,000-strong allied army. In the same month Marshal de Saxe assumed command of France's army of 95,000 men in Flanders. It was the biggest national army seen thus far in the war; it included a fine array of artillery and a superb corps of engineers. As we have seen, the French had already occupied the south-west corner of the Austrian Netherlands in 1744.

Marshal de Saxe now planned to take the north-west corner that included the estuary of the Scheldt, the prosperous commercial heart of the country. After three weeks of tactical manoeuvring, he split his army, sending 45,000 of his troops to lay siege to the Fortress of Tournai which guarded the approach to the Scheldt basin; the other, larger part, of his army he moved forward to take up a strong defensive position on a plain two miles south of Tournai. There he positioned this part of his army near the river on a ridge from which the ground sloped gently downhill towards the south-east, the direction from which Cumberland's army was approaching. He planned that, as it advanced, Cumberland's army would be channelled between the town of Antoing on its left (river) side and the Wood of Barry on its right side onto the open ground rising towards the French army. Marshal de Saxe planned to attack his enemy principally by artillery fire; as the white houses of Fontenoy lay just before his main line of fire the town was levelled and reduced to rubble. He posted companies of infantry in the Wood of Barry and cannon along the ridge between Antoing and the village of Fontenoy to fire on both sides of Cumberland's army as it tried to pass between them.

In this carefully prepared position Marshal de Saxe was content to wait; on 8 May Louis XV joined him. Cumberland, with an army of only some 50,000, did not have the majority in numbers of at least three to one that a more experienced and conventional general would have considered necessary for an assault on such a strong position. Nevertheless, on 11 May he decided to attack. Marshal de Saxe's trap worked very much as he had planned. The allied army, led by the British infantry, approached the French position, as expected, between the wood on one side and the river on the other. As they advanced they found themselves exposed to artillery and infantry fire from both sides and from their front. The Dutch had been ordered to take Fontenoy, but the French troops allowed them to draw very near before delivering a hail of bullets. A few of the Dutch were killed and the others fled; a second Dutch attack was equally unsuccessful. The commander of the British cavalry was killed at the beginning of the battle. He left no orders. The British army was left with its infantry exposed to lacerating fire while its 12 cavalry squadrons were confused and leaderless. Cumberland had not ordered the artillery to take any part in the action. Although things continued to go badly, Cumberland did not choose to order a retreat. He abandoned his position of oversight as the commander of the army to take personal command of the British infantry in what was to become one of the greatest infantry advances of the eighteenth century. The British infantry advanced and for a time came to within 30 yards of the ruins of Fontenoy. Sir John Ligonier, Cumberland's second-in-command, thought that the battle was all but won. But the French cavalry now entered the battle and the allied army was obliged to make a fierce fighting retreat. The battle at Fontenoy was the bloodiest of the war. The French had suffered some 7,000 killed and wounded; but the allied Pragmatic Army had lost over 12,000.

The 20 British battalions employed in the battle had lost more than 4,000 killed and wounded; some regiments had lost over a third of their strength. Of the thousands of wounded who were carried from the field, 600 of the most severe cases were evacuated to the General Hospital now at Mons. It had been set up in accordance with Pringle's instructions. One of the surgeons later wrote that the hospital was 'one of the most commodious we have yet had, each room separated by a wall and our sick recovered well. It is a general fault in all [other] hospitals that the apartments are too large, and contain too many sick, by which the air is infected especially when the house is crowded after an action.'

The 1,200 British wounded who had been captured by the enemy were much less fortunate. When, at de Saxe's request, the Duke of Cumberland sent 105 wagons to carry them away, it was found that they had been badly treated. One of the British surgeons who had been present later wrote:

We surgeons sent to take care of the wounded were made prisoners of war and treated in a very merciless way for not only we but a 1,000 more were stripped of everything of value that we had, *viz* watches, swords, money and clothes and not only so but our very instruments were taken from us although the barbarians saw hundreds continually imploring our assistance. In this unprecedented way we remained three days, numbers dying every hour because we had nothing to dress them with. Then they were flung into waggons and drove along the causeway to Lille and Valenciennes. In this jolting journey you may easily conceive of the misery of the poor wretches most with their legs, arms, etc shattered to pieces . . .When we arrived at our camp we waited on His Royal Highness [Cumberland] and laid before him the matter of our treatment and presented him with a bag of chewed balls, points of sword, pieces of flint, glass, iron etc we had extracted from the wounds.[11]

Cumberland protested, informing Marshal de Saxe that if he intended to make war like a Turk we would 'learn for the future how to receive him'.

Cumberland complained that the provisions of Pringle's Cartel of Frankfurt had been broken. Marshal de Saxe replied that the British army had ignored the Cartel on more than one occasion. Nevertheless, he ordered the release of the captive surgeons and made reparations at the hospital in Lille. In his *History of the War of 1741–57* Voltaire wrote that there 'all the wounded were treated alike and every luxury was placed at their disposal; indeed they were well-nigh killed with kindness and the surgeons had to check the excessive good will of the populace. In a word the hospital was so well organised that wounded men preferred it to lodging in private houses.'[12]

After its defeat at Fontenoy, the British army retired first to its headquarters at Brussels and then northward towards Antwerp which was now the army's only possible exit port from Flanders. The border fortresses had surrendered and, one by one, all the army's former bases at Ghent, Bruges, Breda and Oudenarde fell as the French army swept across the Austrian Netherlands to within a few miles of the border with Germany.

Of the British General Hospitals, one was now at Antwerp and one was still at Brussels. The third, with over 1,000 sick and wounded, had been left at Mons in French hands. But under the terms of Pringle's Cartel of Frankfurt, the patients were safe and were properly treated.

Pringle wrote an account of the health of the army in the months that followed the defeat at Fontenoy.

In May the weather had been warm and dry and favourable both to the wounded and to the troops in camp. In June it became cold and wet and the vernal agues and fluxes became troublesome but only among the men of the two regiments that had recently arrived from England; the old and hardened troops were not affected. In July the weather was dry and mild and at Brussels the troops were encamped on open and elevated ground. By September, few of the battalions had suffered more than twelve sick, a number as low as could be expected in the best of quarters. The beginning of autumn brought cases of dysentery, but again only among the new regiments, and they were easily cured. There was a more general increase in cases of remitting fever but nothing that could be called an epidemic. At Antwerp where the air was moist and the fortress exposed to the exhalation of the marches, there were in all 183 cases of dysentery or remitting fever, a number five or six times greater than in any other corps at that time.

It is clear from what he wrote some time later that Pringle looked back with some satisfaction on the health of the army at the end of the campaign of 1745. The appalling loss of life from disease that had followed the Battle of Dettingen had not been repeated after the Battle of Fontenoy. He wrote:

> Upon the whole, when the campaign ended we had in the hospitals at Antwerp, Brussels and Mons about 1000 sick, a small number when we consider that during this summer there had been in Flanders, besides the cavalry, 29 battalions whereof some had never been in the field before. From the beginning to the end of the campaign exclusive of those who were killed in the battle or died of their wounds, the deaths did not exceed 200.[13]

The true extent of the success of Pringle's reform of the army's medical services is revealed in the figures later published by the Army Medical Board.[14] In the period before he introduced his reforms, from the battle at Dettingen in June 1743 until the end of that campaign, 4,853 patients were admitted to the army's General Hospital; of these 1,037 died, a mortality of 21.4 per cent. In the period after the introduction of his reforms, from the Battle of Fontenoy in May 1745 until the end of that campaign, 3,735 patients were admitted to the General Hospitals; of these 413 died, a mortality of 11 per cent. That improvement was maintained. From the introduction of his reforms until the end of the war, 24,612 patients were admitted to the army's General Hospitals and of these 2,411 died, a mortality of only 9.8 per cent.

Pringle later commented that the fine weather, the dryness of the ground in which the army had set its camps and the very few demands that had been made of the army during the campaign had helped to keep the troops fit and well. Overall, this campaign in the spring of 1745 had been the 'most healthful campaign of the whole war'.

However, the campaigning season of 1745 was not yet over. In July 1745, the Duke of Cumberland had informed the Secretary of State in London that the campaign in Flanders was lost and that the British army might now be better employed elsewhere. Prince Charles Edward Stuart had raised a rebellion in Scotland.

SEVEN

Rebellion: A Very Different Campaign

Man arrayed for mutual slaughter
Wordsworth, *Ode for Thanksgiving*, 1815

Pringle's third military campaign was not, as his first two had been, a campaign in a war between nations. This was a bitter and merciless form of war. This was a rebellion.

Pringle first heard rumours of a possible rebellion early in July 1745. Reports had reached army headquarters in Flanders of a French plot to invade England. It was also reported that the invasion would be supported by a Jacobite rising in Britain. Soundly beaten at Fontenoy in May 1745, the Duke of Cumberland chose to believe the reports. He wrote to the Duke of Newcastle, the Secretary of State in London, suggesting that as the campaign in Flanders was already lost, the British army might be better employed at home. Newcastle dismissed the notion of an invasion and ordered Cumberland to remain in Flanders. Later, it was heard in London that a small expedition had left the French coast, but the notion that Britain was about to be invaded by France was again discounted. It was assumed that the expedition was merely an attempt to divert attention from some more sinister French project being launched elsewhere in Europe. Nevertheless, on 28 July 1745, the Duke of Cumberland wrote again to the Duke of Newcastle, proposing that, if this 'pretend design' of an invasion of Britain should continue, he should be recalled from Flanders with whatever troops were necessary even if there were 'none left here to save this little scrap of country we still have here of the Austrian Netherlands'. The government was again confident that such a move was unnecessary and his request was again refused.

However, on 30 July, the Secretary of State had written to the Lord Justice Clerk in Edinburgh informing him that he had heard that 'the French Court was meditating an invasion of His Majesty's dominions and that the Pretender's son had sailed on the 15th July . . . By some accounts it was said that he was actually landed in Scotland which I can hardly believe.'

The rumours continued. On 2 August 1745, Duncan Forbes, Lord President of the Council of State that managed Scottish affairs in the absence of a Scottish Privy Council,[1] wrote to Henry Pelham, the Prime Minister:

> In a state of profound tranquillity, we have been alarmed with advices, which are said to have been received at London, of intended invasions; and particularly of a visit which the Pretender's eldest son[2] is about to make to us, if he has not already made it. These informations, particularly as to the visit just mentioned, I must confess, have not hitherto gained my belief. This young gentleman's game seems at present to be very desperate in this country; and, so far as I can learn, there is not the least apparatus for his reception, even amongst the few highlanders who are suspected to be in his interest. However, as, when so much is at stake, no advice, how improbable soever, is to be neglected, I have resolved to make my accustomed journey northwards a little earlier than usual; to the end that, though my fighting days are over, I may give some countenance to the friends of the government, and prevent the seduction of the unwary, if there should be any truth in what is reported.[3]

By 19 August, what Duncan Forbes had thought improbable, and the Duke of Cumberland had referred to as a 'pretend design', had become a reality. A proclamation had been issued from Whitehall offering a reward of £30,000 for the capture of Prince Charles.[4] He had been in Scotland since 20 July.

The costly and unexpected defeat that he had suffered at Dettingen in May had persuaded Louis XV of France that Britain must be destroyed. Without a proper army in place to defend it, Britain could be successfully invaded, the Stuart dynasty restored and the Pretender crowned as James VIII and III. The restoration of the Stuarts would be assisted by a Jacobite rising in Britain. Prince Charles would be called on to act as the figurehead of the rebellion; as he would not be required until the invasion had been successful and London had been taken, he would not be informed of what was planned until that time.

However, Prince Charles heard something of the intention to restore his family to the throne and, on 9 January 1744, he set out from Rome on a long and difficult journey to Paris. When he arrived on 3 February, Louis XV was appalled. He believed that the arrival of the prince in Paris would give public notice of his intended invasion of England. Louis commanded the prince to remain incognito while he was in France.

Two weeks later, everything that Louis XV had planned was wrecked. A gale had destroyed his invasion fleet; the ships had already been loaded with the men and the supplies. Louis XV abandoned his plan to invade Britain and left to join his army in Flanders. In May 1745, he had overwhelmed the British army at Fontenoy and thereafter he was reluctant to launch a second expensive attack on Britain. However, Prince Charles was confident that if he were to raise a Jacobite rebellion by himself, and if his rebellion were to show some evidence of success, Louis XV would be ready to send an army to support it. The ideal place to launch the rebellion was the Highlands of Scotland where the social and militaristic organisation of the clans made it possible to raise an army very much faster than it could be done anywhere else in Britain. Jacobite leaders in Scotland had assured Prince Charles that provided he brought with him 6,000 French troops, arms for 10,000 more and 30,000 gold *louis d'or,* a rebellion raised in the Highlands could be successful.[5]

Early in June 1745 Prince Charles began to organise his expedition to Scotland. He borrowed 40,000 livres from a Parisian banker, George Walters. The sum was later increased to 102,000 livres. A consortium of exiled Irish Jacobites operating as privateers from ports in Brittany provided him with two ships:[6] the *Elizabeth*, a 64-gun frigate captured from the British navy, was to carry 700 volunteers from the Irish Brigade, 1,500 muskets and ammunition and 1,800 broadswords; the *Du Teillay*, a small 16-gun commercial raider, was to carry the prince, the seven members of his staff and 4,000 gold louis d'or. The two ships set off from Brittany on 5 July 1745, but off the coast of Cornwall they were met by a British warship, HMS *Lion*. In the encounter the *Elizabeth* and the *Lion* were both badly damaged and returned to port. The *Du Teillay* sailed on alone to land Prince Charles and his seven companions on the Isle of Eriskay on 23 July. From there they travelled to Glenfinnan on the mainland where Prince Charles hoped to gather an army.

His welcome was less enthusiastic than he had imagined. Most of the chiefs whom he had expected to bring out their clansmen in his support had not been there to meet him. Others had come but, since he had come with no troops, no arms and little money, they advised him to return to France. Apart from Clan Cameron, the only clans immediately ready to join the rebellion were those who had some grievance against Clan Campbell, for long a dominating force in the Highlands and now loyal servants of the government. There were known to be some 32,000 fighting men living in the Highlands.[7] At Glenfinnan, Prince Charles was only able to raise an army of 1,500 men, and many of them were inadequately armed.

His early support in France had been equally uncertain. His father, the Pretender, had heard something of his venture but had not given his approval. There had been a number of Jacobites in Paris but their conflicting views had prevented them from forming any agreement on support for a rebellion. In Edinburgh, the leading Jacobites who met regularly at Buck's Club had tried but had failed to send him notice of their disapproval. Firm support had come only from his Irish friends in Paris, Sir Thomas Sheridan, Father George Kelly and John Sullivan.

Nevertheless, on 27 August, Prince Charles led his small army south out of the Highlands, reaching Perth on 4 September. From Perth he again marched south, reaching Edinburgh on 16 September. Although the garrison of the castle refused to surrender, Prince Charles was warmly welcomed by the people of the town and he was royally entertained at the Palace of Holyroodhouse.

In its progress to Edinburgh the Jacobite army had been virtually unopposed. When it was first raised in the Highlands, the only British army in Scotland had been at Stirling under the command of Sir John Cope and it was an army of only 3,850 recently raised and still very raw recruits. Cope had been ordered north into the Highlands to stop the rebel army before it could find recruits and grow into a real threat to the peace and stability of the state. On 25 August, Cope had an opportunity to challenge the rebel army some miles north of Perth but he chose to avoid battle[8] and go north to Inverness where he could expect to find experienced troops to reinforce his small army. With his strengthened army he marched from Inverness to Aberdeen and from Aberdeen he carried his army south by sea to Dunbar, arriving there on the day that the Jacobite army marched into Edinburgh.

On 20 September, Cope moved his army to within a few miles of Edinburgh at Prestonpans where, on a stretch of open and in places boggy ground, he was confident that he could destroy the Jacobite army and put an end to the rebellion. However, on the morning of 21 September one charge by the Jacobite army was enough to make Cope's troops panic, break their discipline and run. The battle lasted for less than ten minutes. All but some 500 of Cope's 2,300 troops were killed or captured; Pringle, who was then still in Flanders, left no record of how the wounded and the sick were treated.

The British government was now, at last, seriously alarmed. It seemed that Britain was 'in danger of being overwhelmed by the bursting of a cloud which seemed at its beginning no bigger than a man's hand'.[9] In London, on 4 October, George II held a council of war. It was usual for the British army to go into winter quarters at the end of October. The troops were not clothed, equipped, or trained to campaign in winter conditions, certainly not winter conditions in Scotland. Nevertheless, the council of war ordered the formation of two new armies. Field Marshal Wade was to command an army in the north-east at Newcastle and Berwick on Tweed. Wade's given task was to destroy the rebel army before it could seize control in Scotland, or, if that could not be done, to prevent it from marching south into England. It seemed improbable that the rebels would attempt to advance into England on the west side of the country. For an army, with its canon and baggage wagons, to pass through the mountainous counties of Cumberland and Westmoreland, where no strategic roads had been built since Roman times, would be difficult; as winter approached it would become almost impossible. Nevertheless, the council of war decided that Sir John Ligonier, the Duke of Cumberland's second-in-command, should be recalled to England to take command of a second army to be stationed at Lichfield in the West Midlands to confront any rebel force that might, in spite of all the difficulties, advance into England on the west side of the Pennines.

Both British armies were to be formed initially from the bodies of troops at hand in England; each would be brought up to a strength of 10,000 men by withdrawing troops from the army in Flanders. In September, ten battalions were dispatched from Flanders. On 23 October, three of these battalions arrived at Gravesend on the south bank of the Thames and marched north to join Ligonier's assembling army at Lichfield. Pringle records that as they had left Flanders before the nights had become cold and their passage across the Channel had been quick and smooth, they had arrived at Lichfield in perfect health.[10]

The remaining seven battalions destined to reinforce Wade's army in the north of England were less fortunate. Pringle records that their departure was delayed and they had still been encamped in Flanders as the weather became wintry. Sickness among the troops had steadily increased. Once on board ship at Antwerp, the sickness rate had increased even further. For many days the transports had been unable to leave harbour because of contrary winds and for all that time the troops were kept confined in the foul unventilated holds of their ships. During the voyage many of the men became 'ill of the remitting fever which was soon converted into a jail-distemper [typhus] and became infectious'.[11] When the first of the transports arrived at Newcastle, a number of houses were taken over as a hospital for those who had become sick during the voyage. But as the men of Wade's original small army also began to fall sick, the hospital became overcrowded, 'the air was soon corrupted' and the numbers suffering from 'jail-fever' (typhus) increased. Nursing and medical personnel also became infected; three apothecaries, four of their apprentices and two journeymen working in the hospital died.

Two of the seven battalions were landed, not at Newcastle, but at Holy Island. When they disembarked, they were in a worse state than those who disembarked at Newcastle. Pringle later wrote that at Holy Island 'their distress was unforeseen and unprovided for'. No fewer than 97 men were taken from the ships in which they had been confined already suffering from 'jail-distemper'; of these 40 died. Soon after the troops had been disembarked, the 'jail-distemper' spread to the local population; one in six of the people of Holy Island died.

On 19 October, Cumberland was ordered to return to England with the twelve battalions of infantry and three regiments of cavalry that were still in Flanders and to reinforce and take command of Ligonier's army at Lichfield. Pringle, who accompanied Cumberland, reported that the troops had arrived at Lichfield in good health. A Quaker group had given flannel inner-waistcoats to the soldiers to protect them from the cold. The weather had been dry during their march and men 'lay only one night upon their arms but at all other times laying in houses and having plenty of straw, fuel and provisions they were more healthy than could be expected in a campaign at that season of the year'.[12]

Meanwhile in the north, the 72-year-old Field Marshal Wade had been, as always, slow to act. It spite of all the urgings of his senior officers, it was not until 31 September that he had moved his army northwards towards Edinburgh. At Morpeth, on 3 October, he was informed that the rebel army had already left Edinburgh and was now heading towards Carlisle. He returned to Newcastle intending to cross from there through a pass in the Pennines to help in the defence of Carlisle. However, crossing the Pennines in winter soon proved impossible and on 21 November he returned once again to Newcastle.

On 16 November, after a long siege, the rebel army succeeded in capturing Carlisle and began to move further into England through the snow and the difficult terrain of Cumberland and Westmoreland. Thereafter, on easier terrain, the rebels continued to advance south through Preston, Wigan and Manchester. Since 25 November, Wade's army had been shadowing the rebels' advance into England but from the other, eastern, side of the Pennines. However, at Lichfield in the West Midlands, Cumberland was lying across their line of advance. On 2 December, the rebels sent a detachment of their army as a feint in the direction of Wales. Cumberland took the bait and moved quickly north and west planning to stop the rebels in major battle on a site that he had chosen at Stone in Staffordshire. All day from 4 a.m. on 3 December Cumberland's army waited in the snow and the wind but the enemy did not appear. With Cumberland safely out of the way, the rebel army had marched south to Derby, entering the city on 4 December.

On the morning of 5 December, at Exeter House in Derby, Prince Charles and his senior officers held a council of war. For the first time since the rebellion began they were facing serious opposition. Cumberland was now marching back towards them from the west. Field Marshal Wade, on his march south on the east side of the Pennines, had reached Doncaster to the north-east. A double agent,[13] who had gained access to the meeting, informed them that an army of 9,000 was approaching from Northampton in the south. Lord George Murray, Prince Charles' Lieutenant General, dismissed the report of an army at Northampton, but no one, not even Murray, doubted that the government had at least 25,000 troops ranged against their army of 4,500.

Murray argued that in any battle they must expect to suffer up to 1,500 casualties, a loss that would leave them unable to fight a second battle or even to conduct an orderly fighting retreat. Prince Charles and the Duke of Perth held that the best course would be to avoid a battle and make a dash for London where they could expect decisive support; France had already assembled a fleet and an army and planned to make a landing on the Essex coast on 25 December.[14] However, Murray's misgivings prevailed. A deeply reluctant Prince Charles was, at last, persuaded that he must abandon his goal of seizing London, the centre of power in Britain. On the morning of 7 December he began to lead his army on a long and difficult withdrawal back into Scotland.

As the Jacobite army began its withdrawal, Cumberland sent his cavalry urgently to the north to retake Carlisle; it had been reported that the town was being looted and devastated by the 400 rebels who had been left behind to hold it. But he decided that, before leading the main body of his army in pursuit of the rebel army, the infantry should be rested for a time in quarters at Lichfield and its neighbouring towns. The men had marched to Stone and back in foul weather and had waited for many hours in the snow on a vacant battlefield. Within days, many of the men had become ill. The Regimental Infirmaries were overwhelmed. At Lichfield, Pringle took over a workhouse as a hospital but it too soon became overcrowded; 'the air was corrupted and the common inflammatory fever changed into one of the jail-kind of which several died'. It soon became clear to Pringle that it was only those who had been admitted to the workhouse who contracted the 'jail like' fever. Those who had been ill of the common inflammatory fever but had not been admitted to the workhouse remained free of the 'jail like' fever.

As we have seen, Pringle was aware that the 'seeds of disease' could be passed from one person to another. From his observations he had concluded that the 'seeds of disease' were carried from one person to another in the foul air of an overcrowded environment. He had shown that, in the army's temporary General Hospitals, the spread of the disease could be halted by preventing overcrowding and allowing each patient his own space. But it would be well over a century before it became known that the 'seeds of disease' could be carried from person to person by ticks, lice and other animal vectors and that these carriers of disease could become lodged and flourish in the walls of old and poorly maintained buildings such as the workhouse at Lichfield. Had he known, Pringle would have understood why it was that, in spite of the careful segregation of the patients, the 'jail like' fever had spread within the workhouse hospital at Lichfield. However, it was here at Lichfield that Pringle first questioned the identity of the fever that he, and everyone in his profession, had once been content to accept as an unremarkable 'continuous fever'. As his experience of the malignant 'continuous fever' increased during his first campaign, he began to think of it as 'hospital fever'. It was now at Lichfield that he decided that 'continuous fever', 'hospital fever' and 'jail fever' were all the same disease. All three were distinguished from other fevers by the same symptoms, high temperature, severe headache, stupor or delirium and the red rash.

From Lichfield, on 9 December, Cumberland, accompanied as always by Pringle, set out to march north following closely behind the retreating rebels. But at Preston, on 15 December, he was ordered to abandon the pursuit of the rebels and return 'with all speed' with his army to take charge of the defence of London. Admiral Vernon, the commander of the North Sea Fleet had reported that a French army had landed on the Essex coast. It soon became clear that the message from Admiral Vernon had been mistaken and the order was countermanded; the pursuit of the rebels was to resume. However, Cumberland and the greater part of his army were already on their way south. The campaign against the rebels had been left to Wade's army of the north. On 27 December, the dilatory 72-year-old Field Marshal Wade was replaced by the arrogant and sadistic Lieutenant General Henry Hawley.[15] Hawley had nothing but contempt for the rebel army: 'I do and always shall despise the rascals.'[16]

Hawley followed and harried the Jacobite army as it retreated through Kendal and Penrith. Jacobite stragglers were captured, tied behind Hawley's horses and dragged to their deaths. After reaching and recapturing Carlisle on 30 December, with his provisions and his men exhausted, Hawley decided to rest his troops in winter quarters. Pringle later reported that, although very tired, the great majority of the men were well and that the few who had been taken ill on the road and had been left to the care of the local country surgeons had all been well treated.

Meanwhile, the rebel army had marched north from Carlisle and there it had been separated into a Highland Division led by Prince Charles and a Lowland Division led by Lord George Murray. The divisions took separate routes to Glasgow; then on 3 January they came together to march on towards Stirling. At the same time a new Jacobite army was approaching Stirling from Perth.

When, in October 1745, Louis XV was informed of the rebels' success in taking Edinburgh, he arranged to send a brigade to reinforce their army. It was commanded by Lord John Drummond (brother of the Duke of Perth) and was made up of the Royal Ecossais, a regiment raised in the Lowlands of Scotland to serve in the army of France, and detachments from each of the six Irish regiments then serving in the French army. On 26 November 1745, Lord Drummond and his brigade of over 1,000 men, a train of artillery and a quantity of arms and ammunition had landed at Montrose. However, by then the Jacobite army had left Scotland, captured Carlisle and was marching south into England. As all the crossings over the River Forth and the Firth of Forth were now held by government troops and by ships of the Royal Navy, Drummond decided not to attempt to join the Jacobite army in England. He established a base at Perth and began to expand his brigade into a second Jacobite army. He wrote that 'by dint of sending out letters, some of them enticing, others threatening I prevailed upon a number of considerable persons to join me and others just to send me their men'. In the following month he increased the size of his brigade from 1,000 men to 6,000; in the second week of January, 4,000 of them marched south with the train of artillery to join the main Jacobite army at Stirling. Together they formed the largest army that the Jacobites were to field at any time during the rebellion. However, Lieutenant General Hawley was not impressed. He believed that 'with everything they have brought from the north they are now 7,000, but that's nothing, they are Scotch and only so many more mouths to feed'.[17]

Lord George Murray had planned to put the rebel army into winter quarters at Stirling as soon as Stirling Castle had been taken. However, by 14 January the castle was still holding out and his troops were still in the open as Hawley's army approached Stirling from the south. On 15 January, he left Lord Drummond's brigade to maintain the siege of the castle and arranged the rest of the army in battle order on open ground south of Stirling. But Hawley was in no hurry to join battle. He was aware that the rebel army was now stronger than it had ever been but he was confident that, even so, it would not dare to take the initiative and attack. On 15 January, he allowed his army to rest, encamped to the south of Falkirk. On 16 January, the rebel army took up its battle position as it had done the day before; again Hawley did not move. On 17 January, the rebel army moved forward to take up a battle position nearer to Hawley's encampment on Falkirk Moor. By 3 p.m. Hawley had set out his army in battle line facing the rebel army. Both the armies were arranged, as was the usual practice, with the infantry, the main body of the army, forming the middle of the line with bodies of cavalry at each end of the line. However, before the opposing lines of infantry had come close enough to engage with each other, Hawley sent a large body of his cavalry to attack the right wing of the rebel line. Hawley had assumed that the rebels would be unable to withstand such an assault, but the Highlanders had their own way of dealing with cavalry; they lay on the ground and, with their dirks, they attacked the bellies of the horses as they were ridden over them. Hawley's cavalry broke. Some went off to their left and away from the battle. However, many more broke off to their right, riding across the front of the full length of the line of the rebel infantry like targets in a shooting gallery. They were shot down. The Highland infantry then threw down their emptied muskets and charged the opposing infantry with their broadswords. Hawley's infantry disintegrated and the battle was effectively over in little more than 20 minutes.[18] Casualties were equally heavy on both sides. Pringle had not been with Hawley's army and he left no record of how the sick and wounded were cared for. Nevertheless, the battle may be judged a victory for the rebels; Hawley's reputation had been badly damaged, the British army had been humiliated and the Jacobite army was free to continue its withdrawal to the north.

From Stirling the rebel army marched to Crieff where it was decided that it should proceed in two separate divisions. Prince Charles was to lead the Highland troops and the artillery, by roads that had been made by Wade, through Dunkeld and Blair Atholl to Inverness. Lord George Murray and Lord Drummond were to lead the Lowland Division and the cavalry through Perth to Dundee, across Angus to Montrose, north to Aberdeen and from there to Inverness.

After the debacle at Falkirk, Hawley was relieved of his command. Infantry, cavalry and artillery units were added to the army and Cumberland took command of all the government forces in Scotland. On renewing the pursuit of the retreating Jacobite army he marched, not directly into the Highlands, but along the coastal route taken by Lord George Murray and Lord Drummond as far as Aberdeen where he had arranged to meet up with a fleet of supply ships carrying more troops, artillery and ammunition.

During the march, the weather had been cold and wet and many of the men had become ill. Pringle was now with the army. His comment at this time shows that although he had made great advances in preventing the spread of disease, his treatment of the individual patient was still entirely conventional.

The autumnal remitting fever disguised with many symptoms of cold, could be traced in the troops that came over from Flanders till the frosts of December put an end to it. But the prevailing disorders were hard coughs, stitches, pleuritic and rheumatic pains, with a few fluxes, the usual consequences of men being exposed to colds and rains on duty or getting wet feet on the march. There were some intermittents [fevers] besides but all with such a mixture of coughs and infarctions of the lungs as made bleeding the most necessary remedy. In general, bleeding was so requisite that in every town through which the troops past and where sick had to be left behind, I, who had been recalled to attend this service, believed the surgeons and apothecaries of the place more than half instructed about the cure of the patients committed to them, when I had inculcated the necessity of large and repeated bleeding, for the men were at this time well fed and from taking cold the blood was easily inflamed.[19]

Cumberland reached Aberdeen on 27 February 1746. Until now the army had been fragmented and scattered and the medical care of the troops had been in the hands of their regimental surgeons and infirmaries. At Aberdeen

Pringle was at last in a position to set up a General Hospital. Some 300 sick had been left behind at Perth or Montrose, but at Aberdeen the army was in good health and, until the end of March, the troops were comfortably billeted at Aberdeen, Inverurie and Strathbogie. But as the weather became cold, with severe frost, snow and easterly winds, Pringle observed that while the men suffered by cold beds, guard duties or by their own conduct, the officers, having warm quarters and being less exposed to cold, escaped. Only at the beginning of March, when the weather was very cold, a few officers suffered attacks of gout. The sick were well lodged in the town hospital and in other large houses where, having free air, they did not become victims of what he was now beginning to call 'hospital fever'.

While the army was based at Aberdeen, Cumberland had been able to spend six weeks introducing new infantry techniques and preparing his troops for battle. Then, on 8 April, as the snow cleared and the weather began to improve, he led his army east to Nairn, ten miles from the position north-east of Inverness where the Jacobite army was already gathered.

Cumberland had an army of almost 9,000.[20] The Jacobite army, after a long and miserable retreat, was a tired and dispirited force of 5,400.[21] Nevertheless, Prince Charles had decided not to retreat further into the Highlands but to turn on his enemy. He chose to fight on an open stretch of moorland at Culloden House. There, late on the morning of 27 April, the two armies faced each other 300 yards apart. Prince Charles was confident that their famous charge made his Highland troops invincible. The charge, although often described as 'wild', was in fact highly disciplined. At the beginning of a battle the Highlanders, armed with broadswords, stood resolutely facing the enemy, waiting until the opposing infantrymen fired their first volley; they then dashed forward to cut the infantrymen down as they were attempting to reload their muskets. However, Cumberland had benefited from the army's bitter experience at Prestonpans. At Culloden his infantry did not fire that crucial opening volley. For 20 minutes the Highlanders waited and for 20 minutes they were torn by Cumberland's artillery. When they did eventually charge, they found that Cumberland's infantry were armed with bayonets and had been taught how to use them effectively against the broadsword. Every man in the line had been trained to ignore the Highlander in front of him and thrust his bayonet into the exposed area below the raised sword arm of the Highlander attacking his immediate neighbour on his right. With highly disciplined troops, every man confident that he would be protected by his neighbour on his left, the manoeuvre was very effective. Cumberland's infantry was not broken by the Highland charge. In the whole battle Cumberland's army suffered only 32 dead and 270 wounded.[22] The Jacobites lost over 2,000 casualties and an unknown number were slaughtered after the battle.

In April 1745, in the aftermath of the Battle of Fontenoy, the Duke of Cumberland had carefully observed the provisions of the Pringle-inspired Cartel of Frankfurt and had vigorously upbraided Marshal de Saxe for failing to do so. After the Battle of Culloden, he applied the provisions of the Cartel selectively. French and Irish soldiers who had fought in the Jacobite army were treated correctly as prisoners of war, but Scottish soldiers who fought in the Jacobite army were regarded as traitors and were shown no mercy. Murder squads were sent out to the fields, parks and scattered buildings in search of rebel wounded. In one of many such incidents 19 helpless men were discovered in a barn on the day after the battle; they were taken out, set up against a wall 'as so many marks to be besported with, and were shot dead upon the spot'.[23] Jacobite surgeons were deprived of their instruments and were refused access to the Scottish Jacobite soldiers who had been taken prisoner. Bystanders, who had taken no part in the battle but were suspected of having assisted rebels to escape from the scene of the battle, were shot.

Pringle had taken over two malt barns to accommodate 270 of Cumberland's wounded. He noted that 'several had cuts of the broadsword which were till then uncommon wounds in our hospitals but they were easily healed as the openings were large in proportion to their depth, as they bleed much at first and as there were no contusions as in gunshot wounds to obstruct a good digestion'. Such wounds were rare in military hospitals in the middle of the eighteen century. Infantry in European armies in the eighteenth century were armed with muskets. Musket bullets were of soft metal that flattened on impact, ripping the soft tissues and causing compound fractures if they struck bones. Probing the wound to extract the bullet frequently led to putrefaction; it was common practice to insert bits of leather or cloth into the wounds to stimulate the production of pus then thought to be essential to the process of healing.[24] If there was a compound fracture of a bone, the inevitable treatment was amputation of the limb, an operation that, if carried out in a busy army hospital, carried a mortality of between 50 and 80 per cent. By contrast, wounds caused by a broadsword blade were rarely associated with a compound fracture of a bone and as the open wounds contained no metal or other debris they could be easily cleaned and closed.

Pringle made separate arrangements for the treatment of the sick. He had set up a General Hospital in two large and 'well aired houses' in Nairn,

12 miles from Culloden. As he had done after the Battle of Fontenoy, he ordered the regimental surgeons to send only the most serious of their cases to his hospital. But, at Nairn, he had found that stricter measures were necessary to prevent the spread of disease. As he explained:

> By this preservation of pure air in the wards it was hoped that all contagion would be moderated, if not prevented; though it was more than ever to be apprehended, from the smallness of the town, the jail filled with prisoners many of them wounded, the prospect of a long encampment and camp diseases, the crowds and filth of the place where the markets of an army are kept and, lastly, the morbid state of the air from the measles and smallpox which had prevailed in the town before the arrival of the army.[25]

On his orders the town's jail was vigorously cleaned every day, all dead bodies were removed at once; and to 'lessen the crowd, part of the prisoners were put on board some ships lying in the roads with a liberty of coming upon deck for the air'.

Pringle's measures proved effective and from April until the last weeks of May the incidence of fevers among the government troops remained low; it was of particular significance that there was no outbreak of the potentially lethal disease that he now called hospital fever. But, at the end of May, Houghton's regiment and three other battalions that had been sent north as reinforcements disembarked and joined the army at Nairn. A few days later, 12 men of Houghton's regiment were admitted to Pringle's hospital suffering from fever. Pringle noticed at once that they did not have the cough and rheumatic pains that were the usual symptoms of the fever prevailing in the army at that time. When they were admitted they were in 'an uncommon stupor'. Pringle recognised their illness as the highly contagious and dangerous hospital fever. At first he assumed that their illness had resulted from their long confinement in the foul air of the ships' holds. But he could not understand why it was that only men of Houghton's regiment had contracted the fever during that long confinement and not men of the other three battalions who had sailed under the same weather conditions, in the holds of similar ships, and for the same length of time. It was only later that he discovered that the disease had come by contact with established cases of 'jail fever'. Some months earlier, a French ship had been captured off the coast of England by ships of the Royal Navy and had been found to have on board troops being sent from France as reinforcements for the rebel army in Scotland. Among the troops were found 36 English soldiers who had served with the British army in Flanders but had deserted to the enemy. From the French ship they had been thrown into jails in England where they had been kept until they could be sent by sea to stand trial by court martial at Inverness. In retrospect, it seemed clear that they had carried the 'seeds' of the fever with them when, by chance, they were embarked on the transport on which Houghton's regiment happened to be travelling to Inverness.

Within three days of landing, six of the regiment's officers had been infected. In the few days that Houghton's regiment was billeted in Nairn and 86 more cases were admitted to hospital. The regiment then moved to Inverness and in the following ten days a further 120 cases were sent back to Pringle's hospital in Nairn. Pringle made an unequivocal decision on a matter that had troubled him for some time:

> The symptoms of the jail-fever are in every point so like those of the hospital-fever, that, as they were formerly only conjectured to be the same distemper they are now proved to be so.

While the army was at Inverness the number of new cases of the disease gradually diminished but when, on 3 June, the main body of the army began its march south, 600 sick, most of them victims of hospital fever, had to be left behind.

Later, while resting at Fort Augustus there were more cases of fever among the troops and the hospital fever spread to the local population. When the army left Fort Augustus in the middle of August, between 200 and 300 had to be left behind; they were carried back to the General Hospital at Nairn. When the army left Fort Augustus, hospital fever was already 'frequent among the inhabitants of that town'. Pringle also noted that, since the middle of February, when the army had arrived at Aberdeen, over 2,000 men had been treated in his General Hospital and of these some 300 died, 'most of them from hospital fever'.[26] The large number of deaths from hospital fever was disturbing. However, if Pringle had not introduced his measures to contain the spread of the infection, the number of dead would probably have been much greater.

In August, the army left Scotland to return to Flanders. The Duke of Cumberland, and Pringle spent the following months in London. Neither Cumberland nor Pringle returned to the army in Flanders until the beginning of the campaigning season in the spring of 1747.

EIGHT

Fever in Flanders: the End of the War

There never was a good war or a bad peace.
Benjamin Franklin, 1789

By the summer of 1746, although the war in Europe still continued, it had already failed to achieve its objectives. In 1740, the Pragmatic Army had been formed to defend the Hapsburg inheritance of Maria Theresa of Austria but her inheritance was no longer preserved intact. Louis XV of France had failed to establish the dominance of the Bourbons over the Hapsburgs of Austria. Frederick II of Prussia still held only part of Silesia. Charles Albert of Bavaria was now the Holy Roman Emperor but he had not taken and kept Bohemia. Elisabeth Farnese, the Queen of Spain, had not found a place for her son in Italy. In the winter of 1745–6, Louis XV of France had conducted a flurry of diplomatic missions and international congresses to find peace terms that would be acceptable to every combatant party in the war, but every party meant to secure a settlement as favourable to its own interests as possible.

Louis XV still hoped to reduce the powers and possessions of Austria. In the summer of 1746, he renewed his campaign to complete his conquest of the Austrian Netherlands. He planned to do so without disturbing the Dutch Republic. The Dutch had contributed troops to the Pragmatic Army that opposed him in 1743 and they had manned the fortresses defending the borders of the Austrian Netherlands against his first invasion in 1745. However, the Dutch Republic was not formally at war with France; it was the close northern neighbour of the Austrian Netherlands and Louis XV saw it as a possible ally.

Louis XV's commander in Flanders, Marshal de Saxe, meant to take the Austrian Netherlands with as little bloodshed as possible by laying siege to the enemy's fortresses while constantly manoeuvring the main body of his troops to draw off the enemy's army without engaging it in battle. On 11 July 1746, the fortress at Mons quickly surrendered and the surrender of the fortress of Charleroi followed on 2 August. The fortress at Namur was more strongly defended but, after it had been besieged for two months, its supplies of food were exhausted. On 1 October, it too surrendered. Marshal de Saxe now assumed that the campaigning season had come to its end, but, on 10 October, on the fields that surrounded the village of Ramoux, he found himself threatened by a large Pragmatic Army. He could not avoid battle.

The French army of 120,000 was positioned on a four-mile-long arc stretching from the River Jaar to the outskirts of Liège; people flocked out from the town to watch the battle. The Pragmatic Army was commanded by Prince Charles of Lorraine; his appointment, ordered by Maria Theresa, had caused the Duke of Cumberland to remain in London. The Pragmatic Army approached the French line from the north. At its centre were 24,000 British, Hanoverian and auxiliary German troops, all commanded by Sir John Ligonier; on its left flank were 24,000 Dutch troops; on the right, on the far side of a ravine and isolated from the rest of the army, were 32,000 Austrian troops. Marshal de Saxe planned to attack first the Dutch who were expected to be as eager to surrender as they had been in the past. When they had given way, he would quickly attack the British; as the Austrians would be isolated on the far side of the ravine, they would be unable to take part in the early stage of the battle. The British would be easily defeated.

However, the battle did not go well for Marshal de Saxe. Bad weather on 11 October prevented the onset of the battle until 2 p.m., leaving only five hours for the nine hours' work that he had planned. When attacked, the Dutch did not behave as expected; they offered strong resistance. Marshal de Saxe was obliged to use his great advantage in manpower and throw battalion after battalion in a 'meat-grinder action'[1] against the British centre. After almost five hours, the British and Dutch forces withdrew across the River Meuse under the cover of darkness. The French had suffered 2,500 wounded and 1,250 dead; the allies lost 5,400 wounded and 1,600 dead. Pringle later wrote that as he had been in Britain at this time he could not give a full account of the casualties suffered by the British army. He reported only that after the battle the General Hospitals had treated some 1,500 sick 'but there was nothing uncommon in the diseases being such as regularly occur in the course of every campaign.'[2]

Nothing had been gained by either side in the battle. Marshal de Saxe had the fortresses that he had taken at Mons, Charleroi and Namur still in his hands, but he acknowledged that the battle had not been the crushing blow on his enemy that he had hoped to inflict. The only satisfaction that the battle had given him was that the French infantry that had failed at Dettingen had, by his training and under his command, been transformed into a force that could match the infantry of 'the fearsome British'.[3]

Before hostilities were renewed in 1747, there had been an important political change. There had been a revolution in the Dutch Republic. The Dutch had long been proud of their liberties; they were industrious and very successful in trading and agriculture; they were the wealthiest nation per capita in Europe; for more than two centuries, they had taken an important part in European affairs.[4] Their constitution had been thought to be one of their glories. Each of the country's provinces had control of its own affairs and the right to elect its own Stadtholder. Only for foreign affairs was there a supra-provincial body, the States General, but nothing it proposed could be put into practice without the agreement of all provinces. No single officer served as a chief executive officer for the whole republic. It was a decentralised system of government that had worked well for a community whose chief interest was in trade and commerce. However, in the middle of the eighteenth century trading had declined, the economy was losing its momentum and now the republic had been invaded. It was clear that the system of government was failing. For many years real power had rested only with the families of great commercial wealth. It had been accepted that the chief member of the House of Orange, the country's nearest approach to a royal house, should hold only two or three of the Stadtholderships and leave all the others vacant. The great majority of the people played no part at all in government.

Early in 1747, there was a demand for change to a more centralised form of government. In particular, it was insisted that the Prince of Orange should be made Stadtholder of all the provinces and that he should always express and openly mount opposition against the ambitions of France.[5] France could no longer look at the Dutch Republic as a possible ally. Marshal de Saxe was now free to attack and keep the key fortress at Maastricht in the Dutch line of defence.

In the spring of 1747, Cumberland returned to Flanders to resume command of the Pragmatic Army. When the campaigning season began, Marshal de Saxe did not immediately make an assault on the Dutch fortresses. He knew that Louis XV was pursuing peace across Europe and he had no wish to sacrifice the lives of his troops unnecessarily. He could afford to wait. The Pragmatic Army was seriously outnumbered and poorly supplied and the alliance that had created it might fall apart. Should that happen he would be able to take both the fortress of Maastricht and the fortress near the coast at Bergen op Zoom without bloodshed. For weeks he manoeuvred his troops to threaten but not to assault the two fortresses while Cumberland shadowed his movements from his main base at Breda.

However, in June 1747, Louis XV lost patience with de Saxe's procrastinations and ordered him to proceed to take Maastricht. On 2 July, in an area of a little over 20 square miles near the village of Laffeld, a quarter of a million soldiers became crowded together in another long grinding battle. De Saxe had an army of 136,000. He was opposed by a Pragmatic Army numbering less than 100,000. After five hours of desperate fighting, the Pragmatic Army was forced to make a fighting withdrawal to the safety of the walls of Maastricht.[6] De Saxe claimed victory but he had suffered 10,000 casualties, twice as many as the allies. He believed that he was no longer strong enough to make a second attack on the fortress at Maastricht. In an attempt to split Cumberland's army, he sent a force of 30,000 to take the fortress of Bergen op Zoom, over 90 miles to the north at the mouth of the River Scheldt. Cumberland sent only seven battalions to Bergen op Zoom but they were not called into action; the fortress was surrendered by its Dutch garrison after no more than token resistance. The butchery that followed in the town was horrendous. Over 2,000 of the civilian inhabitants of Bergen op Zoom were killed and many more were severely injured. Together the pointless slaughter at Laffeld and Bergen op Zoom became a further convincing argument for peace. In October, both armies in Flanders went into winter quarters and the fighting was not renewed.

Pringle wrote little about his last campaign in the Low Countries[7] On his return to the army with Cumberland in the spring of 1747 his immediate concern had been for the high incidence of sickness in the army. Most of the illness was, once again, due to the army's two usual diseases, intermittent fever (malaria) and the flux (dysentery). Troops living on low ground suffered severely from intermittent fever; in some regiments as many 85 per cent of the men were at times unfit for duty. He had found that 'where the soil is barren sand and so little water is seen that at first sight the country might seem dry and healthy this appearance is deceitful. For water is everywhere to be found at a depth of two or three feet; and in proportion to its depth the inhabitants are healthy.' The incidence was particularly high near fortresses around which the land had been deliberately flooded as an integral part of their defences. It was also high in areas where wet ground was sheltered by trees. However, he had also noticed that, even when the incidence of the disease was at its height, it did not spread to the crews of the ships stationed offshore. This he took as 'a proof that the moist and putrid air of the marshes was dissipated or corrected before it could reach them'.

The flux was never as common in the army as intermittent fever, but in the late summer, when the days were still hot but the nights had begun to grow cool 'and from these interchanges to which the men were most exposed, the flux took its rise from cold and damps after the blood has undergone some alteration by continued hot weather'.[8] In 1747, more than half of the soldiers had the disease; even the officers were affected and the disease ran through the neighbouring villages. However, the town of Maastricht escaped although there was constant intercourse between the camp and the town; Pringle concluded that Maastricht had escaped because the 'town, standing on a large river in open country, is particularly well aired and clean'. Pringle's observations were again sound but they could not be explained until, more than a century later, when it was shown that the disease was caused by living micro-organisms.

Pringle's achievement in limiting the spread of infection in hospitals and jails by preventing overcrowding the sick in enclosed spaces was based on his observations and inductive reasoning as advocated by Francis Bacon. But his treatment of disease was still based on the classical theory of the four humours and firmly in accord with Galen's teaching that bleeding was essential in the treatment of every fever.

When the campaign began in 1747 and the battle was about to begin at Laffeld, Pringle had taken charge of the organisation of hospital services. He commandeered a large well-ventilated church at Ravenstein in which he set up a General Hospital. Once again he ordered that the wounded should be cared for at their Regimental Infirmaries and that only when absolutely essential should they be sent back to overcrowd the General Hospital at the army's base. As a result, only 100 of the many British troops wounded in battle were treated at the General Hospital at Ravenstein and there was no outbreak of the dreaded hospital fever (typhus).

In the weeks after the battle, the men who had escaped injury and had been in camp close to Maastricht, remained healthy, but at the end of August the incidence of dysentery began to rise. Pringle recorded that by the beginning of October 'half the soldiers had the distemper, more or less'. However, the patients had been dispersed among the Regimental Infirmaries and General Hospital and all had been 'better aired than was usual'; and the regimental surgeons had been taught how to treat dysentery. As a result there had been very few deaths. But the seven battalions that had been stationed at Bergen op Zoom[9] had been very badly affected; at the height of the epidemic only one in seven of the men had been fit for duty. Overall, the army had suffered a great number of deaths from dysentery but there had been no deaths from hospital fever.

However, from the army's camp at Maastricht the dysentery had spread to the neighbouring villages and it had caused many deaths because, as Pringle commented, 'the peasants either wanted medicine altogether or used what they had been better without'. He also noted that during the epidemic, the people of the town of Maastricht had escaped the contagion although there had been free contact during the epidemic between the people of the town and the people of the surrounding villages. His explanation was that the town of Maastricht stood on a large river and 'was particularly well aired'. He had also noticed that at Bergen op Zoom the troops had been in constant contact with the men of the squadron of the Royal Navy lying at anchor near the town yet they were 'neither afflicted with the fever nor the flux but, amidst all that sickness, enjoyed perfect health, a proof that the moist and putrid air of the marshes was dissipated or corrected before it could reach them and that an open situation is one of the best preservatives against the diseases of a neighbouring low and marshy country'.

During the winter months the epidemic of dysentery had quickly subsided. When the army moved out of winter quarters in April 1748 and marched 30 miles to the north to Roermond, only 500 sick had to be left behind. Few of these were suffering from flux. The majority were men who had been suffering from intermittent fever for some time, either at Maastricht or at Bergen op Zoom. But when the army was at Roermond the number of new cases of intermittent fever had begun to mount; and the number continued to increase later in the spring as the army moved a further 30 miles north-west to Eindhoven in North Brabant.

Pringle described Brabant as the flattest part of the Netherlands with only 'some sand hills and insensible risings which gave the advantage of a few feet in height to some of the villages'. Elsewhere the ground looked barren and, at first sight, it seemed to be dry and healthy, but that appearance was deceptive. Water could be found everywhere at a depth of only two or three feet below the surface of the ground. Every winter large stretches of the countryside were flooded with water drawn from the lower reaches of the River Maas; although the water was run off in the summer, the land that it had covered never became completely dry. During the war years the perpetual wetness of the ground and the constant dampness of the air had been made worse by the flooding of the land round the country's many fortresses as part of their defences. In the summer of 1748, the air had become, in Pringle's words, 'so filled with putrid exhalations' and the sickness that raged through the neighbouring villages had become so severe that the States of Holland had given orders that the water was to be let in again round the fortresses and that its level was to be kept up until winter.[10]

Stationed on the low ground that surrounded Eindhoven, almost the whole army became sick. Only the regiments billeted in the villages of De Lind and Zeist, which were 10 feet and 14 feet above sea level, remained healthy. In regiments billeted elsewhere, so many of the men contracted intermittent fever that by July the Regimental Infirmaries became so overcrowded that some of the patients contracted the dreaded hospital fever (typhus). These men, although they were severely ill, were sent 80 miles to the General Hospital near Brussels; the hospital was on higher ground and the wards were large enough to allow the patients to be well segregated.

This outbreak of hospital fever was successfully contained but as the summer advanced the army continued to have more and more cases of intermittent fever. The Scots Greys were very badly affected; by the end of the campaign there were only 30 men in the whole regiment who had not suffered from intermittent fever at some time. The Scotch Fusiliers had had as many as 300 men sick at the same time, while a regiment of dragoons stationed only half a mile away escaped completely. Pringle commented that 'such was the advantage of that little distance from the marshes, of the wind blowing mostly from the dry ground and of a situation upon open heath somewhat higher than the rest of the country'.

Later, on reviewing the epidemic of intermittent fever, Pringle noted that within a month of being stationed near Eindhoven the total number of cases in the army had risen to over 2,000. That number had increased greatly in August and it had continued to rise in September. It was only early in October that, as the weather became cool, the number of cases of raging fever began to dwindle; by the beginning of winter the epidemic had ceased completely. Pringle wrote that 'it was curious to observe how these intermittents declined with the fall of the leaf. At that time, less moisture ascends and by the trees shedding their leaves, the villages become more open and perflated and of course more dry and healthful.'

However, during the epidemic of intermittent fever it had been the peasants living in the villages who had made up the majority of the victims. In the towns there had been fewer cases and fewer deaths; it seemed to Pringle that the intermittent fever was most frequent among the poor who lived on the ground floors of the houses, who were inadequately nourished and who 'wanted medicine, for, without artificial evacuations [enemas], Nature was able to make no cures but slow and imperfect ones'. That the people had experienced more sickness from fever in 1748 than for many years he attributed to the misfortune that in that year two of its causes had coincided, the flooding of the land round the fortresses and a very hot summer.

In the autumn of 1748, the British army was preparing to leave Flanders. For some months, certainly since the battle at Laffeld, France and Britain had come to accept that they had little to gain by continuing the war. Austria had hoped that, before the war ended, it would have won back the whole of Silesia which, until October 1740, had been its richest province. However, in July 1748, the Austrian Ambassador to Paris acknowledged the predominance of France and Britain in the affairs of Europe[11] and he was aware that they meant to have peace. After further months of negotiation, on 18 October 1748, the Treaty of Aix-la-Chapelle brought the war to an end.

In the middle of November, the British army began to move from its camps at Eindhoven and Breda to the port of Willemstad where they embarked for passage to England. Unfortunately, the winds were contrary and a number of the ships were forced to remain anchored offshore for a month. The men were kept confined below deck, the air became foul and soon there was an outbreak of hospital fever. The outbreak was worst in the ships carrying the patients from the army's General Hospital at Oosterhout. Pringle later wrote that the patients had brought 'the seeds of disease' with them and had then been crowded together in the hold of the ships for over three weeks. The greatest number and the worst cases were in one of the ships in which there were two men with gangrenous limbs. Pringle assumed their wounded and mortifying limbs were not only a source of infection while they were on board ship but also in the wards of the hospital in Ipswich to which they had been admitted on their arrival in England. He later wrote:

> The hospital prepared at Ipswich only for the reception of the sick from Oosterhout was obliged to admit several more from the other transports which by the stress of the weather put in on that coast; so that we had about 400 there and most of them ill of this contagious fever. Now as so many were brought from the hospital-ships in the worst state, the infection and mortality were at first considerable.

But by the largeness of the wards and by billeting in the town every man as soon as he recovered (thereby removing him from the contagion and gaining more room for those who were still sick) the air was purified and the distemper abated sooner than could have been expected. The hospital then broke up after it had continued about three months in England.

The army's campaign in Britain in 1745–6 had been quite different from the earlier ones that Pringle had experienced. Much of it had been conducted in the severe conditions of winter. The army had not campaigned as a single unit but had often been split into widely separated sections. Pringle had not been able to supervise the medical services of every one of these often widely scattered units of the army. Nor had he been able to provide a General Hospital to serve every section of the army. The medical care of the troops had largely been carried out by the regiments' own surgeons and infirmaries. On their marches the regiments were frequently engaged in skirmishes. As they were not equipped to carry their wounded and sick with them, the regiments were often obliged to leave them behind in the care of the local population. There had also been several major battles and just as it had not been possible to ensure that there were General Hospitals available to support the Regimental Infirmaries after every skirmish, it had not been possible to have a General Hospital at hand to care for the wounded and sick after every major battle. Nevertheless, where it had been possible to follow Pringle's methods and standards of care, they had proved effective. The outbreak of hospital fever at Inverness in May 1746 had been contained and there had been no recurrence of the catastrophe that had devastated the army in 1743.

In the campaign in Britain, much of the difficulty had been caused by the nature of the war, its bitterness, its urgency and its chaos. In Flanders in the last months of the war the diseases suffered by the troops were caused largely by the nature of the territory on which the army was stationed and by the conditions in which the army was transported. For over a year the army had been stationed on territory that was flat, low, wet and poorly drained. In the heat of the summer the incidence of first intermittent fever then dysentery had risen to epidemic proportions. When the sick were carried back to England crowded together in the holds of their ships, many of them had died of the malignant continuous fever (typhus).

However, nothing that Pringle wrote as his last campaign in Flanders came to an end conveyed any sense of failure. The army that returned to Britain in 1748 had carried with it hundreds of sick. In all, the General Hospital at Ipswich had been called on to care for 626 patients, most of them suffering from hospital fever; of these 52 had died, a mortality of 8.3 per cent. However, in 1743, after his first battle at Dettingen, most of the sick admitted to the General Hospitals at Fechenheim and Neuwied had also been suffering from hospital fever; the mortality among the soldiers was then 27 per cent, while among their civilian 'followers' it was over 50 per cent.[12] The reforms that Pringle had introduced had clearly been effective.

From his observations in the campaign of 1743 he had concluded that apart from the itch (scabies) and *lues venerea* (gonorrhoea and syphilis) which he believed were common in many populations and were therefore not specific to armies, intermittent fever, the flux and hospital fever were the three major diseases that had afflicted the army during its campaigns and that all had in some way been caused by foul air, the exhalations from the marshes, the foul-smelling vapours from human excrement and the air breathed in crowded hospitals and ships' holds.

Pringle had issued instructions to the army's regimental officers and quartermasters on measures to protect the troops from inclement weather, from fatigue and hunger; he had given them guidance on the siting of camps and the management of the camp sites. He had improved the standard of care in the military hospitals. Particular attention was given to ventilation of the wards; each patient was allotted his own space, his own bed with frequent issues of clean linen. The wards were staffed by trained, well-disciplined female nurses who had been recruited for the purpose. Above all, hospitals were never allowed to become overcrowded. All of these provisions were new to the army. Before being introduced by Pringle they had never been used by European armies, certainly not since Roman times.

However, the regimes of treatment that he insisted should be used had been used for centuries. Bleeding was obligatory in the treatment of every case of fever and it was recommended in almost every other illness. Even in treating coughs and bronchitis, a routine bleeding was to be given before administering drugs to induce sweating or cupping to produce large fluid blisters. Even rheumatism was to be treated by the application of leeches to the affected area.

For the intermittent fever the initial bleeding was to be followed by an emetic three times daily and a purgative once a day; but the mainstay of treatment was Peruvian Bark (the bark of the cinchona tree, the source of quinine). In convalescence fresh vegetables and a daily ration of wine or spirits were recommended as tonics. The treatment of dysentery was similar to the treatment of intermittent fever except that the administration of opiates was forbidden as they tended 'to pen up the wind and fix the cause'.[13] Diet was restricted to rice gruel, mutton broth, or barley water but never milk unless diluted by lime water.

By the end of the campaign of 1748, Pringle's reforms had already brought about major improvements in the health of the army but further improvements were still clearly necessary.

On 8 October 1748, the Treaty of Aix-la-Chapelle was signed and on 6 December the treaty was finally ratified. The war was over. Pringle's appointment as Physician-General to the Army Overseas was ended. He now had to face up to the question that had been troubling him since he first joined the army. Should he return to Scotland?

From the beginning Pringle had been aware that his appointment as an army physician would last only until the end of the war. In a letter from Ghent in November 1742 he told his friend Andrew Mitchell that when the war ended he 'had no other scheme but to return to Edinburgh and the university'. But in the same letter he wrote that Miss N.[14] was 'the only thing that gave [him] any considerable attachment to Scotland'. Pringle had been in love with her since he was 15; she was in her 13th year. The relationship clearly had the approval of her family. His letters to Miss N. were always enclosed in packages addressed to her mother; her letters to Pringle were no doubt read by her mother before being posted. A few weeks later Pringle informed Mitchell that 'the only attachment to Edinburgh I own is to Miss N. but upon my honour there is no engagement nor shall there be till you know of it'.

In a letter on 3 December he discussed in greater detail the difficulties that he was experiencing in making plans for his future.

On the whole the worst day I have had since I have been abroad has been better than my best day at home. You know what complaints I have had, the prospect of an ever dwarfed fortune. So don't think but that at my worst I am satisfied with my present position. To think to have everything to one's wish and have no profession, no prospect is either folly or madness.

In a former letter I balanced accounts between two situations, not that I thought it at all necessary to come to a decision at present for Lord knows what may happen before I can see either of the two places but to accustom myself to think upon the subject that I may be ready when it is necessary. My objection to my nation [Scotland], I have already given. My objection to the other place [London] I have thought of but two, the want of language, the deficit of which I am daily more and more sensible, and the lack of salary. If you think I may come soon to make up that elsewhere I can assure you from experience that either from regaining my physical practice in the place I have left or my chance of enlarging it, they are so inconsiderable that they need hardly come into the question. As for my defects of address and arts, my ungainly manner with new folks they are things that will ever be bars, I imagine, in my way, in any city in the world. As for matters touching Miss N, who is a heterogeneous body having nothing to parallel her in a southern latitude, I will offer them another time.

Pringle's objections to returning to Edinburgh were real and they had increased during the years he was abroad with the army. He was the youngest of four sons; he had inherited very little when his father died. On accepting the appointment of Physician-General to His Majesty's Forces Overseas in March 1744, he had been obliged to resign from his Chair of Philosophy at Edinburgh. He had been made a Fellow of the Royal College of Physicians of Edinburgh in 1735 and had done much to improve the College's *Pharmaco-peia*. But he had been unable build up a practice in a place where he was much better known as a Professor of Philosophy and his prospects of establishing a practice in Edinburgh diminished still further while he was with the army.

The difficulties in establishing himself in London that he had foreseen during his first year in the army had also been real. In the 1740s England was already enjoying a period of increasing prosperity. The wealthy and educated, the people of quality, now formed a new polite society with its own manners of speech, conversation and behaviour. These were the defects of language, address, and ungainly manner that Pringle found in himself in 1742. However, during his years in the society of English officers in the army, he had learned something of the habits and manners of polite London society. In the late autumn of 1743, Miss N. had gently chided him for failing to write to her, but thereafter she had disappeared from his correspondence and was no longer 'the only thing that gave [him] any considerable attachment to Scotland'. However, most important of all, in October 1745, he had been elected a Fellow of the Royal Society of London. When the war came to an end in 1748, Pringle decided to settle in London.

NINE

Observations on the Diseases of the Army

I flatter myself that I may have a work useful to the public.
John Pringle, letter to Andrew Mitchell, 1743

Pringle's life had been transformed by his years with the army. In 1742, he had sought a commission in the army because his income was less than £100 a year and at the age of 35 he felt humiliated by his continuing dependence on more prosperous members of his family. However, for six years his army salary had amounted to £546 a year (present value £102,500).[1] Officers in the army had paid him a fee for his services and each year while the army was in winter quarters, he had earned an income by practising among the local civilian population. It seems probable that while in the army his total annual income was never less than £1,000 (present value £187,800). In 1748, he was financially secure and independent.

Before he was commissioned in the army, he had failed to make his mark either as a practising physician in Edinburgh or as a Professor of Philosophy at Edinburgh University. Since then he had been very successful. He had been an eminent Physician-General to His Majesty's Forces Overseas. In 1745, he had been elected a Fellow of the Royal Society of London. In 1749, he was made Physician-in-Ordinary to the Duke of Cumberland.

In 1743, he had written of his 'defects of address and arts and ungainly manner with new folks, things that will ever be in my way'.[2] In this too, he had changed. In London, in 1749, he was seen as a man of distinction. He was tall and erect with a strong expression and a commanding presence. It was said of him that he paid careful attention to those who had earned his friendship and esteem. Foreigners were always shown every mark of civility and respect. However, it was also said that he had a somewhat dry and cool manner towards men who failed to please him. Nevertheless, he made many friends and, in London, he quickly became a popular and generous host. On Sunday evenings he entertained friends, fellow scientists, soldiers and distinguished visitors who had come to London to meet and talk to him.

In the middle years of the eighteenth century London was 'the hub of a polite transformation'.[3] During the reign of George II, Britain had enjoyed great commercial success, a success that had brought new money to the middle classes but much greater wealth to the upper ranks of society. The elite, the people of quality, had generated a new polite society. They travelled abroad. They acquired new elegant furniture (commodes and secretaires), new porcelain, new hairstyles and even new foods. Their new society had its own genteel manners of speech and conversation. They discovered a new interest in paintings, in books, in music and the decorative arts of every kind. They determined how certain things must be done, how to sit on a horse, how to enter a room, how to take a place at the table, how to hold a glass.[4] As a physician with a practice that included many patients who were known at the Royal Court of St James, Pringle was welcomed into this new society. It was something that he had not known in his years in Edinburgh, but in London it was a society that he found very agreeable.

As physician to the Duke of Cumberland he was obliged to be easily available. In 1751, he moved from his apartment in King Street, St James Square, to a house on the south side of Pall Mall,[5] only a short walk from the Palace of St James although a rather longer walk to the Royal Society in Crane Court. On 14 April 1752, he married Charlotte, the younger daughter of Dr William Oliver of Bath.[6] Dr Oliver was a Fellow of the Royal Society and the principal physician at the hospital that had recently been opened for patients who had travelled to Bath to take the waters at the most fashionable spa in England.

Now settled in London as a physician, Pringle set out to extend his reputation as a medical scientist. In 1750, he published his *Observations on the Nature and Cure of Hospital and Jayl-Fevers*. The book followed an outbreak of jail fever (typhus) in Newgate during the Old Baillie assizes in which the Lord Mayor, three judges and forty other people died. Pringle's commentary was based on his experience of jail fever when serving in the army in Flanders and in Scotland. He attributed this outbreak to the 'putrid air' in London being made more dangerous by the 'perspirable matter of a great number of all sorts of people'.[7] Newgate was cleaned and 'three cartloads of the most abominable filth were carried away but lest the effluvia of such poisons should infest the air the contents of the carts were buried ten feet down some miles out of town'.[8] Newgate, Gatehouse Prison, New Prison, Clerkenwell, Bridgewell and the Old Baillie were all washed with vinegar and herbs were burnt in the courtrooms.

Two years later, Pringle published his *Observations on The Diseases of the Army*. It was the book that, in December 1742, he had promised Andrew Mitchell that he would write. It was to be his most famous work. Seven editions were published in Britain in his lifetime and it was translated into French, German and Italian. An American edition, edited by Benjamin Rush, was published in 1810.

In the first part of his book, Pringle gives a brief account of the British army's campaigns on the continent of Europe and in Britain from 1742 until 1748, the campaigns during which he had made his observations on the diseases suffered by the army. In Part II he classifies the diseases suffered by the troops, making a clear distinction between the pattern of diseases suffered by the army and those suffered by the civilian population. Cases of measles, smallpox and *lues venerea* (syphilis and gonorrhoea) did of course occur in the army, but, as they were no more common among soldiers than among civilians, he did not include them among his diseases of armies.

The diseases of the army fell into to two broad groups, the 'inflammatory' and the 'putrid'. To the modern reader these two names may be misleading; they did not refer to the pathology of the diseases which was at the time still unknown and unknowable. The so-called 'inflammatory' diseases were those which were clearly sited in one organ or part of the body. The 'putrid' diseases were those, notably the fevers, which did not appear to be localised anywhere in the body.

The diseases of the troops differed from those of civilian populations in that they resulted from the lack of appropriate clothing during exposure to bad weather; from inadequate covering when asleep; from being encamped on wet ground; and from insufficient space in barracks and hospitals. Pringle wrote that they were caused by 'the inclemency of the weather, from foul air and from infection'. His use of the word 'infection' is remarkable. Pringle, of course, could know nothing of live micro-organisms; the germ theory belonged to a later century. But in notes that he made during his military campaigns he had frequently written of the 'seeds of disease' being carried from one person to another. He had a concept of the physical carriage of disease as it spread among a gathering of people.

For the most part the diseases due to the severity of the weather occurred in the months when the army was in winter quarters. These were the inflammatory diseases – pleurisies, chronic coughs, consumptions, rheumatisms, inflammations of the brain and inflammations of the bowels – all without fever. Pringle wrote that all these disorders were commonly supposed to be caused by a stoppage of perspiration at a time when the fibres of all the body's organs were most braced and the pores of the skin and lungs most contracted, but he added that 'it is not yet clear whether the cause does not rather depend upon something imbibed from the air'. Here Pringle is accepting Boerhaave's teaching on the fibrous structure of the body's organs but at the same time he is seeking an explanation of the cause of these diseases more in keeping with his own observations.

Pringle notes that the spring is the healthiest season for the army. However, in the summer, as the weather becomes warmer, the fibres of the body become relaxed and the body fluids become 'rarefied and more disposed to putrefaction'. Should there then be a stoppage of the perspiration or any of the other excretions designed to carry off the more putrid parts of the blood, a fever is the result. It might be a remitting fever, an intermittent fever, or a bloody flux. Hippocrates had ascribed these fevers to a failure of the production of bile and for that reason such fevers were still generally called 'bilious'. Pringle proposed that, since it seemed probable that the bile was not the only fluid to be deficient, the word 'putrid' would be more proper'. Pringle was again acknowledging Boerhaave's teaching on the fibrous structure of the body and its reaction to heat. However, Pringle doubted that the relaxation of the body's fibres provoked by exposure to heat was the full explanation of the outbreak of fevers during the army's summer campaigning season. He pointed out that during the summer campaigns the troops were also brought together in camps where they were much exposed not only to heat but also to moisture.

Pringle wrote that moisture was one of the most frequent causes of sickness in the army. In the winter the troops were lodged in damp barracks. During the summer campaigning season they were exposed to the dampness in tents in which the air was never thoroughly dry because of the breathing, the 'constant exhalations', of the men and the heavy rains. The dampness had been particularly troublesome where the army had been encamped in the lower and wetter parts of the Netherlands. But Pringle had also observed that it was neither the canals nor the deep defensive inundations round the fortresses that were so dangerous. It was rather the vapours rising from marshy ground, from meadows that had been flooded and had recently been drained, or from fields that looked dry but had water close below the surface that were the source of the putrid diseases that became common in the dry and hot summers. Pringle's observations were correct, but it was not until the last years of the nineteenth century that it was discovered that the danger was carried by mosquitoes that bred in the wet marshy ground. Pringle was convinced that moisture was itself dangerous.

This moist air, Pringle divided into four kinds. These were the air rising from the corrupted water of the marshes; the air from the human excrement lying about in the camp in hot weather; the air from bedding straw rotting in the tents; and the air in hospitals crowded with men suffering from putrid disorders. Again Pringle's observations were sound, but the full explanation of what he had observed did not emerge until a later century. However, in his *Observations* Pringle ventured some speculations of his own.

It seemed probable to him that the dangerous exhalations from the marshes consisted of more than water; certainly they contained the putrid effluvia from the great quantities of vegetables that rotted in the marshes and innumerable insects that died there. Almost as dangerous as the camps sited near the marshes were those pitched closely surrounded by trees; there the air was not only moist and dangerous of itself but became stagnant and corrupted by the filth of the camp. The foul air caused by the privies and rotting straw of the camp was always offensive. But during outbreaks of the bloody flux (dysentery) the air containing the putrid excrements and effluvia of the sick becomes infectious and even more dangerous. Many of the normally healthy men suffering from the flux might recover easily were it not for the foul air, 'the destructive steams that work like a ferment and ripen the disease'.

However, Pringle believed that the most dangerous foul air of all was that in hospitals, barracks, transport ships and every other crowded place in which the air becomes so confined that it either loses some of its vital principle by being so frequently breathed and rebreathed or becomes loaded with foul steams. It is the 'respirable' matter that, as it is the most volatile part, is the most putrescent. 'It is due to the uncleanliness of such places, to the number of men present in them suffering from the flux, from foul sores and mortifications [gangrenes] that the contagious fever is so frequent and mortal.'

Pringle was confident that foul air, in its various forms, was an important cause of the diseases of armies. At that time irregularities in diet were more commonly supposed to play the major part, but Pringle argued that, if this were the case, then changes in the weather would not have such an obvious effect on the health of the soldiers. Troops of different nations in the same camps but living on different diets would not be afflicted by the same diseases and there would not be such a great variation in the number of sick in different years. He also argued that a soldier, in time of war, receives very little pay and is thus protected against excess in eating, which he judged to be 'the most common error in diet'. The only danger is that when soldiers are not obliged to eat in a communal mess, some spend their money on strong liquors. But when every man is obliged to eat in a group of soldiers and to pay his share of the cost, there can be no errors of diet of any great consequence since almost the whole of his pay must be spent on the common food. The abuse of spirits, the consumption of fruit and the drinking of bad water were also generally said to cause illness. Pringle, however, insisted that together these three causes had never caused the tenth part of the sickness experienced in any of the campaigns in which he had served. Spirits, even when drunk in excess, tended to weaken the constitution rather than to produce any of the common army diseases. If a number of the men became sick after drinking too much, Pringle was confident that many more were prevented from falling sick by drinking spirits in moderation: 'Soldiers often have to struggle with extremes of heat and cold, long marches, wet clothes and scanty provisions. To enable then to undergo such hardships it is proper that they should drink something stronger than water or even small beer.'

Pringle believed that more relevant to the health of the soldier than his diet was his way of life. The life of a foot soldier is divided between extremes of labour and inactivity. At times he becomes ready to sink in fatigue when, carrying the full weight of his arms, his accoutrements and his knapsack, he is made to march long distances in bad weather. But for a man of low rank the great danger is the long periods he spends in idleness. At times the foot soldier has turns of duty and little time for sleep; but these times are rare. Usually when he is off duty he spends too much time asleep which enervates the body and renders it more subject to disease. The cavalryman leads a more regular and even life. He suffers comparatively little fatigue during the long marches and at all times he has the constant but easy exercise in the care of his horse; as a result he enjoys much better health than the foot soldier.

Pringle also gives attention to the soldier's personal cleanliness:

It is well known how necessary it is to keep up the perspiration and also how much the uncleanliness of the person will concur with other things to frustrate that intention. I have observed in the hospitals that when men were brought from the camp with fevers nothing so much promoted that discharge as washing their feet and hands, and sometimes the whole body, with warm water and giving them clean linen. So that the officers judge rightly with respect to the health of the men as well as their appearance when they require cleanliness both in their persons and their clothes.

Sir John Pringle when he was at the height of his international fame in his middle years.

Isaac Newton published *Philosophiae Naturalis Principia Mathematica* in 1687. Many assumed that the method that he had devised to measure the movements of the planets would be useful in solving every problem in science.

Archibald Pitcairn, an Edinburgh physician who became professor of medicine at Leiden in 1682. He taught his students that Newton's new method could play little part in the advance of medical science.

Herman Boerhaave, the professor of medicine at Leiden in the first years of the eighteenth century when Leiden was the most prestigious medical school in Europe.

he Earl of Stair who commanded the British Army in the first British campaign in the War of the
ustrian Succession. He appointed Pringle as the army's first Physician General.

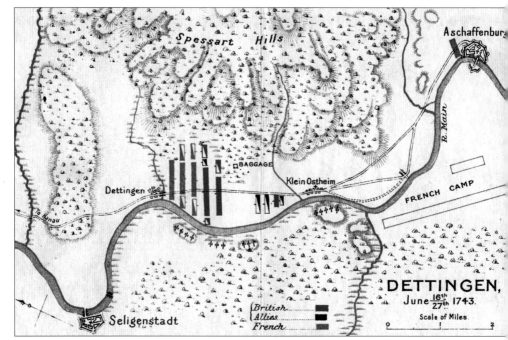

The Battle of Dettingen. This sketch map is of the area between Aschaffenburg and Dettingen from which the Pragmatic Army escaped entrapment.

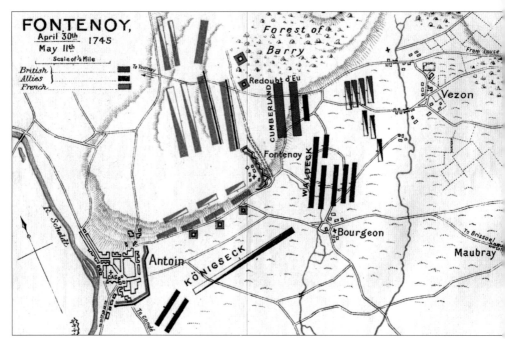

The Battle of Fontenoy. This sketch map is of the area of the battle in which the British infantry fought a celebrated attack but in the end the Pragmatic Army was soundly defeated.

Prince Charles Edward Stuart was summoned by Louis XV from Rome to lead a Jacobite rebellion in Britain. The rebellion was ended at the Battle of Culloden in 1746.

Above. The Battle of Culloden. A tired, hungry, poorly equipped and badly led Jacobite army was easily destroyed by a larger, better trained and better led army commanded by the Duke of Cumberland.

Right. Observations on the Diseases of the Army was first published in 1752. This photograph is of the title page of the seventh edition of 1772.

OBSERVATIONS
Collegii ON THE *Regu*
Diſeaſes of the Army,

IN

CAMP and GARRISON.

In THREE PARTS.
Medicor. WITH AN *Edin.*

A P P E N D I X,

CONTAINING SOME

PAPERS of EXPERIMENTS,

Read at ſeveral Meetings of the ROYAL SOCIETY.

BY
JOHN PRINGLE ..D. F.R.S.
Phyſician-General to his MAJESTY's Forces employed abroad during the late War.

LONDON:
Printed for A. MILLAR, and D. WILSON, both in the Strand; and T. PAYNE, next the Mews-gate, near St. Martin's Church.   MDCCLII.

Captain James Cook had kept his men remarkably free from disease during his first two great exploratory voyages. He and Pringle discussed the plans that he was making for his third voyage in 776.

Above. King George III. Pringle had been a successful physician to members of the royal family for many years but in 1777 he disagreed with King George on the design of lightning conductors.

Right. Sir John Pringle in his middle years. This is one of the very few paintings of Pringle that are known to exist.

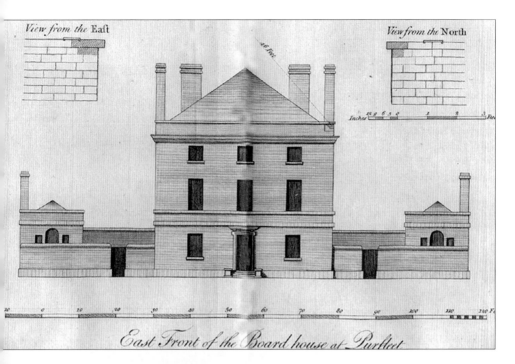

View from the East

View from the North

East Front of the Board house at Purfleet

Above. Board House of Purfleet. In 1772 the Board of Ordnance asked the Royal Society for advice on the installation of lightning conductors on the Royal Navy's powder magazine at Purfleet. The request led to prolonged disagreements within the Royal Society.

Left. Sir John Pringle in his last years.

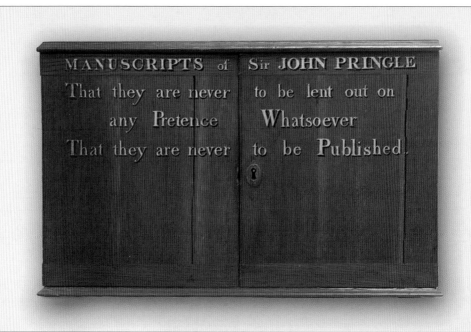

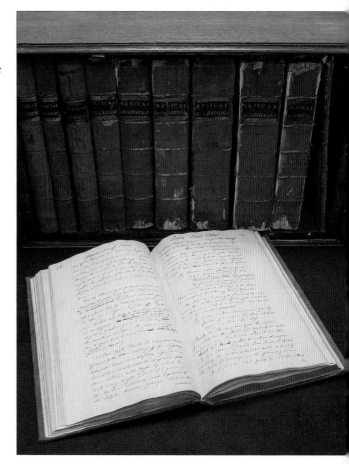

Above. The box in which the ten volumes on Pringle's Medical Annotations were presented to the Royal College of Physicians of Edinburgh in 1781.

Right. Pringle's Medical Annotations after many years in the library of the Royal College of Physicians of Edinburgh.

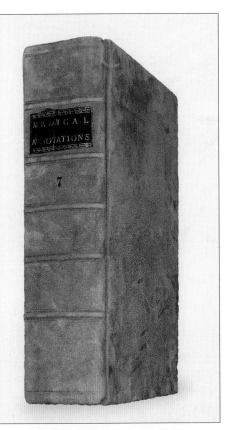

Left. One of the volumes of the Medical Annotations after they had all been rebound in calf in the nineteenth century.

Below. These pages of the last volume of the Medical Annotations show evidence of Pringle's final frustration.

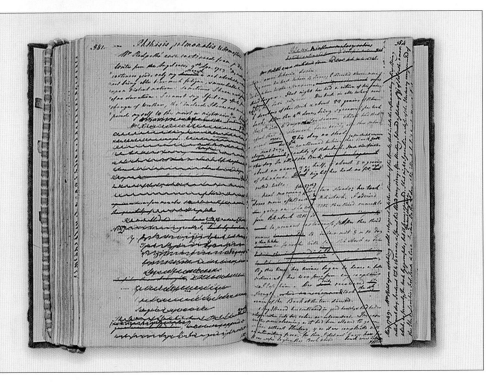

Sacred to the Memory of
Sir JOHN PRINGLE, *Baronet,*
Who was at an early Period of Life
Profeſſor of Moral Philoſophy
in the Univerſity of *EDINBURGH*;
afterward Phyſician to the *ARMY*.
To the PRINCESS of *WALES*.
To the QUEEN and to KING GEORGE III;
PRESIDENT of the *ROYAL* Society;

Member of the *ROYAL* Academy
of *SCIENCES* at *PARIS &c &c*;
His Medical and Philoſophical Knowledge
His inviolable Integrity;
and truely Chriſtian Virtues
rendered Him an Honour
to His Age and Country.
He was born in *SCOTLAND* in April 1707;
And died in *LONDON* in January 1782.

Nollekens. F.

Sir John Pringle's memorial in Westminster Abbey.

Pringle relates lack of personal cleanliness not only to the harmful suppression of perspiration, but also to the incidence and spread of the itch (scabies), the commonest non-fatal disease of armies. It was still unknown that the disease was caused by a parasitic mite. However, Pringle wrote that the itch spreads so easily by contact with 'the foul person or his clothes that one affected man in the same tent, mess or barracks will often communicate it to all the others: this, and the little attention which men of that rank have to cleanliness, make it difficult to keep it under control though the cure of the individual is generally easy'.

Pringle follows his account of the diseases that affect and weaken armies with a general discussion of the ways in which they may be prevented. First he insists that it is incumbent on the officers in command to make rules and other provisions that will enable the soldier to overcome the hardships of military life. The prevention of the soldier's diseases does not depend on medicines or on anything that the ordinary soldier can control but on the orders that he must obey.

To avoid the ill effects of intemperate heat those in command must make certain that their men do not sleep outside their tents and that the tents are covered by foliage that will shade them from the sun; they must order their men to their duties in the early cool of the morning so that, their blood being cooled and the fibres of their bodies braced, they will be well prepared to meet the heat of the day. To avoid the effects of cold every soldier should be provided with a waistcoat; waistcoats would be useful not only in winter quarters but also when the soldiers take the field at the beginning of a campaign or in the last weeks of the campaign. In the winter greatcoats should be issued to soldiers on sentry duty. And at all times of the year the soldiers should have strong boots as it well known how easily men catch cold from having wet feet. The men's bedding is also important. Every tent should be equipped with a blanket. Pringle had noticed how useful their cloaks were to the cavalry; a blanket would be equally useful in preserving the health of the foot soldiers. The only question is whether the expense and the impediment of so much additional baggage would outweigh that advantage.

Pringle proposed a number of measures to prevent diseases caused by moisture. When the troops were to go into winter quarters, the regiments' quartermasters were to examine the buildings offered as barracks by the local magistrates. Houses that had been uninhabited for some time or had any signs of dampness were to be refused. Houses without drainage were also to be rejected. If dry accommodation could not be found, sickness due to moisture could be prevented by providing a generous supply of fuel. When the army was on campaign in the field, diseases due to moisture were to be prevented by digging trenches round the tents to draw off the moisture of the earth and prevent it from wetting the men's bedding straw. It was also important to have plenty of straw and to change it at frequent intervals. One of the advantages of the army being constantly on the move in the course of a campaign was that the damp and rotting straw was left behind. When the encampment had to be fixed in one place even for a few days, tents were to be opened every day for a few hours and the straw taken out once a day to be well aired. And after the men had been exposed to rain when on marches or on sentry duty, they should be allowed to cut down and burn wood to lessen the moisture in their tents.

To prevent diseases due to foul air during the campaign the best answer was for the army to keep on the move; the men would have more exercise, straw would be changed and the old privies would be left behind. When the encampment was on marshy ground, it would be better to flood the fields completely rather than to leave them half dry. From the middle of July or whenever the incidence of the flux began to increase, every man who eased himself anywhere about the camp other than in the privies was to be punished. The privies were to be made deeper than usual, they were to be frequently covered with earth and more new ones were to be dug. It would also be necessary to change the bedding straw very frequently 'it being not only apt to rot but also to retain the infectious steams of those who have fallen ill of the disease. And when an outbreak of the flux begins the sick should not all be sent to one hospital, at least not in such numbers as to vitiate the air and communicate the infection to others.'

During epidemics of the flux the regimental surgeons were instructed to treat minor cases within the camp, preferably in their infirmaries which should always be set up in barns, granaries, or other large and airy buildings that would allow the men's 'steams' to disperse. Only when the infirmaries were fully occupied were patients to be sent the army's General Hospital. Otherwise the General Hospital might be called on to receive many more patients than could be managed even by a much greater number of physicians than the army authorities were willing to recruit to serve a General Hospital. Even if this deficiency were to be corrected, Pringle claimed that it would still be unwise to have only one General Hospital with the army in view of the mortality that always results when numbers of putrid and contagious cases are crowded together in one place.

Pringle also advised that a General Hospital should admit to each ward so few patients that, to someone unfamiliar with the dangers of foul air, the room would seem capable of accommodating twice or three times that number. He insisted that, when the ceilings of the wards are low, part of them should be removed in order to open up the garret space to the circulation of air. Pringle also warned of the difficulty always experienced in convincing the nurses and their sick patients of the necessity of opening the doors and windows for air. He added: 'I have generally found those rooms the most healthful where, by broken windows and other defects, the air could not be excluded.'

These, the first and second parts of his *Observations on the Diseases of the Army*, were, as Pringle had promised in a letter to Andrew Mitchell in 1743, part of a work that he hoped would be useful to the public.

TEN

On Treating the Diseases of Armies

I find a deficiency in the treatments prescribed for diseases.
Francis Bacon, *The Advancement of Learning*, 1605[1]

Pringle addressed the third and final part of his *Observations on the Diseases of the Army* to the physicians and surgeons serving the army. In it he set out his views on how the diseases of the army should be treated. The physicians and surgeons did not form a large or ready audience. In peacetime the army employed very few physicians. Those who were recruited to serve in wartime were chosen from civilian practice and they had little knowledge of war, of armies, or of the diseases that afflicted armies. With very few exceptions the physicians employed were graduates of Oxford or Cambridge and their medical education was firmly based on the ancient teaching of Hippocrates, Aristotle and Galen. Oxford and Cambridge had not yet followed the lead of the medical schools of Leiden and Edinburgh in questioning the theories of classical medicine. To many of the physicians serving in the army the advice offered by Pringle was surprising, perhaps even revolutionary.

By far the majority of the medical officers serving in the army were surgeons. For years they had all been taught their craft as surgeon's mates in a regiment, they held their commissions in that regiment and answered to the colonel of that regiment. Their methods of practice were those traditional in the army and expected by the army. To the surgeons much of the advice offered by Pringle was almost as strange as it was to the physicians.

In the earlier parts of his *Observations* Pringle had questioned the ancient doctrines of Hippocrates, Aristotle and Galen. Their ancient theories did not sit easily with Pringle's own observations and experience of the onset and spread of disease. Pringle believed that the evidence that he had found would justify him in introducing measures to limit the devastation of the army by disease. The success of these measures proved that his action had been fully justified. However, his observations and experience had found nothing that led him to question the ancient treatments of disease, treatments that had been used with faith and confidence for centuries. For that reason, Pringle remained convinced that they should continue to be used. However, he recommended their use not to restore health but to control or mitigate the manifestations of disease. Health was intangible; the sufferings from disease were real.

In the eighteenth century the most dreaded disease was fever. Fever took different forms. It occurred in different circumstances and its causes were mysterious, but fever in all its forms was the disease that was feared and it had to be treated. The treatments that had been used for centuries to rebalance the humours – bleeding to reduce the volume of the blood, drugs to cause sweating, drugs to cause vomiting, clysters (enemas) to empty the bowels – all tended to reduce the fever. Their effects could be witnessed as the fever abated.[2]

In his *Observations* Pringle recommends the use of these measures in treating the fevers that were the principal cause of death in the armies of the time. Before making his recommendations public, he had been careful to consult the works of two long respected authorities, the French physician Ballonius (Guillaume de Ballou) (1538–1616) and the English physician Thomas Sydenham (1624–1689). He had also taken account of the views discussed in his correspondence with three of the leading physicians of his own time, Giovanni Morgagni (1682–1771) in Italy, Gerhard van Swieten (1700–1803) in Vienna and Albrecht von Haller (1708–1777) in Switzerland. His instructions for the treatment of fever published in his *Observations* were confident and didactic.

Pringle writes first on the treatment of the so-called inflammatory fevers, those which occur chiefly in winter and are sited in one part of the body. The most common of these are pleurisy and pneumonia in the lungs and rheumatic pains in the joints. Inflammatory disorders could also occur in the brain, the liver, the stomach and the other abdominal organs. No matter in which of the organs the disease is sited, the fever is to be treated by bleeding, supplemented if necessary by the administration of emetics or clysters. Leeches might be applied at the site of the pain or blisters might be raised on the skin near the affected part. Pringle insists that delay in bleeding, or failure to repeat it often enough in the early stages of the illness, is the chief cause of minor inflammatory illnesses developing into malignant fevers or a fatal consumption. He points out that soldiers are instructed that when they become sick they must report at once to the surgeon of that regiment. The regimental surgeon is therefore in a position to prevent many deaths by the timely and generous use of the lancet. Twelve to sixteen fluid ounces of blood should be drawn at the first and the second bleedings but rather less at subsequent bleedings; it is always best to bleed the patient when he is lying down since this prevents him from fainting before enough blood has been drawn. The patient should also be made to sweat. This is to be achieved by prescribing a draft of vinegar-whey (skimmed milk and white vinegar) with some spirit of hartshorn (ammonium bicarbonate) at bedtime. While the fever lasts, it is necessary to prevent constipation by administering a daily clyster, strong enough to procure two bowel motions each day. As the fever subsides, the patient should be given a little wine, preferably as a cordial of wine mixed in gruel. As to diet, the patient should be kept on watergruel or something similar, but broth must not to be allowed until the fever breaks. Then a decoction of Peruvian Bark (quinine) or the elixir of vitriol (sulphuric acid) completes the treatment.

These principles were to be followed in the treatment of all inflammatory disorders, but some modifications were recommended for particular cases. Examples of these modifications are given in Pringle's directions for the treatment of five of the common inflammatory fevers.

Phrenitis: Inflammation of the brain

Phrenitis (severe headache) most commonly occurs when men are exposed to the full heat of the sun, especially while asleep and 'in liquor' (drunk). It may also occur as a secondary symptom in cases of putrid fever. Primary phrenitis requires immediate, large and repeated bleeding; preferably the blood should be taken from the jugular vein. The pain may be eased by applying three or four leeches to each temple. Symptomatic phrenitis (headache occurring in the course of some other illness) is also to be treated by copious bleeding unless a weak pulse makes bleeding impossible, in which case large blisters must be raised on the head by cupping. Symptomatic phrenitis is usually accompanied by a lack of perspiration. On admission to hospital the patient should therefore have his hands and feet washed with warm water and vinegar. In his civilian practice, Pringle had found it helpful to apply a fomentation to the feet and lower parts of the legs with double flannels wrung out of water and vinegar, made comfortably warm and frequently repeated for an hour or two at each time.

Ophthalmia: Inflammation of the eyes

Soldiers contract ophthalmia from catching cold in the winter or from exposure to the sun and dust during the summer. Severe cases cannot be cured without the loss of much blood unless the necessary effect can be achieved by applying blisters behind each ear for two or three days. Alternatively, two or more leeches may be applied to the lower part of each orbit near the external angle of the eye. In mild cases, Pringle recommends fomenting the eyes with warm milk containing a small quantity of brandy; when pain is intense, the eyes may be fomented with water in which white poppies have been boiled.

Angina: Inflammation of the throat

Angina is most common in the early days and weeks of the summer campaigning season. Its tendency to cause suffocation requires a speedy and large bleeding, repeated next day if the pain has not eased. In all cases a gentle purge is to be followed by daily clysters to 'open up the body'. After the first bleeding, a large blister, raised near the site of the pain, is an essential part of the treatment. A piece of thick flannel moistened with two parts sweet oil and one part of spirit of hartshorn should be applied to the throat and renewed every four or five hours. This causes the whole body to sweat which helps to clear or lessen the inflammation. In cases of quinsy, the patient should gargle a mixture of milk and water in which figs have been boiled, keeping a piece of one of the figs as near as possible to the part affected.

Rheumatism and gout

Pringle notes first that the ancient classical physicians had failed to distinguish gout from rheumatism, giving every affection of the joints the name 'arthritis' whether the joint pain was due to a gouty humour or to an inflammatory humour. Different cases of arthritis were treated differently by the classical physicians according to the site affected as in podagra (pain in the big toe) or ischias (pain in the lower back); as a result the disease had often been very badly managed. In the more recent past, physicians had come to believe that all pains in the joints were caused by catarrh, a humour running down from the head. The popularity of this theory had been unfortunate since the physicians had supposed that catarrh was a cold humour and when there was an excess of cold humour, bleeding was regarded as dangerous and was not used.

Unlike the ancient physicians, Pringle makes a clear distinction between gout, caused in older men by high living, and the inflammatory rheumatism that occurs in soldiers in the prime of life, caused by the factors that cause every inflammatory disease. Pringle insists that while bleeding may not be used in the treatment of old men with gout, the cases of rheumatism met with in the army must be treated by bleeding, not only once but a second and a third time. When the painful joints are swollen, up to 12 leeches should be applied, equally divided between two or more of the affected joints. Drafts containing 40 drops of spirit of hartshorn should be given three times each day. Clysters must be administered daily to prevent constipation and the patient should be kept on the lowest diet that he can be prevailed upon to accept; for food, water-gruel and the like; for drink, barley-water or whey made with vinegar. Should the pain persist in spite of such careful and proper treatment, it should be assumed that the cause is venereal (gonorrhoea or syphilis) or that the soldier is feigning illness.

Phthisis Pulmonale: Consumption (pulmonary tuberculosis)

Pringle lists coughs and consumption together as common inflammatory diseases. A recent cough may prove to be the earliest stage in the development of pneumonia. However, an old and long neglected cough should be regarded as the beginning of consumption; in a series of autopsies on patients who had died of consumption, Pringle had found the lungs full of tubercles.[3]

Colds must therefore be carefully treated from the beginning. Bleeding and a light diet will cure most bad colds. After the first bleeding the cough may be soothed by administering a sweet oil to which has been added a drachm of *syrupus e meconio* (syrup of poppy). However, in cases of chronic cough such soothing medicines are harmful; if the patient is disturbed during the night by his coughing, he should be given an opiate. When, in the early stages of consumption, the patient begins to complain of pain in his chest and is disturbed during the night, Pringle recommends the insertion of setons[4] under the skin near the site of the pain, a cool diet and weekly bleedings of four to seven ounces. When the patient becomes hot and uncomfortable, his sweating should be checked by having him drink barley water or elixir of vitriol.

Pringle devotes the last part of his *Observations* to a long and full account of the diseases which cause the greatest number of deaths in the army. These are the diseases that he has come to call putrid diseases. They usually begin towards the end of the summer and tend to become epidemic in the early autumn. They present in two forms, putrid fevers and bloody fluxes.

The putrid fevers may be either remittent or intermittent. If the army is camped on dry ground the fever is generally remittent (recurring every day); if the army is camped on or near wet boggy land, the fever is generally intermittent, either tertian (recurring in a cycle of three days) or quartan (recurring in a cycle of four days). The chief cause of the fevers is, Pringle believes, an excess of heat and moisture of the air, although in many cases there are inciting causes such as fatigue, intemperance, the checking of perspiration by wet clothes, lying on wet ground, or absorbing noxious vapours.

If untreated, the remittent fevers may become continuous fevers (typhus) and may prove fatal. If the moisture in the air is pure, the intermittent fevers are usually tertian and easy to cure. However, if the moisture in the air rises from stagnant water in which plants, filth, and insects die and rot, the fever is frequently quartan and more dangerous to life.

In treating all of these putrid fevers it is essential to begin by opening a vein and repeating the bleedings as often as seems required by the severity of the symptoms. After the first bleeding the patient should be given a purgative at a dosage that will produce a bowel motion at least twice in four hours. Next day, 20 grains of ipecacuanha and two grains of tartar emetic should be given as a single dose to produce vomiting, to open the bowels and to induce sweating; the dose should be repeated after two hours and again after four hours. The administration of Peruvian Bark must begin as soon as possible during the first intermission between bouts of fever, otherwise the fever may become continuous fever and even more dangerous. Pringle preferred to prescribe Peruvian Bark in the form of one ounce of the fine powder infused overnight in a pint of Rhenish wine; the mixture is given in divided doses in the course of the next day.

Of the bloody fluxes, only outbreaks of dysentery are a major threat to the health of the army. Cases of dysentery usually begin to occur toward the end of the summer, but later these sporadic cases may become an epidemic that lasts for as long as two months. The first symptoms are fever, lassitude and abdominal discomfort. The disorder may at first be mistaken for an autumnal putrid fever. However, within two or three days the bowels become very loose and the watery stools are seen to contain mucus and blood. Thomas Sydenham had described dysentery as an autumnal fever 'turned in on the bowels'.[5] As with the autumnal fevers, dysentery appears to be caused by the heat and moisture of the air; like the autumnal putrid fevers, outbreaks of dysentery are most severe at the end of very hot summers. However, Pringle insists that dysentery is quite different from the putrid fevers. It is contagious. In army camps he has observed that the contagion passes from one sick soldier to the others in the same tent. In a fatal outbreak of dysentery in Nijmegen in the autumn of 1746 it had been observed that the infection was communicated to the people of the town by one affected person. It had also been noticed that the Jews, who had little contact with the general population of the town, had remained free of the disease. Pringle believed that the disease had been spread by the putrid exhalations from those who had first become ill.

In his own experience he had observed that the officers were much less likely to acquire the disease than the men. It seemed that the men, unwilling to eat vegetables and unable to afford the price of fermented liquors, deprived themselves of two considerable antiseptics. Certainly it is known that dysentery occurs most commonly among the poor people who, from foul air, bad diet and filth are those most liable to putrid diseases.[6]

Pringle remarks that there are few acute distempers less likely to be cured by nature or more difficult to treat than dysentery. Haemorrhaging from the bowel requires repeated bleeding, the loose stools require astringents and the pain of the bowels requires opiates. Unless these necessary remedies are used with caution, they tend to aggravate the disease rather than cure it.

Pringle recommends that the treatment should be determined by the stage of the illness and the state of the patient. If the disease is of recent onset, treatment should begin with a modest bleeding; if the patient is already seriously ill, even that should be omitted. If the patient is seriously ill or if treatment has been long delayed, bleeding is ineffective. Until nature alone becomes strong enough to produce a cure, medicines should be given only to coat the bowels against irritation and to control the pain. For this Pringle recommends enemas of a concoction of linseed and starch or of four to eight ounces of mutton fat. If opiates are required to control the pain, they should be given into the rectum.

When the diarrhoea has continued until the patient is exhausted and the pulse has sunk, the danger is already very great although there is still some hope unless the passage of stools has become involuntary. Then opiates have little effect. If there is still any place for medicines, Pringle recommends a composition of Peruvian Bark and snake-root (ageratina) together with a few drops of laudanum (morphine).

These remittent and intermittent putrid fevers had made up the greater part of the yearly burden of disease suffered by the British army while Pringle was Physician-General. But even more deadly was the fever that broke out in the army after the Battle of Dettingen in 1743, at Aberdeen in 1746, and again in the ships carrying the troops back to Britain at the end of the war in 1748. Pringle had quickly recognised that this was the same disease as the fever that so commonly affected prisoners confined in jails. In the army the disease had broken out in hospitals overcrowded by sick patients and among soldiers confined for long periods in the holds of troopships. As we have seen, Pringle had demonstrated that the spread of the disease could be controlled by segregating the victims in generously spaced and wellventilated accommodation.

In earlier parts of his *Observations* he had shown why he had come to refer to the disease as 'jail or hospital fever'. Now he gives a full account of its symptom and signs, drawing particular attention to the fierce headache, the tremor of the hands and the characteristic rash that appears on the chest and back. In the autopsies that he had performed on the bodies of patients who had died of the disease he had found, in some cases, abscesses in the brain and in others he found only scattered areas of inflammation.

Pringle warns that in cases of jail or hospital fever the outcome is more difficult to forecast than in any other fever. When the brain is affected and the patient already delirious, tremulous, blind and unable to swallow, he is very unlikely to recover. The outlook is also very poor for patients already weakened by some other disease. Nevertheless, there is still some chance of recovery if the patient is not delirious, if his body is covered by a gentle sweat, if his tongue is moist, and if his pulse can be quickened by wine.

The first essential in treatment is to remove the patient from the foul air that has been the source of his illness. Thereafter the mainstay of treatment is causing the patient to vomit and sweat by the administration of half a drachm of *theriaca* (an ancient concoction of herbs and honey) and ten grains of hartshorn to encourage the free flow of sweat. Pringle advises that the patient, 'especially the less cleanly sort', should have his feet and hands washed with warm water and vinegar. Some bleeding is essential but large bleedings are harmful as they weaken the pulse and badly 'affect the head' (cause headache and tremor). Pringle finds it safer to bleed the patients by applying leeches to the head rather than by opening a vein. Thereafter the patient is given a twice-daily dose of tartar emetic which not only causes vomiting and loosening of the bowels but also promotes sweating.

Pringle speculates on the nature of jail and hospital fever. It is clear, from the way in which the head is affected, the dejection of the spirits, the general debility, the sunk pulse, the suppuration of the lymph glands, the putrid sweats, the rash and the contagion, that jail and hospital fever is of a truly contagious nature. Although it may differ in some degree from the plague, Pringle believes that it is clearly of the same genus (class). It proceeds from a similar cause and produces the same symptoms; the only distinction is that the plague is attended by swollen lymph glands in the groin and armpits and large abscesses on the back of the neck. The fevers of the genus vary according to the kind and quantity of the virulent miasma that has been received into the blood. However, they all seem to depend on some internal or external *fomes* (carrier) of corruption such as a putrid habit (clothing) or the exhalations from corrupted animal or vegetable substances. He suggests that jail or hospital fever differs very little, if at all, from the disease which arises after battles when the bodies of men have been left unburied to rot on the field.

Pringle reviews what has been written on the nature of such diseases by authorities from Galen in the second century to Frascatorius in the sixteenth century, Thomas Sydenham in the seventeenth century and John Huxham in the eighteenth century. He concludes that when miasma containing an effluvium of putrid substances is received into the blood, it has the power to corrupt the whole mass of the body. The disturbed blood irritates the nerves and causes a variety of spasms, the pulse is at first quickened and later depressed due to the heart receiving too little of the vital principle (oxygen) or due to the weakening of the heart's fibres by putrefaction.

At the end of this final section of his *Observations* Pringle writes:

> It is easy to conceive how incident to all these fevers must be, not only in all marshy countries after hot weather, but to all populous cities, low and ill aired, unprovided with common sewers or where the streets are narrow and foul or the houses small and dirty, where fresh water is scarce, where jails and hospitals are crowded and not ventilated or kept clean, when in sickly time the burials are within the walls and the bodies not deep, when slaughter houses are likewise within the walls or where dead animals and offal are left to rot on the dunghills, when drains are not provided to carry off any large body of stagnant or corrupted water in the neighbourhood, when meat makes up the greater part of the diet without a proper mixture of bread, greens, wine or other fermented liquors; when grain is old and mouldy or has been damaged by the season, but above all, when the houses once infected have not been sufficiently purified. I say, in proportion to the number of these or the like causes concurring, a city will be more or less subject to pestilential fevers or to receive the leaven of a true plague when brought in to it by any merchandise.

Francis Bacon had written that 'if a man will be content to begin with doubts he shall end in certainties'.[7] Pringle was ready to follow Bacon in making decisions on the management of the spread of disease. However, he found it difficult to follow Bacon in making rules for the treatment of the sick. The physician is not at liberty to base the treatment of his patient only on speculation. Ideally, treatments should be of proven value in curing disease, but in the eighteenth century there were still no curing medicines. The ancient classical treatments recommended by Pringle had the authority of many years of experience. However, Pringle limited his expectation of what they would achieve to what those years of experience had demonstrated. They were capable of relieving the symptoms of disease and Pringle used them for that purpose. For the cure of the disease he looked to nature.

Pringle's *Observations on the Diseases of the Army*, first published in 1752, was undoubtedly his greatest work. It was translated into French, German and Italian, and an American edition, edited by Benjamin Rush, was published in 1810. In the nineteenth century it was still listed by the Army Medical Board as essential reading for all medical officers in the British army.[8] It was also studied in America and its translated editions were used across Europe. As the foremost book on military medicine to be published in the eighteenth century, it laid down some lasting principles and established Pringle's place as the father of military hygiene.

ELEVEN

Studies on Putrefaction and Digestion

Physicians know neither the causes of disease nor the true method of cures.
Francis Bacon, *The Advancement of Learning,* 1605

In his *Observations on the Diseases of the Army* Pringle had written of his experiences, his judgement and his great achievements as a successful practising physician. However, he also hoped to make his contribution to the advance of medical science. For 200 years medical science had been seeking a more rational system to replace the ancient mythical system of the four humours, a theoretical system invented to explain everything. Pringle was convinced that the search for a new theoretical system should be abandoned as no system could be expected to explain everything. He believed that real progress in medicine could be achieved by observation, experiment and inductive reasoning.

In 1750, Pringle delivered to the Royal Society the first of a series of presentations that established his reputation as an experimental medical scientist. His subject was putrefaction. As physician to the British army throughout six years of war he had been responsible for the care of a great many soldiers suffering and dying from the so-called bilious fevers. He had carried out many post mortem examinations of the bodies of victims of these diseases and he had concluded that the fevers were not due to any abnormality of the bile but to the putrefaction of body tissues. This discovery had led him to rename the fevers the putrid fevers. It also led him to make a personal study of the process of putrefaction. Pringle's work was inspired by Francis Bacon who, in *The Great Instauration,* had written that 'it is of excellent use to inquire into the means of preventing or staying putrefaction which makes a great part of physic and surgery'.

Pringle's investigation was unique; no such study had ever been attempted.[1] Morbid anatomy was still in its infancy[2] and even in the middle years of the eighteenth century, the techniques suitable for such an investigation were still few and primitive.[3] Pringle could only make his observations on putrefied flesh by sight and smell. His only means of demonstrating change in putrefied material was by chemistry; and chemistry had hardly developed beyond the skill and lore of alchemy. Between 1750 and 1752, Pringle carried out no fewer than 48 experiments on 'the manner in which bodies are resolved by putrefaction and the means of accelerating or preventing that process'. The techniques, the materials and the terminology he used were all drawn from alchemy.

Pringle first studied the history of the subject. He found that it had long been believed by alchemists that as human bodies putrefy they become alkaline. His first experiment was carried out to discover whether or not this was true. In his early observations he recognised two stages in the process of putrefaction of body fluids and body tissues: first they became 'corrupted' as shown by a change in their appearance; later they became 'putrefied' as demonstrated by the unpleasant smell. As his indicator of alkalinity, Pringle used syrup of violets, an agent introduced by Robert Boyle, the seventeenth-century natural philosopher and chemist. Crushed violets were boiled in water, the violet-coloured water was drained off and quantities of refined sugar were added as a preservative. When an acid was added to the sweet violet fluid, it turned red; when an alkali was added, it turned green.

Pringle tested three of the body's fluids – serum, blood and bile. Specimens of serum, blood and bile were left exposed to the air, to become first corrupted and then putrefied. Specimens of the fluids were first corrupted by mixing them in a solution of corrosive sublimate (mercuric chloride); the resulting corrupted precipitate was then allowed to putrefy. Each of these putrefied body fluids was infused in water; none of the resulting watery extracts turned the syrup of violets green.

He next infused specimens of putrid flesh in water; again the watery extract did not turn the syrup of violets green. He therefore concluded that neither putrefied body fluids nor putrefied flesh were alkaline as the alchemists had claimed. To support his conclusion he added drops of oil of vitriol to the watery extracts of all the specimens of body fluids and tissue; no effervescence or bubbles were produced as would have been expected on adding an acid to a liquid containing an alkaline substance.

Alchemists had also claimed that, when distilled, putrescent material gave off large quantities of volatile alkaline salts. Pringle tested a distillate of each of his specimens of putrid serum, blood and bile and found that none of the distillates contained any trace of volatile alkali salts on testing with syrup of violets. However, when he tested urine, he found that it acted

quite differently. Even before the distillation began, the stale urine gave off a
volatile alkali that turned the syrup of violets green; and when its distillation
progressed, it produced even greater quantities of volatile alkali. Pringle was
now persuaded that in the past alchemists had tested only urine and had
assumed that testing the other body fluids would have produced the same
result. For Pringle, his discovery that the vapour given off by putrid urine
was different from the vapour given off by putrid blood, bile and flesh was
hugely significant.

As a clinician, he had always found that the smell emitted from stale urine
was harmless, while the unpleasant effluvia emitted from putrid animal flesh
had often seemed to indicate putrid diseases. Could it be that, far from the
volatile alkali given off from urine being the agent causing putrefaction as
had been supposed by the alchemists, it was perhaps a 'corrector of putrefaction'?[4]

Whether or not this was the case might depend on how the putrefaction had been caused. Perhaps if the putrefaction had begun in a part of the
body because of a failing or obstructed circulation, might alkali salts stop its
progress? On the other hand, if the putrefaction had been caused perhaps
by heat, even if alkaline salts were 'antiseptic' in most circumstances, they
might in these particular circumstances augment the putrefaction. (The
words 'septic' and 'antiseptic' were invented by Pringle and were used here
for the first time.)[5]

He answered this question by studying the effect of alkaline salts on
animal tissue before putrefaction had begun. He applied salts of hartshorn
(ammonium chloride and ammonium carbonate) and spirit of hartshorn
(aqueous solution of ammonium) to a great variety of animal substances and
found that in every case these alkaline salts delayed the process of putrefaction no matter how it had been caused.

Pringle next compared the antiseptic strength of alkalis with those of
acids. Salts of hartshorn and spirit of hartshorn were applied directly to
specimens of dried serum and to dried whole blood. Samples from each of
these preparations were put into equal volumes of both acid vinegar and
alkaline salts of hartshorn. After a month, the pieces in alkali were still as
sound and free of putrefaction as those in the acid.

In a further experiment he compared the action of the salts of
hartshorn with the action of sea-salt which had been known for centuries to prevent the putrefaction of stored fish and meat. In one glass phial
he placed a specimen of lean beef in a measured quantity of water and
added salts of hartshorn; into a second phial, he put the same quanti-

ties of lean beef and water but added sea-salt in place of the salts of hartshorn; and in a third phial, the same quantity of lean beef and water but without adding either sea-salt or salts of hartshorn. All the glass phials were kept at a temperature of approximately 100 degrees Fahrenheit in a lampfurnace. After 18 hours, the meat in the phial containing neither sea-salt nor salts of hartshorn had become putrid; a few hours later the meat in the phial containing sea-salt had also become putrid; after a further 24 hours the meat in the phial to which the alkaline salts of hartshorn had been added still remained 'sweet'.

He extended this trial by placing in separate containers three slices of beef, one dusted with sawdust, one dusted with bran, and the third dusted with hartshorn. All three containers were placed on a windowsill where they were exposed to the sun. By the fourth day, the beef dusted with sawdust and the beef dusted with bran were quite putrid while the beef dusted with the alkaline hartshorn was still 'sound.' After subjecting a number of other alkaline salts to the same tests, and achieving the same result, Pringle was satisfied that all alkaline salts must be assumed to be antiseptics.

Pringle had shown that acids and alkaline salts had strengths as antiseptics; he now proceeded to investigate the effect of combining the two. The two mixtures that he tested were vinegar saturated with salts of hartshorn and lemon juice saturated with salt of wormwood. He found that in both cases the antiseptic effect of the mixture of acid and alkali on flesh was very much less than the effect of either the acid or the alkali acting alone.

At a meeting of the Royal Society on 28 June 1750, Pringle was able to present a table showing the comparative antiseptic strengths of all the salts that he had investigated. In making each comparison, he used as a standard a series of four wide-mouth phials, each containing a piece of lean beef in two ounces of water; 30 grains of sea-salt had been added to one of the phials and 60 grains of sea-salt to another. The salt to be assessed was placed in the fourth phial containing the same volume of water and the same weight of beef as the three standard phials. The phials were corked, placed in a lampfurnace and kept at body heat. A salt that delayed the putrefaction of the beef for as long as did 60 grains of sea-salt was graded 1, a salt that delayed it rather longer was graded 1+, one that delayed it for twice as long was graded 2, one that delayed for more than twice as long was graded 2+, and so on up to, in one case, a grade of 30+.

A table of the comparative powers of salt in resisting putrefaction[6]

Sea-salt	sodium chloride	1
Sal Gemme	potassium carbonate	1+
Tartar Vitriolated	potassium sulphate	2
Spiritus Mindereri	ammonium acetate	2
Sal Diureticus	potassium acetate	2
Sal Ammoniac	ammonium chlorate	3
Nitre	potassium nitrate	4+
Salts of Hartshorn	ammonium carbonate	4+
Salt of Wormwood	potassium carbonate	4+
Borax	sodium borate	12+
Salt of Amber	succinic acid	20+
Alum	potassium aluminium sulphate	30+

Pringle now turned his attention to the antiseptic power of resins, gums, plants and other substances of vegetable origin. He tried many such substances and found antiseptic in over 30, from the exotic myrrh from Arabia to the more mundane pepper and mustard. He had hoped to assess the comparative strength of these antiseptics as he had assessed the power of the alkaline salts, in phials of water. However, when he prepared emulsions, solutions, or infusions of these vegetable substances, he found great variation in the readiness with which they 'imparted the virtue [the antiseptic principle] to the water'.[7] An emulsion of the resin sagapenum (a resin from a species of ferula) showed very little antiseptic activity perhaps because 'all the antiseptic principle fell with the grosser parts to the bottom'. The shrub camphire, a source of henna,[8] showed great antiseptic activity although 'most of the camphire flew off and stuck to the phial'.[9] Pringle had to be content with the very general and unmeasured conclusion that a great many vegetable substances have antiseptic properties.

However, he was particularly pleased by the results of his assessment of the antiseptic properties of Peruvian Bark, which is now best known as the source of quinine. Pringle had cared for many cases of intermittent fever while physician to the army; he had performed autopsies on a number of those who had died; and he had found evidence that seemed to indicate that intermittent fever was caused by a putrefaction of body tissue. He had also treated every case of intermittent fever by the oral administration of Peruvian Bark, and the great majority had recovered. For many years it had been known that Peruvian Bark was helpful in relieving fevers, but why it was so particularly effective in treating intermittent fever was unknown. Pringle recorded his laboratory assessment of the Bark:

> I made a strong decoction of the Bark and infused a piece of flesh in two ounces of it. The flesh never corrupted tho' it remained two or three days in the furnace after the standard was putrid. In this time the decoction became gradually limpid whilst the grosser part subsided. By which it appears that a most minute portion of Bark intimately mixed with water is possessed of a very extraordinary antiseptic force.[10]

When Pringle had first demonstrated the antiseptic properties of a number of substances in the laboratory he had written that 'we may presume that the same taken by way of medicine will, *caeteris paribus* [all things being equal], prove antiseptic'.[11] Peruvian Bark had now been shown to be a potent antiseptic; it had been administered as a medicine for many years; it had already been successful in overcoming the putrid intermittent fever.

The implications were startling. The concept that a specific medicament given by mouth could cure a specific disease was quite incompatible with the ancient classical teaching that disturbances in the health of the body must be corrected by measures to restore the balance of the body's four humours. It was also incompatible with the more recent notion promoted by Pringle's teacher Herman Boerhaave that the human body was essentially a hydraulic machine and that its disorders responded to the laws of physics; and it was incompatible with the notion of his illustrious contemporary in Edinburgh William Cullen that the functions of body were subject to control by the central nervous system.

Pringle was confident that he had shown how much real progress could be achieved by setting aside the dogmas of classical learning and futile attempts to create a theoretical model of health and disease that would explain everything. He believed that he had made a contribution to the theory and practice of medicine by observation, experiment and inductive reasoning as prescribed by Francis Bacon. His account of his discoveries was commended by the Royal Society and later published in full in its *Philosophical Transactions*.[12] In 1752, the value of his work was recognised by the award of the Royal Society's Copley Medal.

In the months that followed, Pringle made a further series of presentations to the Royal Society that were less well received. In these presentations he gave an account of a large number of experiments that he had been prompted to perform by a comment made by Francis Bacon. In 1648, in his *Historia Naturalis et Experimentalis ad Condendam Philosophiam*, Bacon had written that the putrefaction of flesh was analogous to the fermentation of vegetables. Could it be that in the process of human digestion, the putrefaction of flesh spread by contact to the vegetables in the diet causing them to ferment?

First, Pringle addressed the question of whether or not putrefaction could be shown to be contagious. In the Bible, at Leviticus, Chapter 13, the contagious nature of putrefaction had been described at some length. Bacon had claimed that putrefaction was contagious in his *Advancement of Learning* in 1605.[13] However, Bacon had produced no experimental evidence to support his assertion. In one very simple laboratory experiment Pringle now provided that evidence:

> A thread being dipped in the yolk of an egg already putrid, a small portion of it was cut off and put into a phial with half of the yolk of a new laid egg diluted with a little water. The other half, with as much water, was put in another phial and both being corked were set by the fire to putrefy. The result was that the thread infected the fresh yolk; for the putrefaction was sooner perceived in the phial that contained the thread than in the other.

This was in keeping with Pringle's clinical observation while serving with the army that when soldiers suffering from putrid diseases were admitted to overcrowded hospital wards their putrid diseases quickly spread to the other patients. His laboratory experiment had also demonstrated that:

> putrefaction may be advanced quicker in confined than in free air for as the most putrid parts are also the most volatile, they incessantly issue from the corrupting substance and are dispersed with the wind; but in a stagnation of air they remain about the body and by way of ferment excite it to corruption.[14]

This seemed to be in keeping with his experience that the spread of infection could be largely prevented by keeping hospital patients with putrid diseases as far apart as possible, each in his own space in very well-ventilated wards.

Satisfied that putrefaction could indeed spread by contagion, Pringle made a number of experiments in which vegetables were brought into contact with putrefying meat. He discovered that unlike garlic, onions, horseradish, cabbage and many other vegetables, the farinaceous vegetables, wheat, barley and oatmeal, fermented very readily on contact with putrefaction.

In *The Advancement of Learning,* Bacon had stated that new learning and new discoveries were worthless until they had been made useful to man.[15] In this spirit, Pringle set out to use his discoveries in establishing 'how far aliment [food] ferments in the stomach, the various causes of indigestion and the cause and cure of heartburn'.[16] In planning this overly ambitious investigation, Pringle found it necessary to make four unfortunate assumptions: that a mixture of meat or fish, bread and water was a fair representation of a normal meal; that digestion takes place entirely in the stomach; that digestion could be equated with fermentation; and that apart from the animal source of putrefaction and the material being fermented, saliva is the only factor involved.

In the first experiment of his investigation, he made a number of standard test mixtures each of two drachms of fresh meat with the same amount of bread and one ounce of water. Each mixture was beaten into to a pulp and put into a closed glass phial. All the phials were then kept in a furnace at a temperature of 100 degrees Fahrenheit. After a few hours the mixtures began to ferment; after two days the fermentation was so strong that 'if the corks had not sometimes given way the phials must have burst'. During these first two days the smell was the smell of putrefaction. But, as Pringle reported,[17] what followed was totally unexpected. On the third day the smell of putrefaction began to abate and before the fermentation process had ended it had gone completely. At the end of the experiment, the fluid in the third-day phials tasted acid and had the normal smell of fermented liquors. Pringle concluded that the acid formed by the fermentation of the bread had suppressed the process of putrefaction.

After repeating this experiment many times, substituting fish for the meat and oatmeal or barley for the bread in the standard test mixture, Pringle concluded that 'all animal substances, putrid or tending to putrefaction, are endowed with the power of raising fermentation in the farinacea'.[18]

Pringle now repeated the experiments, adding fresh saliva to the standard mixture. He reported that:

if the saliva is sound, in sufficient quantity and well mixed with the food, it retards putrefaction preventing immoderate fermentation, flatulence and acidity in the *prima viae* [alimentary tract]. However, if the saliva is insufficient or not properly mixed with what is swallowed, the food putrefies causing very strong fermentation that generates excessive quantities of air in the stomach and bowels. However, when putrid rather than fresh saliva was added this not only brought on fermentation sooner but made it stronger and more productive of air.

Pringle now repeated all of these experiments, replacing the bread with the vegetables, spinach, scurvy grass (*cochlearia*) and asparagus. All the vegetables were made to ferment with varying degrees of vigour. The vegetables were next replaced by four ounces of milk; after six hours the milk was seen to ferment very strongly indeed. Pringle concluded that 'since milk may be considered as the juice of grass and various other vegetables we may judge how prone all vegetables were to ferment with anything putrid'.

Pringle claimed that, as these processes that had taken place in the glass phials of his experiments were the same as the processes of human digestion, it could be concluded that fermentation begins in the human stomach whenever there is an animal substance present to act as a ferment and vegetables to be fermented. He acknowledged that many people were able to survive on a diet that included neither meat nor fish. In such cases it was most unlikely that fresh saliva alone could compensate for the lack of animal flesh; however, he was confident that milk contained sufficient 'animal fluid' to promote and maintain adequate fermentation. He therefore suggested that 'the common people in poor countries' who ate a diet of bread and other farinaceous foods but no animal flesh survived and were able to work because they drank milk. It was only when, because of age or infirmity, they were unable to work and had no milk that they became subject to indigestion, became less healthy and were 'shorter lived'.

In a final presentation to the Royal Society, Pringle offered an account of his new understanding of the process of human digestion. He 'presumed' that, after every meal, fermentation begins in the stomach. As the fermenting material passes into the intestinal tract it becomes disunited and a fermentation gas is loosened. The saliva moderates and prolongs the fermentation and checks any too great a propensity of the animal substances to putrefaction. Provided that the saliva is sound and in sufficient quantity, the food has been well mixed and there is not too much of it, fermentation passes without any tumult and generates little gas. But when too much has been eaten or swallowed without due mastication, when the meats are tough or fat, when the saliva is too small in quantity or not intimately mixed with the food, the formation becomes tumultuous. The stomach swells and this great commotion, being attended with unusual heat, brings an uneasiness called the heartburn.

Pringle's second series of presentations to the Royal Society was received with some interest, but the Society did not publish it in its *Philosophical Transactions*. Perhaps too much had been assumed and too much of it was mere speculation. However, Pringle was unrepentant. He continued to publish the work on putrefaction and digestion just as he had presented it to the Royal Society as an appendix to his *Observations* in every one of its many editions until the end of his life.

TWELVE

The Raids on Rochefort and St Malo

I am tired and sick of war. Its glory is all moonshine.

General Sherman, 1879

Pringle's marriage to Charlotte Oliver lasted for little over a year. On 21 May 1753, they agreed a deed of separation. Charlotte died 20 months later in December 1754.[1] After her death, Pringle's domestic life in London settled into a pattern that continued almost unchanged for over 20 years. In the mornings, at his house in Pall Mall,[2] he was at home to eminent physicians, scientists, statesmen and military men, many of whom had come to London to meet him. On Sunday evenings, he was host to gatherings of old and new friends, among them: Sir Andrew Mitchell, now British Ambassador to Berlin; Benjamin Franklin, scientist and envoy from Pennsylvania; Lord Stanhope, politician and scientist; Richard Mead, the king's physician; John Ranby, the king's surgeon; Captain James Cook in the weeks before his last voyage to the South Seas; Major General James Wolfe before he left for his campaign in Quebec; and the young scientist Joseph Priestley. Almost every gathering included at least one distinguished visitor from overseas.

Pringle was an accomplished musician. He played the violoncello whenever possible with a group of other amateur instrumentalists. He loved music; it may be assumed that he was in the audience at Covent Garden for the first performances of Handel's new oratorios and later for the recitals given by the young Mozart in the concert halls of Piccadilly.

He continued his researches and regularly attended the meetings of the Royal Society; in 1753, he was elected for the first time to the Council of the Society. He was enjoying a very full and active professional life in London. Then, in the summer of 1757, he was recalled to the army. Once more Britain had been drawn into war with France. The Treaty of Aix-la-Chapelle that ended the War of the Austrian Succession in 1748 had left a very uneasy peace. In February 1755, Frederick II of Prussia had informed his ambassadors in London and Paris that he expected that Britain and France would soon be again at war.[3]

Already there was open and bloody conflict between British and French colonial armies in North America and between the forces of the British and the French East India Companies in India. Neither of these conflicts had led to a war in Europe, but war in Europe was approaching for other more pressing reasons. Both France and Austria were aggrieved by the terms that the Treaty of Aix-la-Chapelle had forced on them. France had been made to dismantle and destroy her naval and military bases at Dunkirk and elsewhere on its Channel coast. In 1755, France was openly rebuilding and strengthening these bases and assembling an army that was clearly intended for an invasion of Britain. The British government hired troops from Hanover and Hesse to strengthen Britain's dangerously small army. On 16 January 1756, Britain made a pact with Prussia (The Westminster Convention); in it Prussia undertook to protect King George's Electorate of Hanover from attack by France; in return Britain agreed not to assist Maria Theresa of Austria should she make war on Prussia.

Britain was still preparing to meet the invasion by France when, on 24 February 1756, the Admiralty in London received intelligence that, at Toulon, the French were gathering a large expeditionary force with the openly declared intention of seizing Britain's naval bases at Minorca and Gibraltar. In London, it was at once understood that France's objective in launching this operation was to draw off to the Mediterranean Britain's principal defence against invasion, the Royal Navy's Channel Fleet. The Channel Fleet was kept on station but Admiral Byng was dispatched to the Mediterranean with a small squadron of 12 poorly prepared ships of the line to defend Minorca. When Byng reached Minorca on 20 May, he found that French troops had already occupied the island and were besieging St Philip's Castle, the citadel of Port Mahon, while the French escort fleet was lying off the island, shielding the siege from British intervention. Byng immediately engaged with the larger and stronger French fleet, but after four days of manoeuvring he had failed to defeat or disperse it. Byng and the captains of his 12 warships now agreed that, since they had found it impossible to raise the siege of Port Mahon and had no land force capable of retaking the island, their proper course was to withdraw to defend Gibraltar.[4] Byng's small fleet sailed west leaving the British garrison at Port Mahon to surrender four weeks later. However, Byng and his captains had been mistaken in their forecast of the intentions of their enemy. The French did not go on to attack Gibraltar. The French expeditionary force returned to Toulon, leaving only a garrison to hold Port Mahon. Admiral Byng was later tried by court martial. The 12th Article of War stated:

> Every person in the fleet who through cowardice, negligence or disaffection shall not do his utmost to take or destroy every ship which it is his duty to engage, every such person so offending and being convicted thereof by the sentence of a court-martial shall suffer death.

Byng was found guilty and executed on the quarterdeck of his flagship for 'not doing his utmost' to save Minorca.

Outmanoeuvred and humiliated, Britain now formally declared war on France. Within weeks, Prussia was at war with Austria. As Frederick II had foreseen, Maria Theresa of Austria had made plans to recover the part of the rich province of Silesia that she had lost to Prussia in the war of 1740–8. As Prussia had by far the most powerful army in Europe, Maria Theresa was in need of a powerful ally. For 25 years Britain had been Austria's most important ally, but, in 1748, Britain had betrayed Maria Theresa's trust by ending the war of 1740–8 before Austria had succeeded in driving the Prussian army out of Silesia. And when, in the Convention of Westminster in 1756, Britain formed a defensive alliance with Prussia, Maria Theresa's long-standing enemy, Austria's partnership with Britain dissolved completely. In May 1756,[5] Austria formed an alliance with France,[6] an alliance that was later joined by Russia, Saxony and Sweden, and then Spain. The objectives of this new alliance were to recover Silesia for Austria but also to overrun and partition Prussia. In August 1756, Frederick II decided to pre-empt this onslaught by marching south to destroy Austria's main army, now deployed in Bohemia.

By 1 October, Frederick II had overrun Saxony and defeated the Austrian army at Lobositz, 40 miles north of Prague. As it was now winter, he withdrew to reorganise his army. At Frederick's urgent request, King George II sent the Duke of Cumberland to take command of a new Army of Observation to protect Hanover and the right (western) flank of the Prussian army from attack by France. In the spring, Frederick II led his army into Bohemia. By 1 May, he was within a few miles of Prague and with some difficulty he managed to drive off the Austrian army and lay siege to the city. But on 18 June 1757, at Kolín, a town 15 miles to the east of Prague, he met the full force of a well-led Austrian army and was soundly defeated.

The Duke of Cumberland's Army of Observation was now without support in confronting the French army bearing down on Hanover. On 27 July, at Hastenbeck, 25 miles south of the city of Hanover, Cumberland was overwhelmed. At the convention held after the battle, Cumberland agreed to withdraw north to the Channel coast and there disband his Army of Observation.[7] By doing so he left Hanover and Prussia open to invasion by the French. Outraged, King George II dismissed Cumberland from his command and never gave him another. Frederick was equally angry that he had been so cravenly deserted.

However, it was now that, at last, Frederick II received valuable assistance from Britain. Britain provided him with a subsidy of £400,000 and paid smaller subsidies to the other well-disposed princes in north Germany. Frederick was able to rebuild his army and begin to drive out the Austrian troops that had made their way into southern Prussia. To replace Cumberland's disbanded army he appointed one of his best generals, Prince Ferdinand of Brunswick, to command a new army made up of troops from Hanover, Prussia, Hesse and the other northern principalities. Its task was to drive the French forces out of Hanover. To weaken the strength of his enemy, Frederick II asked Britain to create a diversion by attacking the French naval bases on the Atlantic and Channel coasts. To protect such vital assets the French would be obliged to keep a large part of their army in France rather than send it to fight in Germany.

The target chosen for the first of these raids was Rochefort on the Atlantic coast of France. In the summer of 1757, an expeditionary force of ten battalions of infantry, two battalions of marines, a troop of light horse and two companies of artillery was assembled on the Isle of Wight. Pringle was called from London to supervise the organisation of the expedition's medical services. As the Chief of Staff and Quartermaster of the expeditionary force was his friend James Wolfe, the measures that Pringle ordered for the protection of the health of the troops were faithfully put in place.

It was unfortunate that from the beginning the officer chosen to command the land force, General Sir John Mordaunt, believed that his army, numbering less than 9,000, was inadequate for the purpose. While the naval commander of the expedition, Admiral Sir Edward Hawke, continued to be confident of success, at every stage Mordaunt found reasons to withdraw. When the expedition's departure from the Isle of Wight was delayed, Mordaunt claimed that the operation could not be carried out within the time scale that had been set; the time scale was amended by the government. When the expedition reached the Basque Roads, the channel leading into the port of Rochefort, it had to cruise within sight from the shore for two days as it waited for a favourable combination of wind and tide. Mordaunt claimed that the advantage of surprise had been lost and that the operation should be aborted; Admiral Hawke disagreed and pressed on. As the fleet approached Rochefort, Mordaunt demanded that, before any troops could be landed, the fort that overlooked the harbour must be put out of action. Hawke agreed to bombard the fort, but, before any of his ships could fire a shot, the fort lowered its flag and surrendered.

Parties of troops were landed, but, after three days of diligent reconnaissance of the town and its surroundings, it was discovered, that during the British expedition's hesitant approach, a mixed force of 8,000 French regular soldiers, militia and coastguards had been assembled to oppose it. General Mordaunt decided not to accept the risk of landing his troops; he feared that, should the attack fail, it would prove impossible to re-embark the troops on the transports quickly enough to allow them to make their escape from the harbour. Exasperated, Admiral Hawke used his guns to destroy the fort commanding the harbour and carried the expedition back to England. General Mordaunt was court-martialled on a charge of disobedience. As his orders had allowed him considerable discretion, he was acquitted; but King George removed him from the army staff and he was never given another command. In spite of Mordaunt's failures, the raid on Rochefort had served its purpose. To defend his naval bases against further assaults, Louis XV gathered 80,000 men from his main army, leaving few troops available to counter Prince Ferdinand's advance towards France.

In his account of the raid on Rochefort, Pringle made no comment on the success or otherwise of the expedition or on the conduct of its commanders.[8] He confined his attention to matters relating to the health of the army. At the beginning of June 1757, the troops intended for the expedition were mustered at Dorchester, Chatham and Barham Downs, in all a force of ten battalions each with a complement of 780 men. In the last week of July, they were assembled at Newport on the Isle of Wight. As no General Hospital was to go with the expedition, the troops were to be served by the regimental surgeons and the Regimental Infirmaries. On his arrival at Newport on 26 August, Pringle's first task was to visit the infirmaries and decide which of the men were unfit to go with the expedition; 55 men were discharged from the expedition. After careful inspection, Pringle was satisfied that the troops were properly encamped on dry ground and that the regimental surgeons had set up their infirmaries in suitable buildings in Newport. However, on 28 August, the weather changed and there was a long period of heavy rain. During that time there was an outbreak of the flux (dysentery). The disease was milder than the bloody flux suffered by the army in Flanders in the 1740s and there were never, at any time, more than four or five cases in any of the battalions; it seemed to Pringle that the flux only became severe if the patient had not been adequately bled at its onset. Only four men died while the army was at Newport; one died of smallpox, one of a remitting fever, one of pneumonia and only one of the flux. However, when the expedition embarked on 5 and 6 September, as many as 88 soldiers who had contracted the flux had to be left behind in hospital at Newport.

Pringle had made every effort to ensure that the transports carrying the troops to Rochefort remained free of disease. The Admiralty had allocated transports at the customary rate of one ton per man, but Pringle believed this allowance of space was inadequate. He appealed to the Commander-in-Chief of the Army, his old friend Sir John, now Viscount, Ligonier, and the rate was raised from one ton per man to one and three-eighths tons per man. Pringle instructed the expedition's officers, and especially the regimental surgeons, that they should allow the men to go up on deck when the weather was fair; to ensure that the men always had a free flow of clean air, to keep the hatchways open as far as the weather would allow and at all times to see that the ships' scuttles were kept open. He also recommended that the men should be made to change their linen every day and, whenever possible, to take their bedding on deck to keep it well aired. Every transport ship was provided with a large quantity of vinegar, enough to scrub clean all the floors and walls below deck. When it was suspected that the air was about to become foul, a loggerhead (an iron ball attached to a long wooden handle) was to be made red-hot and thrust into a pitcher of tar; the resulting sanitising fumes were to be diffused through those parts of the ship where the men were to sleep.

The expedition was at Rochefort for only ten days. When it reached England on 5 October, it had not been expected after such a short time. The War Office had ordered that the expedition should first capture Rochefort and then hold it for as long as it served its purpose. No plans had been made for the early return of the expedition or for the return of the various regiments to their home bases in different parts of Britain. As a result the troops were not disembarked until 17 October; by then, nine of the expedition's ten regiments had been confined on board ship for upwards of five weeks.

However, during the whole operation the weather had been warm and free of rain. This, together with the measures that Pringle had put in place to ensure that every soldier had clean and adequate well-ventilated space, had resulted, he believed, 'in the troops suffering much less sickness than could have been expected of the same number of men on shore at that season of the year'.

The chief complaints had been 'slight distempers that soon yielded to bleeding'. But, if by chance the patient had not been bled and his illness had been allowed to grow worse, he had been confined to the ship's hold. Some 30 men who had been confined in this way had contracted jail fever (typhus); however, with very few exceptions, these cases had all occurred on the same transport. That transport had not been fitted with scuttles when it was built and it was not well-ventilated. Pringle's instructions had not been followed; the hatches of the hold had not been kept open, even at night; the sergeant in charge had kept them shut as he had believed that fevered patients should always be protected from cold air.

When the expedition returned to Britain, five of its ten battalions landed at Southampton and the others at Portsmouth. Among the battalions landed at Southampton fewer than 20 were sick. However, the ships landing at Portsmouth included the hospital ships carrying the wounded and the transports carrying the seriously ill. To take care of the sick and the wounded a hospital was set up in the barracks in Portsmouth; in all, 80 patients were admitted. Of the sick, only five died; one died of jail fever in its acute stage; two others had suffered relapse after showing some early signs of recovery; one died of the flux; and the other died of an undiagnosed illness.

A year later, in the summer of 1758, Pringle was again recalled to the army. Prince Ferdinand had been successful in removing the French invasion forces from Hanover and was now planning to drive the French back across the Rhine. Once again he asked Britain to create a diversion by attacking one of France's major naval bases. The target for this second raid was St Malo on the Channel coast of France. It was to be commanded by the Duke of Marlborough, supported by his very influential chief of staff, Lord George Sackville. It was formed of thirteen battalions of infantry, nine troops of light dragoons, three companies of artillery and a large siege train, a force of over 13,000 men; it was to be carried and supported by five ships of the line, ten frigates, five sloops, two bomb-ketches, two fire ships, a hundred transports and numbers of store ships, cutters and tenders under the command of Commodore Richard Howe; the navy also provided a covering fleet. It was a formidable expedition.

It reached St Malo on 4 June and two brigades landed unopposed. The surprise had been complete and the landing was said to have been 'little more than a parade'. By the evening of 7 June, the army was encamped on the heights overlooking the fortified town of St Malo. That evening Marlborough rode forward to make his own reconnaissance. To the south of St Malo, he saw below him the port of St Servan, crowded with shipping. St Servan was not fortified, it had no other local defences and it was out of range of the French guns at St Malo. That night Marlborough seized his opportunity and sent in his light cavalry armed with blazing torches. St Servan was set alight; by morning four French warships, sixty-two merchantmen and great quantities of stores had been destroyed.

However, the main body of the army had not met with such success. It had found that the poor state of the roads and the rough sodden ground made it impossible for the siege train and the artillery to be moved forward on the town of St Malo. Lord Sackville, who was never among the first to court danger, persuaded Marlborough that without the siege train and the artillery there could be no hope of destroying its fortifications and taking St Malo. Marlborough agreed to abandon the operation. By 12 June, his army had been fully reembarked and the fleet was waiting for a fair wind to carry it back to England. For the British government this was a great disappointment, but it had not been a failure. The French army had detached the whole Maison du Roi (the equivalent of the Household Division of the British army) and all the elite regiments of Hainault to go to the defence of St Malo. Prince Ferdinand was now free from the threat of attack by France and by the end of June his army had crossed the Rhine.

In his account of this brief campaign, Pringle again made no comment on the success or failure of the operation or on the quality of its leadership.[9] He recorded only matters related to the health of the 13,000 men who had made up the expedition's land force. They had assembled at Newport in the middle of May. As had been the case in the raid on Rochefort, no General Hospital was to go with the expedition. Medical and surgical care was to be provided by the regimental surgeons and their infirmaries. Pringle's first task was to visit all the Regimental Infirmaries; he found 286 men to be unfit to join the expedition and they were discharged. He then had the transport ships prepared for the voyage as he had prepared them for the raid on Rochefort. The troops embarked on 26 and 27 May; they remained on board the transports for 16 days until the expedition sailed for St Malo on 5 June. When, following the sudden collapse of the operation, the expedition returned to England, the men were kept on board the transports for a further 26 days until they were disembarked at the Isle of Wight on July 6. Although the troops had been on board ship for a total of 44 days, the illnesses they had suffered were mostly mild fevers; there had been a number of cases of the flux and many more of rheumatism; the itch (scabies) had been almost universal throughout the army. But there had been no outbreak of the lethal jail fever; of the 73 men who had died of disease, fewer than half had died of jail fever.

Pringle was now satisfied that, in these brief campaigns in 1757 and 1758, he had provided further evidence of the effectiveness of the measures that he had introduced during the war in Europe in 1740–8 and had described in his *Observations on the Diseases of the Army* in 1752 and 1753.

In the autumn of 1758, Pringle did not retire on half pay. He resigned as Physician General to the Army in Europe and returned to his practice in London. However, he did not abandon his interest in the health of the army. He published further editions of his *Observations* in 1761, 1764, 1768, 1775.[10] As he explained in the preface to the 1768 edition, he had made very few additions to what he had written in the first in 1752. In the later editions he had only 'taken an opportunity of expressing with more confidence some of my former remarks and by omitting others which I had advanced without sufficient evidence'. He had presented his *Observations* as 'a foundation for others to build on'. However, he had written only of the diseases suffered by the army in the campaigns in which he had served in Europe. Although he had been kept well informed, he had chosen not to publish his comments on the health of the army in the campaigns in North America and the West Indies and in peacetime Britain. However, he recorded observations privately in his Medical Annotations that have never been published. The campaigns in North America and the West Indies had been very different from the campaigns in which he had served in Europe.

THIRTEEN

The Health of the Army in North America, the Caribbean and Britain

Here is yet a postscript.
Shakespeare, *Twelfth Night*, II, v

In the 1750s the British army was at war in America. Pringle's book *Observations on the Diseases of the Army* was first published in 1752. By then Pringle no longer had responsibilities or duties in the army, but he still had great interest in its health.

North America

England and France had been in conflict in America since the seventeenth century. In 1667, the Treaty of Breda had established France's dominion over Canada and Canada had been renamed New France. In 1620, the Plymouth Company and in 1623 the Massachusetts Company had established colonies on the north-eastern seaboard of America; although these were private enterprises they had been granted Royal Charters and they had acknowledged the ultimate authority of the British government over their activities. They therefore came under British sovereignty and in law they were agents of the Empire.[1] Together the colonies became New England; they expanded southwards and in 1664, the Dutch town New Amsterdam had been taken over, it had been renamed New York and had become the key centre of New England.

By 1750, New France stretched from the southern shores of Newfoundland, westward to the Great Lakes and from there south over the headwaters of the Mississippi and was reaching further south down the Mississippi valley to establish secure and effective contact with the French colony of Louisiana. The French were bent on strengthening their hold on the Ohio Valley, the most disputed part of the territory linking New France with Louisiana; the New England colonies were attempting to expand westward into the territory that the French were so desperate to hold. Both New France and New England built chains of forts along the Allegheny and Ohio Rivers, the notional border that separated them. In 1754, George Washington, then the commander of a battalion of colonial militia, attacked Fort Duquesne, the key fort in the French chain; the attack failed. Britain sent out reinforcements of regular infantry; in July 1755, General Braddock led a mixed force of regular troops and colonial militia in a second attempt to seize Fort Duquesne. The result was a disaster; of the 1,373 men making up the British force only 459 survived unharmed;[2] Braddock was one of those killed.

Six months later Lord Loudoun was sent out as Commander-in-Chief of the army in America. The Loudouns and the Pringles were old family friends. Lord Loudoun had been of great service to Pringle in his first months as a physician to the army in Flanders. He now renewed Pringle's contact with the army's Physician-General Richard Huck. Huck had trained as a surgeon's mate in the army and had served as a surgeon during the Jacobite Rebellion of 1745. It was then that Pringle had met him and had encouraged him to take leave from the army and to study medicine at Aberdeen. After taking his medical degree, Huck had returned to the army as a physician. Until the end of the war in America, Huck kept Pringle regularly informed of the health of the army and the difficulties faced by the army's medical services.

In addition to Huck as Physician-General, the medical staff of the army consisted of four surgeons, three apothecaries, twelve surgeon's mates, and ten hospital mates. They were distributed to General Hospitals at New York, Albany, and Halifax, Nova Scotia. These General Hospitals remained at these sites throughout the campaign, but, as the troops were widely scattered and the only practical way to convey patients over long distances was by boat along any convenient river, whenever possible, a temporary Flying Hospital was set up near the site of any fighting by the army. However, the burden of the care of both the wounded and sick remained very largely with the regimental surgeons and their infirmaries.

The campaign did not go well. On 3 August 1757, a French force of 3,000 regular troops, 300 militia and 2,000 Native Americans overwhelmed the garrison of Fort William Henry, the British stronghold at the southern end of Lake George. After the battle the British wounded left on the ground were slaughtered and scalped by the Native Americans. The slaughter was later depicted in Fenimore Cooper's novel *The Last of the Mohicans*. Similar atrocities were performed by France's Native American allies in later battles, adding greatly to the bitterness of the war.

On 10 August, a force of French regular troops, local militia and Native Americans captured the British Fort Oswego on Lake Ontario. Some 1,700 soldiers surrendered along with numbers of civilian workmen, women and children; many of them were slaughtered and scalped. When Fort Oswego was recaptured ten months later, it was the only success achieved during Lord Loudoun's time as Commander-in-Chief.

In January 1758, Lord Loudoun was recalled and General James Abercrombie took his place as Commander-in-Chief of the army. At the same time Major General Amherst was appointed commander of a second army and was given the task of capturing Louisburg on Cape Breton Island, New France's only entry port in the north.

In July, Abercrombie, with an army of 18,000, attempted to capture the French Fort Ticonderoga on the shore of Lake Champlain. The French force was only 4,000 strong, but, after a series of blunders, Abercrombie allowed himself to be defeated. For the British army, it was the bloodiest battle of what had become known as the French and Indian War. Abercrombie lost 3,000 men either killed or wounded.

In London, William Pitt was now Secretary of State and head of the war administration in London. He informed Parliament that:

> The succour and preservation of America cannot but constitute a main object of my attention and solicitude; and the growing dangers to which our colonies may stand exposed demand resolutions of vigour and dispatch.[3]

For Pitt the war in Europe was important as it kept much of the French army occupied in Europe and not in America. He meant to defeat France by depriving her of her lucrative empire in North America.

Pitt now gathered all the financial, administrative and military power into his own hands.[4] Abercrombie was dismissed. He was replaced by Major General Amherst who had been successful in taking Louisburg in June 1758; Major General James Wolfe took Amherst's place at Louisburg.

In December 1757, Brigadier General Forbes had been sent 370 miles eastward with a force of 7,000 regular troops and some local militia to capture Fort Duquesne. As his army approached it in November 1758, the French garrison troops, suddenly abandoned by their Native American allies, evacuated and burned Fort Duquesne to the ground. Forbes rebuilt the fort and then moved forward into the Ohio Valley.

In the spring of 1759, Major General Amherst was ordered to march north along the River Hudson and then by Lake George, Lake Champlain and Lake Ontario to take Montreal. He gathered at Albany an army of 6,000

regular troops (King's Troops) and 5,000 provincial militia (the Connecticut Regiment, New York Regiment and Massachusetts Regiment). He was
two months later than had been planned when he set out on what was to be
a long and difficult march of over 500 miles. He met his first major obstacle
on 21 July when his progress was halted at the French-held Fort Ticonderoga
at the south end of Lake Champlain. Amherst laid siege to the fort, but after
three days the French garrison blew up the fort and withdrew to a defensive
position on the shore of the lake where it had the support of four French
warships. Amherst made no further progress in his march to Montreal that
year; in October, he put his army into winter quarters. He rebuilt the fort
and began the construction of a fleet of boats to carry his troops northwards
along Lake Champlain. In the spring of 1760, he continued the march; he
captured Montreal on 8 September 1760.

Before the St Lawrence River was blocked by ice at the beginning
of the winter of 1759–60, Major General James Wolfe had launched an
amphibious force of 200 ships, 18,000 sailors and 9,000 troops along the
St Lawrence to take Quebec. After the Battle of the Plains of Abraham
on 13 September 1759, the French signed Articles of Capitulation. In the
battle the British and French had suffered almost equal numbers of killed
and wounded; both commanders, Major General Wolfe and Major General
de Montcalm, were among those killed. During the winter that followed,
Quebec was held by a garrison of 6,000 men. Adequate supplies of food
and fuel were impossible to find. By April scurvy had reduced the number
of men fit for duty to less than 4,000 and they were starving and suffering
the effects of intense cold. Quebec would have been easily retaken by the
much fitter French army but for the arrival of a British fleet when the St
Lawrence became free of ice. The French army retreated to Montreal where,
on 8 September, it surrendered to Major General Amherst's larger army.
The campaign in America was over.

For the British troops the campaign had been long, difficult and bitter.
In a long letter written from New York on 5 December 1760, Richard Huck
provided Pringle with an account of the health of the army during the last
years of the campaign. During this time, Huck had been with Amherst's
army as it made the final push for the surrender of Montreal.

On a route of nearly five hundred miles, except for two miles halfway
between Albany and Oswego at Fort Stanwix, the troops were carried by
batoes (a corruption of the French word *bateaux* meaning boats). They
carried with them the chief part of their provisions, artillery and other stores
for the campaign. This was a laborious task; the men were much exposed to

both heat and cold as they were frequently obliged, while hot and sweating, to jump up to their middles in cold water to drag their batoes over shallows, rocks and stumps of trees. The waters of the creeks and rivers were reckoned to be unhealthy. Many of the men attributed their dysentery to drinking it; greater numbers had their feet swollen, excoriated and ulcerated by working in it.

The army had set out at the end of May 1759. When it arrived at Oswego on 7 August, the men had cut down trees and cleared the ground on which they had chosen to site their camps. The provincial troops had chosen to camp on swampy ground; although few of them died, many became very ill. At Oswego bread and salt pork made up the major part of the men's diet. They all drank water, but the regulars (the King's Troops) also drank the spruce beer which was provided by the army as a prophylactic against scurvy. From June until the beginning of August the weather was warm, the temperature rising to 86 degrees Fahrenheit. Then, on 20 August, the weather became cold and until October there was heavy rain. Of Amherst's army, now only 5,038 strong,⁵ only 560 were regular King's Troops. Of the King's Troops 81 (14 per cent) were sent to a Flying Hospital set up at Oswego; the great majority were suffering from scurvy, venereal disease, or both; 9 (17 per cent) died. Of the 4,478 from local provincial regiments, 420 (9 per cent) were admitted to the Flying Hospital and of these 162 (34 per cent) died.

On 10 August, the army set out for Montreal. Until then only the few suffering from smallpox had been sent all the way back to the General Hospital at Albany; but before the army left Oswego almost a hundred cases had to be admitted to the Flying Hospital. There the disease had been 'very mortal', in part because the hospital was small and overcrowded and in part because there was no convenient place to which those recovering from the disease could be sent. Many of those recovering in the hospital from smallpox had died of the flux (dysentery).

Before the army moved north, the sick in the Regimental Infirmaries were reviewed. Many cases of flux had been admitted to hospital at Oswego; some who had been returned to duty relapsed and were readmitted to hospital. Huck described in detail the various ways in which the disease was treated. He had found 'a gentle vomit with ipecacuanha' to be the most useful treatment; opiates checked the diarrhoea but a second dose always made it worse; he had tried blistering (raising blisters in the skin by applying heated cups) but he had found that unhelpful. He had also admitted to hospital a few cases of a slow fever (possibly typhus) which began with shivering, nausea, vomiting and great debility; it lasted for weeks during which the patients became languid, stupid and at times delirious. Medicines and blistering were 'of little service' and the patients were very often 'carried off at last with a putrid diarrhoea'.

At the end of September 1760, as the army returned south after taking Montreal, it halted briefly at Oswego. It left behind in hospital 304 sick and wounded. The sick were almost all provincials; in less than a month 110 of them had died. In October, the Connecticut Regiment had passed through Oswego. Huck had examined all the men and those who were unwell and unfit to continue were sent home. Some 400 continued on the march south; before they reached Albany almost 80 had died; others died within a few days of their arrival. At Albany those who were unwell but could walk or sit on a horse were taken home by relatives or friends. Huck believed that at home a great many more of them died. Of the men still with the Connecticut Regiment more continued to 'fall down'; by the end of October the number fit for duty was very small. The New York Regiment, as it followed the Connecticut Regiment on the march south, 'suffered in proportion from the negligence of their officers, for their men died everywhere on the road and in the woods and many lie unburied to this day or have been eaten by wolves'.

Remarkably, the British regular troops continued to be relatively well. The men of the 55th Regiment, who had left New York in the spring and had been to Montreal by way of Oswego, were entirely healthy. They told Huck that they had only lost one man from sickness in their last three campaigns. Huck speculated on the cause of so much sickness among the provincial troops. They were not paid until they returned home at the end of the campaign and did not have the money to buy an alcoholic drink when wet or the other conveniences that would help to conserve their health. Many of them were boys or old men and had not been fit enough for service. Huck added a comment in a letter to Pringle:

At home provincials, especially the Connecticut people, live in a kind of ease and affluence that renders them incapable of bearing hardship without injuring their health. They cannot stir in the mornings without their tea or chocolate or bear sleeping on the ground in place of a feather bed. I do not know if it is owing to the pampered manner in which they are brought up but they certainly have not the strength and stamina of Europeans. One may generally know a country born man after two or three days by his face.

West Indies

In 1752, the islands of the West Indies were all in the possession of Britain, France, Spain, or Holland. After the outbreak of war, the tasks of the British navy and army were to secure the continuing productivity of Jamaica, Barbados, the Bahamas and the Windward Islands and to protect the convoys of merchant ships homeward bound to Britain. After the capture of Louisburg, the object of the operation ceased to be commercial and became territorial. In London, it had been the intention that Louisburg should be held until the end of the war when it could be restored to France in return for the restoration of Minorca to Britain. However, Pitt disagreed. His aim was to drive the French completely out of America; he insisted that Louisburg must never be returned to France. His plan was to capture Martinique, one of France's most valuable possessions in the West Indies. He was confident that, at the end of the war, France would be willing to accept Martinique rather than Louisburg in exchange for Minorca.

An expedition commanded by Admiral Moore and Major General Hopson set out from England on 12 November 1758 and arrived at Martinique on 17 January 1759. The whole army of 4,400 was landed, but Hopson found the island's citadel heavily fortified while the dense jungle surrounding it made it impossible for him to bring his artillery into position. He therefore withdrew the expedition from Martinique and moved north to capture the neighbouring and equally rich French island of Guadeloupe. On 24 January, the troops landed unopposed at Basseterre on the south of the island. The French army had withdrawn to an impregnable position on high ground. By the end of January, Hopson had abandoned the attempt to take the enemy's position by frontal attack and he had failed to find an alternative strategy. Already 1,500, over a quarter of his troops, were sick and unfit for duty and he himself was dying.

Admiral Moore decided to take independent action. On 7 February, he sailed with a force of 800 marines and two companies of the 42nd Royal Highlanders (Black Watch) for Fort Louis on Grande Terre, a peninsula on the eastern side of the island. Within six hours he had taken Fort Louis and had established a bridgehead on what was a very promising position from which to launch a drive to complete the conquest of Guadeloupe. However, Hopson was unable to take advantage of the opportunity that Admiral Moore had created; he remained ill and inactive at Basseterre.

When Hopson died on 27 February, 1,600 of the men at Basseterre were sick and a total of 1,400 of the worst cases had already been evacuated to Antigua. So many men had died that the expedition seemed on the point of destruction. However, Colonel John Barrington, Hopson's successor, rallied the troops, strengthened the army's defences at Basseterre and, leaving behind a garrison of one depleted battalion of infantry, on 7 March he conveyed his remaining 1,500 men by sea to Fort Louis. There he exploited the bridgehead that had been created by Admiral Moore. After two months of difficult soldiering, on 1 May the French Governor of Guadeloupe capitulated. But in four months a British army of 4,400 had been reduced to a weak remnant of less than 1,300.

Before leaving Guadeloupe in February 1761, Richard Huck sent Pringle an account of the diseases that the army had suffered during its time on the island. Much of the information had been provided by a surgeon, Mr Blair, who had been in practice on the island for many years. As was expected of a medical man of the time he related the incidence of the diseases to the weather and the climate.

First, Huck described the usual pattern of disease of the island. On Guadeloupe, the rainy season began at the beginning of June and continued for three months. During these months the weather was hot and close and the wind was constantly from the north-east. Most days it rained heavily for an hour or two and thereafter, for the rest of the day, it was fair but hot with only a slight breeze; there were, however, frequent brief but violent storms of thunder and lightning. During these rainy months there was always an outbreak of putrid fevers. Towards the end of the rainy season, dysentery also began to break out; it often continued until November. Those most affected by the fevers and dysentery were the soldiers and 'the lower people' of the island who were 'either inattentive to their health or obliged to expose themselves to the wet and the moisture'.

From the end of September until Christmas it was cooler and there were frequent showers; in these months intermittent fevers (malaria) became very common. Then from Christmas until February the weather was agreeable, cool in the mornings and evenings but hot in the middle of the day; the intermittent fevers became even more prevalent among the soldiers because of 'the interchanges of heat and cold, especially while on sentry duty'. From the end of February until the beginning of June was the healthy season. The weather was still cool in the mornings and evenings. The intermittent fevers continued among the soldier but there were no epidemics.

He offered no definitive explanation of the sickness that had devastated the army during the campaign to conquer the island. The sickness was at its height between the end of February and May, normally the months of Guadeloupe's healthy season. However, he did discuss two diseases that had occurred in the army but were not part of the normal pattern of disease on the island. The first was scurvy. It most commonly presented as wounds and other minor injuries that had failed to heal; thereafter it went on to cause a severe general debility. In retrospect its occurrence among the soldiers was easily explained. On the voyage from England to the West Indies the men had been confined on board ship from 12 November 1758 until 17 February 1759 on a diet of bread, salt pork and water. After landing they had continued on the same diet; in an alien and hostile country it was impossible to purchase or otherwise acquire a supply of fresh food. Meanwhile, the French army enjoyed a more generous diet and had their own local source of fruit and vegetables; they had remained free of scurvy.

The second disease was an unfamiliar fever. The chief presenting symptoms were 'a violent pain in the pit of the stomach, great sickness and violent vomiting of yellow stuff, rarely with any purging. When the pulse sank, as it was apt to do, the patient was then in great danger of his life.' This distemper, in which the patient almost always turned yellow, was the 'most fatal and frequent of the putrid fevers' suffered by the army in Guadeloupe. An army officer, Captain Forbes, had informed Huck that in 1757 he had been sent to Senegal in West Africa with four companies of infantry, each of 100 men; while there, 330 of the men had died of what seemed to him to be the same fever.

Pringle was greatly interested in what Huck had informed him about the scurvy that had caused so much trouble in the army. He wrote to Captain Gordon of the Marines who made the voyage round the world with Admiral Anson in 1740–4. Anson had set out with eight ships and 1,900 men and had returned with one ship and fewer than 500 men; the great majority of those who did not return had died of scurvy. Captain Gordon's reply was not as helpful as Pringle had hoped.

He reported that he had scarcely been troubled with any symptoms of the scurvy during the whole of his voyage. This he attributed to his manner of living. He ate salted meat only twice a week and on those days he drank more than his usual allowance of water; he kept some of his water for the days in which he ate vegetables 'such as peas, rice etc.'. He believed that in general the disease was much increased by the scarcity of water. He had bought wine at Madeira and he drank about a pint of it each day. The common allowance of brandy, half a pint a day for the common men, he thought very proper if it was diluted with water. He had reached the island of San Fernando without any symptoms of scurvy, but after the departure from there, feeling a lassitude and fearing scurvy, he had taken some drops which purged, vomited and sweated him violently and, as he believed, prevented the disease. Lord Anson had used the same medicine.

Pringle wrote to Thomas Dundas, a doctor who had been on Lord Cathcart's expedition to Antigua in 1740 and might provide some information about this mysterious fever as it appeared on board his ship. The doctor replied:

> My hurry has been so great that I have scarce had time to consider the papers you have put in my hands. I think that the fever and yellowness proceeds from a general corruption of the fluids which at length become so acrid as to destroy the vessels. For what is called the black vomit and the humour that frequently comes from the eyes, ears and noses of a coffee colour is nothing but extravastated blood. As to the method of cure the best chance is in throwing in the Bark as an antiseptic in small quantities on the very first remission of the fever which commonly happens on the second day.

Pringle also wrote to William Miller, a doctor who practised in Antigua. He replied:

> You desire I would let you know my opinion on the points with regard to the Yellow Fever in the West Indies. It is a disease only incident to newcomers and as I have lived altogether in the country where my practice has chiefly been since I came to the West Indies, I have not had so many opportunities of observing the disease as a practitioner who has lived in the town.
>
> I am of the opinion that the distemper commonly called Yellow Fever is different from the putrid and bilious fevers which are common both in the natives and in strangers. It is more obscure and deceitful and the most fatal I have ever known and which perhaps has no characteristics till the symptoms of death appear which are sooner or later as the patient has been longer or shorter from a cold climate. The more robust and healthy the patients are the more rapid the progress and sudden death.

These and other inquiries provided Pringle with some of the information that he had hoped to collect.[6] There can be no doubt that at Guadeloupe the British army had been devastated by yellow fever. Yellow fever was not fully described and generally recognised until 1855.

Peacetime Britain

From its publication in 1752, Pringle's *Observations* had attracted great attention not only in the British army but also in the other armies in Europe. The book had provoked a new level of interest in the health and welfare of the ordinary soldier. However, Pringle had written only about the health of the British army while on campaign in wartime. In 1758, two army physicians, Richard Brocklesby[7] and Donald Monro[8] began a review of the health of the army when it was not on campaign abroad but stationed peacefully at home in Britain. Their findings were published by Brocklesby in 1764[9] and repeated by Monro in 1780.[10] They painted a distressing picture.

Britain had a small army. At the end of the long and harsh period of Cromwell's military government it had been generally agreed that the country should never again have a standing army. However, in 1722, Walpole had established an army of 22,000 men. In 1757, that number had been increased to 100,000. There had been barracks in Ireland since 1713 and in Scotland since the Jacobite Rebellion in 1715. However, in the 1760s, Brocklesby could find only two permanent barracks in England, one at Chatham and one at Portsmouth. He condemned them both. They were miserably damp, poorly ventilated and totally devoid of drainage; 'they bred disease and swept off men like a perpetual pestilence'. Elsewhere in Britain, troops were billeted in ale houses or in cheaply hired decrepit barns or dilapidated dwellings. No attention was paid to their personal cleanliness or to the state of their dress except when they were on parade. The men were paid sixpence a day and the great majority of them had no communal messing; they catered for themselves and many chose to live on a diet of bread and cheese and to spend the rest of their money on alcohol. Most had been medically examined, at least to some degree, when they were recruited, but thereafter no routine checks were ever made of their health. The regimental surgeons, often men of many years of service with the army, were paid only four shillings a day, a sum that had remained unchanged for a hundred years. They were allowed £30 a year to pay for the hire of accommodation for a Regimental Infirmary and to pay sixpence a day to a nurse chosen from among the soldiers' wives to do whatever washing was ever done. The patients' basic rations of bread and meat were supplied by the regiments to which they belonged; extras such as milk, eggs, vegetables and fish were bought in the local market by the infirmary sergeant and paid for by a stoppage of two shillings and sixpence a week levied on each patient. The medicines used in the infirmary were also paid for by stoppages from the soldiers' pay, one penny a month from privates and a penny three farthings from non-commissioned officers; any money left unspent at the end of the year the surgeon was allowed to keep. It was not uncommon for the surgeon to augment his meagre income by buying only the cheapest medicines.[11] Brocklesby's description of the typical Regimental Infirmary was damning:

> Most commonly the habitation hired for an infirmary has for some time been unoccupied with walls all damp, the boarded floors half rotten and the roof in several places open above. I have indeed seen such a cottage stuffed with 40, 50, or 60, nay with 70 or 80 poor soldiers lying heel to head, so closely confined together with their stinking clothes, foul linen, etc that it was enough to suffocate the patients as well others who were obliged to approach them.

It was evident from his report that Brocklesby had concluded that the care that Britain's soldiers received when stationed at home was very much worse than the care that they enjoyed during their campaigns overseas; when on campaign 'nothing was more conducive to recovery than the continued attention to cleanliness, frequent shifting of foul linen and bedding and invariably a free and almost uninterrupted current of fresh air by treating the patients in tents'.

In later editions of *Observations on the Diseases of the Army* Pringle writes something of scurvy in the text and he makes brief mention of yellow fever in an appendix. He makes no comment on the care of the men of the army in Britain in peacetime.

FOURTEEN

Life in London

I must have liberty with as large a charter as the wind.

Shakespeare, *As You Like It*, II, vii

He that will not apply new remedies must expect new evils for time is the greatest innovator.

Francis Bacon, *On Innovations*, 1625

The publication of Pringle's *Observations on the Diseases of the Army* in 1752 had been a triumphant success. Within a year a second edition had been produced in response to the interest created by the first. A third edition followed in 1761. Further editions were published during the next 20 years. In 1766, he had been made a baronet, Sir John Pringle of Pall Mall. He had been elected a Fellow of the Royal College of Physicians of London, *speciali gratia*. He had been a Fellow of the Royal Society since 1745, and had since been a member of its Council. He was Physician in Ordinary to the Queen and the Duke of Cumberland. In the 1760s he was one of the most eminent physicians in London.

In 1763, Pringle bought a new and larger house on the north side of Pall Mall. He collected books for his library. He bought paintings and drawings. He played his violoncello, often with a group of other talented musicians. Every morning, old friends, new admirers and young protégés from Britain and other parts of the world came to call on him. On Sunday evenings his gatherings were attended by an ever-widening circle of men distinguished in science, politics, philosophy, medicine, exploration, history and military matters. Pringle was an excellent host. He had charm and he had wit and was able to make himself agreeable to everyone. But, although he was invariably courteous, to most of those whom he met, he was always somewhat distant. Pringle preferred to cultivate close and lasting friendships with the few who shared his interests and for whom he had the greatest respect. With his friend Jan Ingen Housz he discussed the new theories of photosynthesis.

With his friend Joseph Priestley he discussed the properties of the 'factitious or artificial airs',[1] carbon dioxide, oxygen and hydrogen. With Captain James Cook he discussed the measures required to preserve the health of seamen on long voyages of exploration. He advised the Prime Minister, the Earl of Bute, in choosing suitable items for his collection of electrical apparatus.[2] Through these and many other friendships he had acquired a voice on the public issues of the time.

One of his oldest friends was the philosopher and historian David Hume. They had met first in Edinburgh when Pringle was Professor of Philosophy at Edinburgh University.[3] Since then they had met from time to time in London and in Edinburgh and they had continued to write to each other, exchanging views on philosophy and on other subjects of mutual interest. In 1765, the subject was poetry. Some years earlier, James Macpherson, a Scottish poet and private tutor, had been introduced by his employer to the playwright John Hume and the Reverend Alexander 'Jupiter' Carlyle, a Moderator of the General Assembly of the Church of Scotland. Macpherson was a native Gaelic speaker who had collected some pieces of what he claimed was ancient Gaelic poetry. Hume and Carlyle encouraged him to translate some of the poetry into English. They showed his early translations to Hugh Blair, Professor of Rhetoric and Belles Lettres at Edinburgh University who was considered to be an authority on the various forms of written composition. Macpherson and Blair immediately came together; Blair was looking for 'something sublime' from an ancient society while Macpherson wished to show that the people of the Scottish Highlands shared many of the characteristics of the Ancient Greeks and that they had their own Homeric epics.[4] In 1761, Macpherson had begun to publish a series of *Fragments of Ancient Poetry collected in the Highlands of Scotland and translated from the Gaelic Language.* Two epic poems followed, first *Fingal* and later *Temora.* He claimed that the author of these pieces was Ossian, a blind poet and harpist of the third century; that Ossian's poems had passed down by word of mouth through many generations of the Gaelic community in Scotland; and that he had translated them into English.

There were many in Edinburgh who were happy to be persuaded that Macpherson had revealed the existence of a long-forgotten Scottish Homer. When, in 1765, Macpherson published a collected edition of *The Works of Ossian,* the book added to what was already becoming an international sensation. The English Romantic poets of the time were all inspired by it. It was translated into 26 foreign languages. The Italian edition became one of Napoleon's favourite books. The King of Sweden named his son, Oscar, after a character in one of Ossian's great epics.[5] Goethe, Schiller and Victor Hugo were all consciously influenced by it. However, Pringle's reaction was distinctly cool and even somewhat cynical. In a letter to David Hume on 9 May 1765, he wrote:

> Ever since Mr Macpherson published his second volume I began to be a sceptic about the whole production and I found that not only in this country but in France the wits were all persuaded that there was nothing, or next to nothing, genuine in it. However now Dr Blair having adduced such a cloud of witnesses to prove Mr Macpherson's honesty as to that particular I do not apprehend that there can be any more objections made.[6]

David Hume, who was a sceptic not only on religion and but also on many other matters, took a decidedly sceptical view of everything that Macpherson had published. Hume and Pringle conveyed their objections to Dr Blair, but, as Pringle had forecast in his letter to Hume, Dr Blair was not open to their objections. The dispute over the authenticity of Macpherson's work lingered for many years. However, Pringle had no doubt. He dismissed Macpherson as a fraud.

For Pringle the authenticity of Macpherson's work was only a passing interest. He was already playing his part in one of the great events of the eighteenth century, the separation from Britain of her 13 colonies in North America. He had been drawn into this momentous affair by his friend Benjamin Franklin.

Franklin had been born in Boston, Massachusetts, in 1706. In 1724 he had crossed the Atlantic to London where he had spent 18 months working at Samuel Palmer's printing house in Bartholomew Close. After his return to Boston, in 1729 he had moved to Philadelphia where he had set up as a printer and proprietor of the *Pennsylvanian Gazette*. Between 1749 and 1752 he made a number of studies of the nature of electricity that, in 1753, won him the Copley Medal of the Royal Society of London. He was made a Fellow of the Royal Society in 1756. In these same years Franklin had become a prominent member of the Pennsylvanian Assembly.

Pennsylvania was at that time still owned by the descendants of the William Penn who had founded the colony in 1677. Unfortunately, the Penn family had continued to insist on exercising the owner's right to appoint the Governor of Pennsylvania, an arrangement that had led to perpetual discord between the privately appointed Governor and the democratically elected Pennsylvanian Assembly. In 1757, as a self-appointed envoy of the Assembly, Franklin travelled to London to persuade the leading members of the British government to resolve the difficulty by making Pennsylvania a Crown colony with a Governor appointed by the Crown. Georgia had been made a Crown colony in 1732 and the new system of government had proved acceptable both to the people of the colony and the government in London.

When he arrived in London in July, Franklin had very few friends there.[7] However, at one of his first meetings of the Royal Society, he was introduced to Pringle and they discovered that they had a common interest in electricity. By 1758 the two had become close friends.[8] They played chess and together they visited the more intellectually inclined coffeehouses in London.[9] Franklin became a regular guest at Pringle's Sunday evening gatherings and there he met men distinguished in politics, science and history. It was at Pringle's house that Franklin met Lord Stanhope and the Earl of Bute,[10] two of the politicians whom he thought might be helpful in securing a less troublesome system of government for Pennsylvania. Pringle continued to introduce Franklin to potential allies in political circles in London, but one of Franklin's chief allies was to be Pringle himself.

Every summer Pringle and Franklin spent several weeks travelling in Britain or Europe. In June 1759, they made a 'long and happy tour in Scotland'.[11] They travelled first to St Andrews where Franklin was to be made an Honorary Doctor of Law. From June until September, they were the guests of the President of the Royal College of Physicians of Edinburgh, Sir Alexander Dick, at Prestonfield, his house at Edinburgh. At dinners and other gatherings in Edinburgh, Pringle introduced Franklin to Adam Smith, William Robertson, William Cullen, Lord Monboddo, Lord Kames, James Watt and Alexander Carlyle, the most influential of the literati and scientists in Scotland.[12] In the summer of 1762, they visited the Netherlands where Pringle introduced Franklin to a number of the distinguished men whom he had come to know during his years at Leiden University and later during his first months in Flanders as physician to the army.

However, by the autumn of that year, Franklin had made no progress in his campaign to have Pennsylvania made a Crown colony. He went home to Philadelphia, but within two years he had returned to Britain armed with a petition drawn up by the Assembly of Pennsylvania to be presented to King George III. However, the Privy Council refused to allow Franklin an audience with the king and again nothing was achieved.

On 22 February 1765, Franklin's problem changed suddenly and fundamentally. The British Parliament passed a Stamp Act that required the colonies to pay a tax on 'every newspaper, book, almanac, legal document and deck of cards'.[13] The sums to be collected were modest and the revenue was to be used to help meet the cost to Britain of the colonies' wars with their Native American neighbours. However, as Franklin was quick to point out, the Act had been passed by a Parliament in which there had been 'no members from America to represent the condition of their country'.[14] Franklin was certain that in the colonies the Stamp Act would provoke a storm of protest. The protests were as loud and as hostile as Franklin had predicted. On 18 March 1766, Parliament repealed the Act but in doing so it emphatically declared that it 'had, hath and of right ought to have, full power and authority to make laws and statutes of sufficient force and validity to bind the colonies and the people of America'. For the people of the colonies this pronouncement was intolerable. All 13 colonies began to look for a more acceptable relationship with Britain and they appointed Franklin as their envoy. Franklin and Pringle set out together to study the systems and the instruments by which other central governments managed their distant and dependent territories.

It had been arranged that, early in June 1766, Pringle would travel to the spa at Pyrmont in Hanover to drink the waters.[15] On 14 June, Franklin joined him. The people of Hanover were subjects of King George and Franklin and Pringle found Hanoverian officials very ready to discuss the nature of their relationship with the British government. On 19 July, Franklin and Pringle were invited to a meeting at Göttingen University and were elected members of their Royal Society of Scientists. In 1767, they travelled to France where they were formally received by Louis XV; they were later warmly welcomed as guests of the king and queen at Versailles. In the summer of 1771, they were to spend three months in Ireland and Scotland to discover whether the relationship that these somewhat detached nations were attempting to forge with the expanding British Empire could serve as a model for the American colonies.[16] But by then the situation had changed once more.

At a dinner party in London in January 1769, Pringle had introduced Franklin to David Hume.[17] At that time most American colonists, including Franklin, still regarded themselves as British citizens living in a transatlantic part of Britain, bound by a fixed British constitution and subject to British law. Hume thought otherwise. He argued that throughout its history the British constitution had never been fixed and unchanging and that the liberties of a people should not be determined by law, but should be rooted securely in the natural and universal rights of man. Hume had made these views clear in his books. His books had been available in the American colonies since 1756, but his views had not been popular.[18] However, as the relationship between the American colonies of the British government deteriorated, Hume's ideas began to seem much more attractive.

Franklin and Hume had become good friends. In the winter of 1771 Franklin spent three weeks with Hume in Edinburgh. There they debated the future of the American colonies. They later continued their debate by letter. However, their deliberations were overtaken by events. Following the destruction of shiploads of tea in Boston harbour ('Boston Tea Party') in December 1773, the local government of Massachusetts had been suspended and the colony had been put under military control. The descent into war now seemed inevitable. During his years of talking and travelling with Franklin, Pringle had continued to believe that the break with the American colonies could and should be prevented. His friend David Hume thought otherwise; and Franklin had come to agree with Hume. In a letter to Hume in January 1774, Pringle wrote:

> I consider as the main cause of the difference between our two opinions to be the firm persuasion I have had that the Americans never wanted to separate from us until we attempted to impose a tax on them but on the contrary they considered themselves as a happy people and took pride in being part of this great and flourishing empire. Even in this sad reverse of circumstances do we not find the principal colony, Pennsylvania, charging their deputies to the Congress to listen to no terms of accommodation that infer a separation from the mother country. And indeed what men in their senses, in those parts, could ever enter into a scheme of that kind whilst they enjoyed all the blessings of plenty and freedom? Another point we differ in is with regard to the conquest of Canada by our troops in the late war. You are of the opinion that it encouraged this revolt whilst I imagine it had quite the contrary effect. Supposing the colonies had meditated a revolt would they not rather have availed themselves of assistance from a neighbouring French settlement than to have waited until they have seen so large a province and so strong a place as Quebec possessed by the mother country from which they were to break of their allegiance.[19]

Franklin returned to Philadelphia in 1775. They continued to write to each other and Pringle continued to argue against independence for the American colonies. David Hume, however, believed that a break was the proper outcome. By promoting the concept of universal rights of man he had lent strong support for the rebellion. When it succeeded, Hume played a defining part in the wording of the Declaration of Independence. He persuaded Franklin to change the beginning of the second sentence of Thomas Jefferson's draft of the text from 'We hold these truths to be sacred and undeniable that all men are born equal' to 'We hold these truths to be self-evident that all men are born equal.' By making this change the statement that all men are born equal was seen to be based on reason rather than on an article of religious faith.[20]

Pringle had made every effort over a number of years to assist Franklin in finding a system of government that would make it possible for the American colonies to remain happily within the British Empire. He deeply regretted their failure to agree but his friendships with Hume and Franklin remained unchanged.

Pringle continued to take an active interest in public affairs, but at the same time he continued his activities as a medical scientist. From 1760, he published work on a number of subjects in the *Philosophical Transactions* of the Royal Society. However, he did not publish the results of his private project. His great ambition was to control the health of the general population as he had controlled the spread of disease in the army by a method based on Bacon's principles of observation, reason and experiment.

During his years as Physician-General to the Army, Pringle had come to believe that this must be possible. He had identified inflammatory disorders (colds, coughs and rheumatism), intermittent fever (malaria), the flux (dysentery) and severe continuous fever (typhus) as the principal diseases suffered by the army. He had observed that outbreaks of colds and rheumatism were clearly associated with cold and wet weather; intermitent fever with siting the army's camps on marshland in summer; dysentery with billeting troops in inadequately drained properties where they were exposed to the effluvia of rotting waste; and typhus with overcrowding in transports and hospitals. Simple reasoning had indicated that the introduction of measures to protect the troops from exposure to each of these sets of adverse factors would reduce the number of soldiers dying from disease. As Physician-General he had the authority to introduce the appropriate measures. The measures proved to be effective and when applied throughout the army, the incidence of disease had been greatly reduced.

When Pringle retired from the army and set up in civilian practice he began to collect, in the volumes of his private Medical Annotations, details of cases in his own practice and the cases of other distinguished physicians whom he had consulted. However, the diseases of the civilian population were many and their causes were obscure. In civilian medical practice the emphasis was not on prevention but on treatment and even if effective measures of treatment could be found, they could not be imposed on the civilian patients as he had imposed his preventive measures on the troops. Indeed, there was no control over any of the measures that were being offered to the public. Medical practice in the middle of the eighteenth century was an open and highly competitive market.

This was particularly true of the society in which Pringle practised. His practice centred on the Royal Court of St James. His patients were the aristocrats of the royal household, their friends, their associates and their dependents. They were the leaders of a new polite society.[21] By the 1750s, profitable overseas trade, expansion in the economy and low taxation had brought Britain to new levels of prosperity. Unprecedented increase in the numbers of the population prevented the labour force from winning its share of the new wealth.[22] It was a time in which the poor were getting poorer and the rich were getting richer and creating a new society with expensive tastes. Health was for sale.[23]

The rich were less liable than the poor to die of contagious diseases, but they suffered the consequences of over-indulgence in food, alcohol and sex. They were also afflicted by gout, ulcers of the legs, headaches, deafness and depression, all chronic disorders that were not fatal but were difficult to cure. A wealthy member of London's polite society might first choose to consult one of London's fashionable 'regular' physicians, a Fellow of the Royal College of Physicians who had been trained in classical medicine for 11 years at Oxford or Cambridge and then at one of London's teaching hospitals. The regular physician would have settled in one place in London and patiently built up his practice on talk of his personal qualities and his successes. But, if the physician failed to relieve the complaint, the patient might consult two or even more other 'regular' physicians. Or he might consult a quack who would not have built up a practice in one place but would move from place to place attracting patients by advertising his special knowledge and skills.

However, the distinction between regular physician and quack was far from absolute. The treatments offered by regular physicians were based on the classical theories of Hippocrates and Galen, theories that were already suspect, and the treatments were at best unreliable. Even the most eminent of regular physicians resorted to inventing their own special cures. Dr Richard Mead FRCP purveyed his mysterious *pulvis antilisus* as a cure for rabies; Edward Jenner FRCP sold his secret lozenges as his treatment for indigestion; Dr Paul Chamberlain FRCP marketed teething necklaces.[24]

Quacks were not constrained by ancient authority; they lived by imagination, invention and bold experiment in treatment. A great many of their imaginings were bizarre and their inventions useless. Many quacks had studied medicine at a reputable university but had seen no advantage in taking a degree; in the eighteenth century as many as 90 per cent of the students studying at Edinburgh University's medical school, then the leading medical school in Britain, had chosen not to take a degree. However, it had been quacks who had introduced inoculation and the use of mercury, antimony, opium, and Peruvian Bark, all useful and reliable medicines.[25] And from the 1750s both regular physicians and quacks dabbled in the therapeutic use of electricity.

In eighteenth-century London it could not be assumed that the treatments offered by quacks were necessarily less rational or more dangerous than those offered by regular physicians. The most famous quack in London in the second half of the eighteenth century was James Graham. Like Pringle, he was a Scot; he had been briefly a medical student at Edinburgh. Like Pringle, his interest in electricity had been stimulated by a meeting with Benjamin Franklin;[26] like Pringle, Graham lived and practised in a house in Pall Mall in London; and again like Pringle, he drew his patients from London's wealthy and sophisticated polite society. His most enthusiastic patron was the Duchess of Devonshire. However, unlike Pringle, his treatments were not based on ancient classical theory but on his claim that 'by air, by magnetism, by musical sounds, by subtle, cordial and balsamic medicines, by chemical energy and by positive and negative electricity [he had] an absolute command over the health, functions and diseases of the human body'.[27]

He described his treatments as miraculous and infallible. He sold pills that he claimed to be the distillate of powerful electrical fluids. At his Temple of Health at his house in Pall Mall, patients with such common complaints as rheumatism, gout, deafness, noises in the head, or depression were offered electric ('galvanic') therapy; they were not subjected to electric shocks; they sat on a 'magnetic throne' and were gently engulfed in streams of an invisible superfine electrical fluid. However, Graham was less interested in the cure of specific ailments than in the promotion of health, and sex was his key to health. He claimed that 'the genitals are the true pulse and infallible barometer of health'.[28] His aim was to promote the health of the patient and of society by stimulating the libido. He gave 'libidinous' (Graham's own description) lectures to audiences of up to a score of ladies and gentlemen while he sat naked in a bath full of earth. In the room 'garlands, mirrors, crystals and silver ornaments are scattered about in profusion'. Music preceded each lecture from 5 until 7 o'clock. Dr Graham then presented himself and delivered his lecture. When this ended, there was a long silence which was suddenly interrupted by an electric shock given simultaneously to the whole audience by conductors hidden under the cushions that covered their seats. As Graham emerged from his earth-filled bath, 'a pretty woman under the form of the Goddess of Music' sang six short pieces and then vanished.

For the treatment of infertility or other sexual difficulties, Graham claimed in his advertisements to have at his Temple of Health:

> the most astonishing method to recommend which will infallibly produce a genial and happy issue, my Celestial Magnetico-Electrico Bed, which is the first and only ever in the world. It is placed in a spacious room to the right of my orchestra which produces the Celestial fire and vivifying influence; this Celestial Bed is supported by six massive brass columns with Saxon blue and purple satin, perfumed with Arabian spices in the style of the Seraglio of a Grand Turk. Any gentleman and his lady desirous of a progeny and wishing to spend an evening in the Celestial apartment in which coition may, on the compliment of a £50 banknote, be permitted to partake of the heavenly joys it affords by causing immediate conception accompanied by the soft music. Superior ecstasy which the parties enjoy in the Celestial Bed is really astonishing and never before thought of in this world; the barren must certainly become fruitful when they are agitated in the delights of love.

Graham claimed that children conceived in his 'Celestial Bed' were certain to be healthy and would therefore be welcome additions to the health of the nation.

Graham's practices represented the absurdity of which an eighteenth-century quack was capable. Pringle's own practices represent the heroic methods of treatment used at this time by the most distinguished of regular physicians. In the case quoted here from Pringle's notes the patient survived:

An eight year old boy, a pupil at Eton School, was taken ill with a fever, supposed to be owing to catching a cold. I saw him on the third day when the fever was high and the patient delirious. He had not been bled for two days. I ordered bleeding of seven ounces and common salt of wormwood draughts with three ounces of the tincture of rhubarb till he had a motion. Next day his back was blistered and the day after I ordered two leeches to be attached to each temple to be left there until they fell off themselves and the blood to stop itself but though he lost a lot of blood his symptoms continued. His legs and arms were blistered but with no better result. On the seventh day the delirium rose to new heights, he had slept none of the preceding night, had raved incessantly and struggled to get out of bed. His seeming too low to bear further bleeding, his head was shaved in order to have it blistered and at the same time twelve grains of Homburg's sedative salt which was to be repeated every six hours till further orders. After that, whether from the medicine or from the shaving of his head, he fell asleep and had a good deal of rest during the night. Next day the delirium threatened to return, a dose of the same salt was given and the patient lay quiet soon after taking it. In the morning a sweat broke out over all his body which seemed to relieve his head for he was sensible, lay easy, his pulse was slow. Seeing him in this good way I returned in three hours and found his face pale, his pulse quite sunk and his body in a cold clammy sweat, in a word he seems expiring. I ordered a servant to lie in bed beside him in order to give him heat and at the same time I made him swallow some warm white wine with spirit of hartshorn. By that means he seemed to be restored to life. The weather was then piercingly cold with frost and snow, the room was very cold and the nurse had neglected to put a warm cap on his head after his head was shaven. For two or three days I found it proper to make the servant lie with him to keep him warm. His cordial was the whey and hartshorne or a jelly melted with a spoonful of brandy in it. After this time he recovered fast without taking any other medicine than a drop or two of a laxative in the convalescent state.

Pringle was aware that much of the guidance that members of the public received from their medical advisers was confusing and contradictory and the treatments that were prescribed were often irrational, unpleasant and ineffective. To resolve the patients' uncertainties and to improve the standard of care that they received Pringle hoped to devise a system based on observation, experiment and reason, the principles of Francis Bacon.

Pringle had begun to record his observations not according to a pre-set questionnaire or some other strict plan of inquiry but as the occasion arose. After many years, his records filled ten folio volumes of his Medical Annotations, all carefully bound in rough calfskin. In all, 259 separate subjects (a disease, a treatment, or a theory) were discussed; the discussion of a subject might begin early in one of the first volumes and continue at intervals in succeeding pages in the same volume and in the pages of subsequent volumes. As a result, the arrangement of the entries on any one subject (the complete 'article' as Pringle described it) is haphazard; each volume does contain a helpful index.

Many of his Medical Annotations are his observations on cases of special interest that he had encountered in his own practice. Many more are observations given in answer to requests for information that he had addressed to physicians known to have expert knowledge or unique experience; a number of these communications are in Latin, French and German.

From his enquiries Pringle discovered that, even for the most common acute illnesses, few physicians claimed to have complete confidence in the treatment they were using.

On the Treatment of Worms

Comment from a London physician, Dr Young:

> All the signs of the presence of worms are fallible and sometimes children and adults will have them without any sign at all, being first discovered in the stools or found in the intestines after death. Most medicines recommended for worms are ineffectual, and no wonder, since most of them have been prescribed on a false theory. The following are found to answer best. Mercurials if there is no fever. Vitriol Alba [zinc sulphate] when diluted for adults for it is not to be given to children. Rhubarb is of use chiefly as a purgative. Copper in all its preparations is a powerful medicine but too rough for children. Vitriol Coral [sulphate of cobalt] I have given with success and I have known it to have very extraordinary effects in removing obstructions to the abdominal viscera.

Pringle received reports on the treatment worms from several physicians. Each one described a single case in which his treatment had been successful. Dr G. claimed:

to have known a Lady much troubled with worms that had resisted several mercurial remedies and clysters at last cured by this method. She began with a purge and then took a quantity of a teaspoonful of the down of [the herb] *vicia hirsuta* on a large spoonful of syrup pectoral [a common cough medicine] every morning she fasted and drank nothing for two hours after. This continued for nine or ten days; she took another purge and was cured.

On the Treatment of Cephalgia Hemicranium (Migraine)

Pringle had consulted Dr Fordyce who suffered from migraine; he made a note of Fordyce's reply:

Dr Fordyce observes that bleeding is the first thing to be done and that the nearer the blood is taken to the part affected the effects are more sensible. After bleeding the patient is to be vomited especially if he complains of indigestion. He recommends drawing water from the nostril by Sal Ammoniac. He lays great strength on the use of valerian which cured him after he had laboured under the condition for four years. But he says that a blister to the head or neck does more service than a thousand other remedies.

On the Treatment of Haemorrhoids

Pringle had consulted a surgeon, Mr Girle, who advised:

for inflamed and painful piles that come out, a deep incision in each single pile to let out the blood. He says he has in this manner opened six or seven ounces of blood at once. It is done without any danger and gives immediate ease. Some women subject to this distemper are generally worse about the time they menstruate, before and after the period.

In the most painful piles, the bleeding that comes of itself does not always give relief but on the contrary sometimes makes the pain rather worse, as in the Case of Lady A., whereas bleeding with leeches always mitigates or removes the pain not only when they can be applied to the piles themselves but also to the anus when the piles do not come out as in the case of Lady M.

Pringle found that there was little agreement on the treatment of the three most common chronic disorders that physicians were called to treat in eighteenth-century Britain. These were palsy, dropsy and gout.

On the Treatment of Palsy

The palsy that most concerned physicians at that time followed a fit of apoplexy (a stroke). The palsy was paralysis extending down one side of the body resulting from the damage to the brain caused by the leaking or clotting of blood. Pringle consulted a number of eminent physicians on their treatment:

> Dr Hall, physician to St Thomas's Hospital, esteemed by his brethren as a judicious physician and no theorist, trusted in most palsies the external application of blisters and afterwards to a liniment compounded of half an ounce of liniment saponis [castile soap, camphor, oil of rosemary dissolved in alcohol] mixed with one ounce of tincture of cantharides. His chief internal medicine was mustard seed.
>
> Dr Hales of Teddington told me of his having known more than one paralytic receiving benefit by drinking every night at bed time a draught of mustard whey made in this manner: To half a pint of boiling milk add a spoonful of made mustard, separate the curd and drink the whey.
>
> Dr Gresham, physician to St George's Hospital acquainted me that the most successful method that he had seen used for the cure of a palsy in that hospital was by repeated blisters in the nape of the neck, spine or upon the shoulder of the arm affected and giving large dose of camphor but he owned that he had scarcely known any instance of perfect cures except of them brought into the hospital within a few weeks after the seizure.

Pringle used his own treatment. When called on to treat the 'Earl of S', who had suffered three apoplectic fits in three years, 'in order to prevent a return, a seton was put into his neck'. A seton was a tape of woven cotton. It was inserted by making two parallel incisions in the skin, inserting the leading end of the seton through one incision, passing it under the skin and withdrawing the leading end of the seton through the second incision. Both ends of the seton were then left loose. The seton inserted in the Earl of S 'continued there during his life and apparently with good effect for he never suffered a relapse though he lived for ten or twelve years without observing any strict regime of health and died of quite a different distemper with his faculties as entire as could be expected of any man at that time of life'.

On the Treatment of Dropsy

Dropsy described the accumulation of fluid in the lungs, abdomen and lower legs causing breathlessness, distension of the abdomen and swelling of the ankles.[29] One physician wrote of his way of treating dropsy:

> In the ordinary way I began with purges which diminished the patient's strength but not the water. The common diuretics had little better effect. In short, after repeated trial of several medicines, he received no considerable benefit from any one of them excepting from garlic and Dutch Gin which last was made into a punch. These indeed sensibly promoted expectoration and urine to that degree that he was almost freed from his difficulty in breathing, his cough and watery swelling. His dose of garlic was two cloves morning and evening swallowed whole and a gill of Dutch to a pint (English) of water as all his liquor for the first 24 hours except for a glass of wine when faintish. I have observed that the volatile spirits agreed particularly well with hydropic patients when faint.

In a case of dropsy being managed in consultation with Sir Edward Hales, the prescribed treatment was quite different. The patient had first been given a diuretic:

> He had passed two quarts of urine in the next 48 hours and his legs were reduced almost to their natural size but he complained of lowness of spirits and restlessness more than ever. At this visit we changed the draught to an ounce of quicksilver to be swallowed every day between breakfast and dinner with ten grains of rhubarb at bedtime to be taken every night or as often as was necessary in case of costiveness, that is to prevent too long a stagnation of the quicksilver in his bowels. As we were sensible that most of the water in his legs and belly was emptied and no more was to be expected of diuretics we thought that something had to be done to relieve his breathing and cough from whatever cause it was proceeding. Sir Edward Hales being again consulted, we proposed [to continue] the quicksilver, as having from experience learned its good effect in various types of asthma. As a palliative we directed two teaspoonfuls of the tincture of camphor with forty drops of Elixir Paregoric [camphorated tincture of opium] to be taken once or twice in every four and twenty hours.

On the Treatment of Gout

Pringle explains that the onset of acute gout begins with twinges of pain in the small joints of the hands and feet, restlessness during the night, irritability and dyspepsia. In some cases the throat is sore and there may be attacks of asthma. As the first fit of gout continues the patient is wakened during the night by agonising pain often in the right big toe.

In the eighteenth century it was believed that gout was caused by some form of indigestion. Drug treatment was therefore aimed chiefly at the relief of the abdominal symptoms. Measures for the relief of the acute joint pain are rarely mentioned in Pringle's Medical Annotations but it was customary at that time for the patient to be advised to keep the affected limb at rest and to apply a poultice to the lower leg. A popular poultice was the rye flour poultice devised by Mr Howells, the Purser of HMS *Thunderer*:

> Take one pound of rye flour, four ounces of yeast, two ounces of common salt with half a pint of hot water, mix into a poultice and apply it to the soles of the feet which will first invite the disorder then carry it off by perspiration without breaking the skin. It is renewed every 12 hours.

Pringle described a case of acute gout that he had treated himself:

> Captain Walker, 28 years of age of a gouty family, had never been troubled by gout himself. He had enjoyed good health only subject to indigestion which he ascribed to over fatigue at sport and drinking a large draught of small beer when sweating. I was called to see him on 25 November 1757. That morning he had been taken suddenly ill with a distension of his stomach from wind which by pressing on his diaphragm straightened his breathing. He was either belching or retching as if to vomit. He could not lye [sic] a minute still but constantly tossed about in his bed. Before I came a surgeon had taken away only 6 ounces of blood from the arm but finding that he was not relived by the opening of the vein but grown faint I ordered a blister to his back opposite his stomach and bled him again.

Here, as always, Pringle relied heavily on bleeding. In this case, to relieve the dyspeptic symptoms, he also prescribed *aqua mentha piperita* (peppermint water) and guyacum resin.

Pringle described a case of chronic gout treated by Sir Edward Hales:

Mr Soames, of gouty parents, began to be troubled with gout at the age of 26. He is now above 50. When in Paris he had often been blooded. At times the gout has affected his bowels and lungs. Once he had an obstinate costiveness in which he vomited several doses of physic which could not get through. It was at last relieved by Sir Edward Hales who gave him a large dose of guyacum dissolved in a draught. He commonly had regular fits of gout but as they come frequently and linger longer and sometimes left vague pains he was advised to wear a flannel waistcoat next the skin, day and night, summer and winter and to drink an infusion of garlic prepared in this manner. Take 19 heads of garlic, prick with a pin and put them into a quart of water to be infused for 48 hours. Half a pint of this water is to be drunk morning and evening for ten days. Then discontinued for as long and begin anew. He now has had fewer fits and he observes that he came sooner to the use of his limbs after each fit.

On the Treatment of Fever

For centuries regular physicians had accepted that bleeding the patient was the essential treatment in every case of fever. However, in the eighteenth century a few physicians had become conscious of its risks. An extract of a letter from Dr Robert Whytt of Edinburgh reads:

> Leeches I have used with remarkable success in the beginning of fevers and also before the pulse begins to fall, when the eyes are inflamed, the patient delirious or somewhat comatose. But towards the end of fever when the pulse is less firm and instead of comatose symptoms [indicate] rather too great a mobility of the nervous system as I was afraid to apply blisters so I have thought of laying leeches to the temples but was afraid that if the patient died soon after the friends would have accused the taking away of blood against which they have no small prejudice.

Pringle's Medical Annotations show that the treatments used by the leading physicians of the eighteenth century were usually ineffectual, often unpleasant, and on occasion dangerous. However, in the case of one of his own patients, his curiosity discovered something new.

James Douglas, 14th Earl of Morton, had his first attack of abdominal pain in 1742 when he was 29 years old. The pain was localised to an area 'in the pit of his stomach' that could always 'be covered with a shilling'. The

pain had persisted for over two months. At times he had been free of it for
a few hours; at other times it 'threw him into an agony making him breathe
quick and occasioning an oppression of his spirits'. The trouble had recurred
in 1746 when he had been a prisoner in the Bastille in Paris and again
while he was travelling from Scotland to London in the winter of 1754–5.
In London he had consulted Pringle who 'advised a low diet, eating little
animal food and drinking no wine but perceiving that under this course he
sensibly fell away in spirits'. Pringle found it 'proper to allow white meats
and some glasses of wine'. He tried a number of different medicaments
but with little effect. In the spring of 1756, Morton went to Bath where he
drank the waters for three weeks but there had been no improvement. From
Bath he set out for Scotland and arrived there in perfect health. In 1762, his
symptoms returned but were eased by restricting his diet to 'soup, chicken
and other light meats' and confining himself to two or three glasses of wine
at dinner and by 'taking a vomit of ipecacuanha and 20 grains of rhubarb' at
bedtime. In March 1767, his symptoms again became severe. Pringle advised
him to keep to the same diet and to 'drink spa water with a little Rhenish
wine and, to correct the acidity, to take doses of powdered oyster shell
throughout the day'. On this regime Morton enjoyed some degree of relief
from pain. In January 1769, he returned to Scotland and for some months
he was free of pain. However, when he returned to London in August, the
pain recurred and his health began to decline. On 11 October, his pain
became unusually severe. He began to vomit mouthfuls of coffee-coloured
fluid and next day he died.

An autopsy was performed by the anatomist John Hunter. He found
'close by the pylorus of stomach a round hole about the diameter of a pea
and a quart of fluid in the cavity of the abdomen which seemed to have been
contained in the stomach'.

Morton had suffered a perforation of a peptic ulcer. Peptic ulcers,
and their complications, were not generally recognised until late in the
nineteenth century and a definitive treatment of the disorder was not
introduced until the twentieth century. Pringle had investigated Morton's
disorder as thoroughly as was possible in his time. His account of Morton's
illness occupied five folio pages of his unpublished *Medical Annotations*.
Although his observations failed to reveal any evidence that might have
contributed to an understanding of the nature of the disease or point to any
form of treatment, Pringle had at least found something new.

The case of Mr Chapel's son led to another new understanding. In his
Medical Annotations, Pringle wrote:

Mr Peter of Chapel's son died of a fever at 11 years old. From the time he was a few months old he began to be sickly and his head was observed to grow larger in proportion to his body. The child, however, enjoyed tolerably good health and got through the common diseases of children such as the small pox. He had very slow parts and a weak understanding but he was not an idiot. What he learned was with great difficulty but what he once gained he retained better than other children. His hearing and his other senses were dull. Upon examination of the body I showed that the head was almost double the size that might be expected at that age. The sutures of the skull were however in a natural state but on opening the cranium we found a pint of clear serum in the ventricles, that is in the centre of the brain. For the medullary and cortical substances were no thicker than the palm of my hand. It is scarce to be doubted that the water had begun to be collected when the head was observed to grow large and it gradually increased afterwards with the growth of the body as long as the sutures kept open. There was perhaps always some absorption of the old and in proportion some new serum although it is not to be conceived that the first serum collected could keep so long unputri-fied.

Pringle's description of hydrocephalus was more accurate than that published by his friend Robert Whytt in 1768[30] and matched almost exactly that published in the last years of the nineteenth century by Sir William Osler. In 1892 Osler still acknowledged that 'the cause is unknown'.[31]

However, Pringle had some satisfaction in discovering that the measures that he had introduced for controlling the spread of infection in the army were being used in civilian practice. In a letter to Pringle in January 1758, Dr Simson of St Andrews wrote:

This winter I have seen many children ill of chin-cough [whooping cough] but I have learned nothing specific. I perceive that crowded nurseries were like daily engraftments of the infectious matter of the cough as in most epidemic diseases. This misfortune was inevitable in poor families but well it was for the rich that they were possessed with the notion that a change of air was necessary. Many divided their children among their neighbours. Several, by my advice, had the nursery divided in different parts of the house.

Until he retired from practice, Pringle continued to record in his Medical Annotations details of cases that might possibly lead him to finding something that he could correct by observation, reason and experiment.

FIFTEEN

Triumph and Frustration

Each player should accept the cards life deals him.
                                        Voltaire (1694–1778)

Old age hath yet his honours and his toils.
                            Alfred Lord Tennyson, 'Ulysses', 1842

In 1770, Pringle was 63 years old and living comfortably in London. His years as Physician General to the army had relieved him from the anxieties and humiliations of poverty in his early years. His career had continued to flourish and he had acquired a handsome fortune.[1] At his house in Pall Mall, he had an excellent library; his collection was principally of books on medicine, philosophy and history, but he also had there everything that he required to improve his command of Greek and for his study of the New Testament. He was still collecting paintings and drawings. He still played the violoncello. His gatherings on Sunday evenings were as popular as they had ever been. In the mornings he continued to be at home to anyone of interest who wished to meet him. He could now spend some time at his club where he enjoyed conversations with distinguished and wellinformed friends. The club met in a property owned by Mr Wharton, a grocer.

In 1774, he was made Physician in Ordinary to King George III. He had already been made Physician in Ordinary to the queen. Pringle was admired in Britain and across Europe for his achievements in controlling the spread of disease among the men and maintaining the health of an army. His discoveries had become known when he published his *Observations on the Diseases of the Army* in 1752 and his fame had grown as new editions of the book were published and translated. He had been awarded member-ship of the Academy of Science at Haarlem, the Royal Society of Sciences at Göttingen, the Royal Academy of Sciences at Madrid, the Society of Amsterdam, the Royal Academy of Medical Correspondence in Paris, the

Royal Academy of Sciences at Paris, the Imperial Academy of Sciences in St Petersburg, the Society of Antiquaries in Cassel, the Medical Society of Hanau, and the Royal Academy of Science and Belles Lettres in Naples.

Pringle received large numbers of letters of comment, questions and debate from Britain, the British colonies and from Europe. Unfortunately, he had long made it his practice to destroy every letter that he received; but before doing so he replied carefully and courteously to them all.[2] His extensive correspondence grew still further when he became President of the Royal Society.

Pringle had been elected to the Royal Society in October 1745. Sir Richard Mead, the leading physician in London, and his friend Andrew Mitchell, the Under Secretary of State for Scotland, had signed the certificate recommending him as a Fellow. In 1750, Pringle had published his 'Observations on the Nature and Cure of Hospital and Jayl Fever' in the *Philosophical Transactions of the Royal Society* as a long letter addressed to Sir Richard Mead. It was an account of Pringle's experience during the outbreak of disease that followed the Battle of Culloden and was the first publication of his discovery that hospital fever and jail fever were the same disease. It was also his first publication in making his case for improvement in the standard of hygiene and care in hospitals. In the next two years he published in the *Philosophical Transactions* a series of papers that he had presented to the Royal Society on 'Septic and Antiseptic Substances'; he was awarded the Royal Society's Copley Gold Medal. He had published 'An Account of Several People Seized with the Gaol Fever, Working in Newgate' in the *Gentleman's Magazine* in 1750; it was published again in the *Philosophical Transactions* in 1753. These papers were written at the time when he was also writing the first and then the second editions of his great work, his *Observations on the Diseases of the Army*.

In the next few years he had published, again in the *Philosophical Transactions,* several papers on a range of subjects, not all of them medical: 'Fragility, Flexibility and Dissolution of Bones' in 1753; 'An Account of the Earthquake Felt at Glasgow and Dumbarton' in 1755; 'An Account of the Agitation of the Waters in Scotland and Hamburg' in 1756; 'An Account of the Virtues of Soap in Dissolving the Stone' in 1757; 'An Account of the Case of the Late Honourable Lord Walpole' in 1757; 'Some Remarks upon the "Several Accounts of the Fiery Meteor Which Appeared on Sunday 26th November 1758"' in 1759. He also arranged the publication of a number of papers that had been written by others. They included works on archaeology, geology, mathematics, music, electricity, and the virtues of mineral waters.[3]

Pringle had also played a useful part in the administration of the Royal Society. He had been elected to the Council of the Society in 1753, 1763, 1710 and again in 1772. In November 1772, he was elected President of the Royal Society. This he regarded as the highest honour that he had received and he intended to ensure that his time as its President was a successful period for the Society.

First, he changed the process of awarding the Royal Society's Copley Medal. In 1709 Sir Geoffrey Copley had donated £100 to the Royal Society to help finance the performance of experiments. In 1731, it was agreed that the interest on the sum should be used to provide an annual award of £5 for the best experiment. In 1735, it was decided that, rather than cash, the award should be a medal. Since then a gold medal had been awarded to the winning scientist each year at the Royal Society's Anniversary Meeting, but it had always been presented in a very simple way that took only a few minutes. The Copley Medal was (and still is) the Royal Society's oldest and most prestigious award and Pringle believed that it should be awarded with appropriate ceremony.

In 1772, his first year as President, the awarding of the Copley Medal was more formal and lasted much longer. It began with a well-informed discourse in which Pringle described the career of the scientist who was to receive the award, discussed the subject of the work being honoured and commended what it had achieved. He gave a similar discourse in his second year as President. The Royal Society agreed that he should present a discourse at every future presentation of the Copley Medal and that they should all be published in the *Philosophical Transactions*.

The first of Pringle's lectures was given at the awarding of the Copley Medal to the Reverend Joseph Priestley in November 1772. Priestley was a dissenting clergyman and a chemist who had discovered 'dephlogisticated air' (oxygen). His award was for the experiments he had described in his paper 'Observations on Different Kinds of Air'. In his discourse, Pringle discussed the history of the investigation of the nature and contents of air since the time of Galileo, Torricelli, Otto von Guericke, Boyle and Hooke.

In 1773, the medal was awarded to John Walsh. He had been Secretary to the Governor of Bengal but on his return to Britain in 1759 he had developed an interest in natural history. He received the award for a paper that he had given to the Royal Society on the electrical properties of the torpedo.

The torpedo was a fish common in the Mediterranean; it had long been believed that handling a live torpedo fish was an effective treatment for severe headache (migraine). Walsh's experiments had shown that the operations of the torpedo fish and the operations of an electrical apparatus were so alike that both must be activated by the same fluid. Pringle discussed the history of the study of the torpedo fish since Aristotle, Theophrastus, Athenaeus, Pliny, Plutarch and Galen.

In 1774, the medal was given to Reverend Nevil Maskelyne, His Majesty's Astronomer at Greenwich, for his paper 'Observations Made on the Mountain Schehallien for finding its Attraction'. In his *Principia* Newton had written that the movement of the planets depended on the attraction, the 'gravitation', which they had for each other. Although his theory had been generally accepted, it had not yet been proved. Maskelyne had proved mathematically that attractions did exist between the stars and the earth and between the stars and a mountain. He had shown that when a star on the meridian was observed from two positions, one on the north side of the mountain and the other on the south side, a plumb line was seen to be attracted by the mountain towards the north by the observation of the south side of the mountain and towards the south by observation on the north side. At the presentation of the medal to Maskelyne, Pringle gave a 'Discourse on the Attraction of Mountains' that described the investigation of the movement of the planets from Pythagoras and Cicero to Copernicus, Tycho Brahe and Kepler.

In 1775, the Copley Medal was presented to Captain James Cook for his account 'The Method Taken for Preserving the Health of the Crew of His Majesty's Ship *Resolution*, during Her Late Voyage Round the World'. This was the account that he had already given to Pringle and that had led to their discussion of the prevention and treatment of scurvy. At the presentation of the medal Pringle gave a 'Discourse upon some late improvements of the means for Preserving the Health of Mariners'. In it he discussed at length the much-debated problem of the prevention and treatment of scurvy. He gave particular attention to the dreadful experience of Anson's voyage round the world.

The Copley Medal was not presented again until 1777 when it was awarded to John Mudge, a physician who was also an amateur maker of parts for telescopes. For many years the best reflecting telescope had been the one designed by Sir Isaac Newton. However, it had a glass parabolic speculum which did not allow a truly satisfactory image. Newton had known that the deficiency could be corrected by using a metallic rather than a glass parabolic speculum, but he had been unable to find a way of producing one. By a long and careful process of grinding and polishing, Mudge had succeeded in making one; he was elected a Fellow of the Royal Society. At the presentation of his Copley Medal, Pringle gave a 'Discourse on the Invention and Improvements of the Reflecting Telescope'. He began with references to Galileo and Kepler, but his talk was principally on the work of Gregory and Newton.

At Pringle's last presentation of the Copley Medal in 1778, the award was made to Charles Hutton of the Military Academy at Woolwich for a paper on 'The Force of Fired Gun-Powder and the initial Velocity of Cannon-balls determined by Experiments'. It had been chosen 'to evince how condu-cive those experiments may be to the improvement of an art of public concern as well as to the advancement of Natural Knowledge'. Pringle gave a 'Discourse on the Theory of Gunnery'. It was a learned account of the development of gunnery since the Kings of Judah, 800 years before the birth of Christ.

Pringle's discourses were all published in the *Philosophical Transactions* soon after they had been given at the Royal Society.[4] They had all been prepared with the greatest care and he was pleased that they had been well received. However, the discourse that he gave at the presentation of the Copley Medal to Charles Hutton on 30 November 1778 was his last. There had been difficulties that he had found intolerable in the advice being given by the Royal Society on lightning conductors. It was a subject that the Society had discussed for over 40 years. In 1734, a Fellow of the Society, Dr Cookson, had reported that he had found that lightning had altered the polarity of a compass and that knives struck by lightning had become magnets. His observations were confirmed by other members of the Royal Society. In 1744, Gowin Knight had published the results of his 'Experi-ments on Natural and Artificial Magnets' in *Philosophical Transactions* and had been awarded the Copley Medal. However, more important observa-tions were reported in March 1747 in letters written by Benjamin Franklin in Philadelphia to Peter Collinson in London. Collinson, who had been a very active Fellow of the Royal Society since 1728, was a partner in a family business that had extensive trade with the colonies in America. Since 1730 he had chosen books for the Philadelphia Public Library and it was one of these books which had first stimulated Benjamin Franklin's interest in electricity. Since then they had continued to write to each other. Franklin had reported that his experiments had confirmed the electrical nature of lightning and that he had discovered that lightning could be attracted by pieces of metal. He reported later that, if mounted on the roof of a building, metal points would secure the building against damage from lightning. In 1750, he had introduced two essentials in the design of the lightning conductors. The lightning should be drawn by pointed spindle heads which should be kept in good communication with water by wires running down from the spindle heads to the sea or to some other water source. In 1753, Franklin was awarded the Copley Medal for these discoveries; after his return to Britain in 1755, he was elected a Fellow of the Royal Society.

In 1752, John Canton, a young schoolmaster and Fellow of the Royal Society, had been awarded the Copley Medal for a work confirming Franklin's discoveries. In London, Canton, Collinson and Franklin had continued to work together on lightning. In 1763, three other Fellows of the Royal Society, William Heberden, William Watson and Edward Delaval, had published studies of the damage caused by lightning strikes on a number of buildings. They had concluded that had the lightning conductors been fitted as Franklin had described, the disasters would have been prevented.

In March 1769, the Dean and Chapter of St Paul's Cathedral had asked the Royal Society for advice on the best method of mounting lightning conductors to protect the cathedral's buildings. Franklin, Watson, Canton, Edward Duval and Benjamin Wilson were appointed as an appropriate committee to provide the answer.

Benjamin Wilson was an accomplished portrait painter who had been elected a Fellow of the Royal Society and had been awarded the Copley Medal in 1760 in recognition of his 'Treatise on Electricity' and his more recent experiments on electricity. In 1764, he had published a paper entitled 'Considerations to Prevent Lightning from Doing Mischief to Great Works, High Building and Large Magazines'. In it he had disagreed with Franklin and had advised that the top of the buildings should remain 'without any metal above them, either pointed or not, by way of a conductor. On the inside of the highest part of the buildings, within a foot or two of the top, it may be proper to fix a rounded bar of metal and to continue it down to moisture on the ground.'[5] The report of the Society's committee to the Dean and Chapter of St Paul's had made no reference to this disagreement and had advised that the lightning conductors should be fitted on the cathedral's building as Franklin had described.

However, in 1772, Pringle's first year as President of the Royal Society, the disagreement continued, but now Benjamin Wilson made his views widely known. The Board of Ordnance had asked the Royal Society for guidance on the installing of lightning conductors on the navy's powder magazine at Purfleet. The members of the committee appointed to provide an answer were Benjamin Franklin, William Watson, Henry Cavendish, John Robertson, Edward Delaval and Benjamin Wilson. They reported, as before, that the best method of installing lightning conductors was that advised by Franklin. The report was signed only by Franklin, Watson, Cavendish and Roberson, but appended to the report was a brief statement by Wilson: 'I dissent from the report in that part which recommends that each conductor should terminate in a point. My reason for dissenting is that such conductors are in my opinion less safe than those that are not pointed.' He repeated his objection in a letter addressed to the Surveyor General of the Board of Ordnance on 8 December 1772. At a meeting of the Council of the Royal Society a letter was presented from Franklin, Watson, Cavendish and Robertson in which they stated that they saw no reason to change the advice that they had offered. There were further meetings on the subject at the Royal Society and all the relevant documents were sent to the Admiralty.

When he was elected President of the Royal Society, Pringle had assumed that, like previous presidents, he would continue in office until he died. However, he found it very difficult to manage this long-lasting dispute. On 26 October 1773, he wrote to his friend David Hume in Edinburgh: 'You kindly invite me to return to my native country and mention its superiority in sense and knowledge and inducements.' In the letter he thanked Hume for his kindness in taking charge of restoring and making his house in Edinburgh habitable, a house that 'he had not thought of almost since leaving Edinburgh'. In 1773, Pringle was already beginning to think that he might, at some time, leave his troubles in London and return to Edinburgh.

Benjamin Wilson continued to make his objections and by 1777 he had won the support of the king. In December 1777, the king sent for Pringle to advise him that the Royal Society should withdraw its recommendation of pointed conductors. Pringle stated that he 'could not change the laws of nature'. The king replied: 'Perhaps, Sir John, you had better retire.'[6] The dispute continued. Wilson presented the king with a detailed account of the experiments that had convinced him that pointed lightning conductors were dangerous; he sent copies to the Royal Society and to the Board of Ordnance. The Royal Society appointed a large committee to settle the dispute. Several proposals that support should be given to Wilson's view were all heavily defeated. However, the trouble continued and Pringle began to consider whether he could continue as President of the Royal Society. The meeting of the Society on 8 January 1778 was the first time at which he did not take the chair. He did not attend the meetings on 29 January, 19 March, or 26 March.

Pringle was preparing to resign from presidency of the Royal Society and to withdraw from his life in London. He had settled his religious struggles. Born into a long established Presbyterian family he had attended church regularly and faithfully and he had accepted the teaching of the Church of Scotland. But, after he left home, he had lived in other countries and had met people of other faiths, he had begun to question what he had been taught as a child. After a time, he had taken a sceptical view of the confident dogmas of every one of the divisions of Christianity. However, in July 1767, Pringle and Franklin had travelled to the University of Göttingen where both were to be made honorary members of the Royal Society of Sciences. At Göttingen, Pringle had met the theologian John David Michaelis and they became friends. In a correspondence that lasted for some years, Pringle was able to discuss the unsettled state of his faith. Michaelis persuaded him to improve his knowledge of Greek and to make his own careful study of the Bible. Pringle was grateful to Michaelis for his help; in 1773, he arranged the publication of Michaelis's *Epistolae, de LXX Flebdomadibus Danielis*. Pringle continued to spend much of his time studying the Bible and reading sermons. After some time he became convinced that the doctrine of the Trinity was not to be found in the Scriptures; they asserted the unity of God and Father of Mankind. In 1774, Pringle became a Unitarian. After many years, he was at last confident in his faith.

However, he had another difficult and private problem. He was suffering deep disappointment over the failure of what had been for over 30 years his greatest ambition. While he served as physician to the army he had witnessed the onset and the course of the diseases that killed many more soldiers than were killed in battle. He had seen that the conditions in which the soldiers lived and marched made them liable to become diseased and that it was the conditions in which they were treated when they were ill that caused so many of them to die. As a student of philosophy at St Andrews he had given great attention to the ideas of Francis Bacon. In facing the problems of the diseases of the army he had followed the method advised by Bacon. He had observed the course of the diseases very carefully; he had reached a rational hypothesis that the rapid spread of the diseases could be prevented by introducing methods to avoid the overcrowding of the sick in hospitals, in ships or elsewhere; he had subjected these methods to a trial. The trial had proved that they were effective. He had proved that the great loss of an army's troops from sickness was not inevitable during campaigns as had always been supposed. He had described the observations that he had made, the conclusion that he had reached and the success of the measures he had taken to prevent the outbreak of disease in the army in his *Observations on the Diseases of the Army*. It was this that had made his reputation.

However, he had not been content with this success. He believed that it must be possible to improve the health of the general population as he had improved the health of the army. For 30 years he had tried to find some factor that caused illness in the general population that he could correct rationally. He had filled the pages of ten volumes of his Medical Annotations with notes on illnesses that he had seen or on illness that others had seen. He had kept notes on his correspondence with experts on every form of illness. However, he had found nothing helpful in the stories of those suffering from gout, yellow fever, breathlessness, pregnancy, stroke, scurvy, anaemia, or any other of the multitude of illnesses. He had recognised a new disease in 1743; he had called it influenza, but he could not prevent it. He had described the perforated ulcer that had caused the death of Lord Morton, but it was something that he did not understand. He could know nothing of the causes of these diseases. It would be many years before some understanding of these diseases was revealed by bacteriologists, pathologists, biochemists and other scientists. Pringle had worked hard to achieve his ambition, but he had achieved nothing. By 1778 the last pages of the last volume of his Medical Annotations were deformed by deletions and random scratches that seemed to indicate frustration or even despair.

Pringle was a proud but solitary man. On 30 November 1778, he resigned from the presidency of the Royal Society at its Anniversary Meeting. Sir Joseph Banks was unanimously elected to take his place. A number of the Fellows had made great efforts to persuade him to continue as President but he was firmly determined to go. He did not explain why he wished to leave an office that he had been so proud to hold. The failure of his long but very private ambition to find a new way to improve the practice of medicine played the major part. His public failure to manage the conflict within the Royal Society had been a continuing humiliation. Or it may have been that he was now 71 years old and hoping for peace of mind in his last years. It was probably all three acting together that caused his decision.

For a time he continued in his practice in London. His first patients at the Court of St James had been the Duke of Cumberland and the Dowager

Princess of Wales but both were now dead. However, some patients were still ready to travel to London to consult him; his friend David Hume had come from Edinburgh to consult him during his last illness. He still had many fashionable patients in London society. His Sunday evening gatherings were as popular as ever, but he now had small dinner parties on other evenings at which he always had at least one foreign guest; on one evening the eight men present were one Scotsman, one Englishman, one Welshman and five others from overseas. He frequently spent a couple of hours at his club at Wharton's in the Strand where he would meet and talk to Lord Charles Cavendish, the Bishop of Exeter, William Heberden, Richard Huck and Sir George Baker. However, few of his first London friends were still alive. He could no longer communicate with the friends he had made while he was a student at Leiden. Gerhard van Swieten had become a Fellow of the Royal Society; he had been physician to the Empress of Austria and had reformed the country's university and its teaching of medicine; he had died in 1772. Albrecht von Haller had become a Fellow of the Royal Society and had been Professor of Medicine in the new University of Göttingen; he had also died in 1772.

In 1781, Pringle decided to leave London and return at last to Scotland. He sold his house in Pall Mall, his library and his collection of paintings and travelled north and settled in his house in Edinburgh where he was warmly welcomed by the Royal College of Physicians of Edinburgh. He was made a member of the Society of Antiquaries of Scotland. However, the weather was cold and he could find very few of his old friends; Colin Maclaurin had died in 1746 during the Jacobite Rebellion; Sir Andrew Mitchell had been Ambassador to Prussia for many years and had died there in 1771; David Hume had died in 1776; Sir James Clerk of Penicuik was already ill. After only five months Pringle returned to London. He took an apartment in King Street, St James Square, and quietly resumed his London life. On 14 January 1782, when he was with his friends at Watson's, he had a severe fit. He was looked after by Dr Huck but four days later he died. He was buried in St James's Churchyard, Piccadilly, and his heir, Sir James Pringle, his brother Robert's son, arranged for a memorial to be placed in Westminster Abbey.

The memorial comments graciously on Pringle's integrity and his Christian virtues. It records that he had been Professor of Moral Philosophy at Edinburgh, Physician-General to the British Army and President of the Royal Society. It also records that he had been Physician to both the King and Queen. However it records nothing of what he had achieved in an early stage of the development of modern medicine.

Throughout his career Pringle treated his patients according to the directions set out in the texts of Hippocrates and Galen. The understanding of disease and its treatment had advanced very little since their time. Pringle accepted what he had been taught of the ancient learning because, like all other learned physicians of the eighteenth century, he had no better guide.

However, Pringle had been a professor of philosophy. He had given great importance to the works of Francis Bacon and particularly to Bacon's belief that problems could best be solved by observation, inductive reason and experiment. On becoming physician to the army Pringle observed that the army could be destroyed by disease. How the diseases were spread remained unknown (the theory of germs would not even be discussed until late in the next century). It seemed reasonable to Pringle to suppose that some 'seeds of disease' carried the illness of one soldier to other soldiers and that this transfer could be limited by keeping patients each in his own clean, uncrowded and well ventilated space. In campaigns in which he maintained these conditions in the army's hospitals the spread of disease was limited, the mortality from fevers was dramatically reduced and the army was saved from disaster. This was Pringle's great achievement. In 1752 he published his findings in his Observations on the Diseases of the Army. Editions of the book were still being published in the nineteenth century. His discovery earned him an honoured place in the history of medicine.

However, even before the publication of the first edition of his book, Pringle was eagerly attempting to find some similar way to improve the health of the civilian population. Over the years that followed he filled ten volumes of notes of his search in his Medical Annotations. However he found nothing. Something of what he hoped to find was made possible only in the next century by the advance of the new medical sciences. Pringle would never know of such advances. After some thirty years of frustration he lodged his Medical Annotations in the library of the Royal College of Physicians of Edinburgh in the hope that another Fellow might, at some time, continue his disappointing search with more success.

Notes

Prologue

1 Hoppryngill was spelled in many different ways. It had been pronounced with the emphasis on the second syllable. The first syllable was not used in ordinary speech. In the written form it changed in time to Pringill and then to Pringle. Only the head of family (or chief of the Clan), Hoppryngill of that Ilk, continued to use that form and style until 1737.

2 James Bruce Pringle, direct descendant of Pringle's brother and historian of the Pringle family, personal communication.

3 In 1455, the Pringles (or Hoppryngills) formed, through bonds of man-rent, an allegiance with the Kers of Cessford that lasted for 150 years.

4 The king achieved an uneasy compromise. He formally appointed bishops but they were largely ignored.

5 Harris, T., *Restoration: Charles II and his Kingdoms* (London, 2005), p. 105.

6 Statement made to the Scottish Privy Council. Ibid., p. 113.

7 James Bruce Pringle, personal communication.

Chapter 1 Early Years

1 There were six children: 1. Robert who inherited Stichill; 2. Gilbert who married Margaret, the heiress to Hoppryngill of that Ilk; 3. Walter who became an advocate and Sheriff-Depute of Roxburghshire; 4. John; 5. Margaret who married Sir James Hall of Dunglass; 6. Katherine who married William Hamilton of Bangour.

2 Prebble, J., *The Darien Disaster* (London, 1968), p. 197.

3 The War of the Spanish Succession.

4 Devine, T., *The Scottish Nation* (London, 1999), p. 10.

5 Clerk of Penicuik, quoted by Fry, M., *The Union* (Edinburgh, 2006), p. 252.

6 James Bruce Pringle, personal communication.

7 Lockhart, G., *Memoirs Concerning the Affairs in Scotland* (London, 1714), p. 95.

8 Roxburghe was one of the pallbearers at Sir Isaac Newton's funeral.

9 Grant, R., *The University of St Andrews* (Edinburgh, 1970), p. 83.

10 From the beginning the studies of students at St Leonard's had been supervised by regents, each regent taking charge of one year's intake of students and following the same students through the full years of their course of study. In 1702, the University of St Andrews appointed Pringle as a 'fixed' professor to teach Greek to the students of all three of the university's colleges.

11 Dingwall, H., *A Famous and Flourishing Society: The History of the Royal College of*

Surgeons of Edinburgh (Edinburgh 2005), p. 68.

12 The apothecaries were supervised by the Royal College of Physicians of Edinburgh.

13 The University of Edinburgh was at that time still known as the Town's College.

14 Pitman, J., 'The Journal of James Boswell: Part I', *Proceedings of the Royal College of Physicians of Edinburgh*, 1990, vol. 19, pp. 67–77.

15 James Boswell claimed that Pringle first went to Amsterdam to prepare for a commercial career. His claim was reported by Andrew Kippis (Kippis, A., *Six Discourses by Sir John Pringle* (London, 1783), p. iv) and since then it has been quoted by others. But, given all the circumstances, Boswell's claim seems improbable and is incompatible with what is known of Pringle's time in the Netherlands.

16 Jacobites was the name given to those who favoured the restoration of the Stuarts to the throne.

17 Landes, D. S., *The Wealth and Poverty of Nations* (New York, 1999), p.138.

18 Van Strien, K. and de Wittlaan, W. A., 'Medical Student at Leiden and Paris: William Sinclair', *Proceedings of the Royal College of Physicians of Edinburgh*, 1995, vol. 25, p. 294–306.

19 Innes Smith, R. W., *English Speaking Students of Medicine at the University of Leiden* (Edinburgh, 1931), p. ix.

20 Van Strien and Wittlaan, 'Medical Student at Leiden and Paris', p. 301.

21 Ibid., p. 306.

22 His graduation thesis was entitled '*De Marcore Senili*' *(On the Decay of Old Age)*.

23 Van Swieten, G., *Boerhaave's Aphorisms Concerning the Knowledge and Cure of Diseases* (London, 1724).

24 Van Swieten, G., *Commentaries upon Boerhaave's Aphorisms Concerning the Knowledge and Cure of Diseases* (Edinburgh, 1776).

Chapter 2 The Theory of Medicine: Boerhaave and Pringle

1 Hippocrates was a legendary figure. His works were written by a number of authors.

2 Porter, R., *The Greatest Benefit to Mankind* (London, 1999), p. 60.

3 Ibid., p. 65.

4 Ibid., p. 77.

5 Principe, L., *The Scientific Revolution* (Oxford, 2011), p. 6.

6 Williams, R., *The Lords of the Isles* (London, 1997), p. 216; National Library of Scotland, Gaelic Medical Manuscript ADV MS IV.

7 Ziegler, P.,*The Black Death* (London, 1997), p. 172.

8 Bacon, F., *The Advancement of Learning*, quoted by Porter, *The Greatest Benefit to Mankind*, p. 244.

9 Gribbin, J., *The Fellowship: The Story of a Revolution* (London, 2005), p. 95.

10 Porter, *The Greatest Benefit to Mankind*, p. 181.

11 Galileo, G., *Discoveries and Opinions* (New York, 1957), p. 27. Translated by Stillman Drake.

12 Gleick, J., *Isaac Newton* (London, 2003), p. 51.

13 That is by continuous change like the acceleration of an aircraft on taking off rather than by incremental change such as adding individual books to a library at regular intervals. Watson P., *Ideas: A History* vol. II (London, 2005), p. 79.

14 The word gravity had long been in use meaning weight or influence. Newton was the first to use it in the sense of the force drawing heavy bodies together.

196 Saving the Army

15 The Newtonian Style: In devising his System of the World, Newton first observed and calculated, the position and movement of one planet. He then added to his system the observations of a second planet and then a third and so on until his series was complete. From these many meticulous observations and ingenious calculations he constructed an experimental model representing the movements and changing relationships of one planet to another. This initial model was no more than a well-informed guess. But it was then compared repeatedly with the movements of the planets as they were seen in further observations. Following each of these comparisons the model was adjusted to conform as far as possible to what had been observed. These comparisons and adjustments were repeated until the model achieved an acceptable fit with what could be observed.

16 Grabiner, J., 'Newton, Maclaurin and the Authority of Mathematics', in I. B. Cohen and R. S. Westfall (eds) *Newton: Texts, Backgrounds, Commentaries* (New York, 1995), pp. 846–7.

17 Ibid., p. 843.

18 Gregory had constructed a practical reflecting microscope; Newton later used Gregory's design in constructing his own microscope.

19 Guerrini, A., 'Archibald Pitcairn and Newtonian Medicine', *Medical History,* 1987, vol. 31, p. 77.

20 Lindeboom, G., *Boerhaave* (Methuen, 1968), p. 66.

Chapter 3 Physic, Patronage and Philosophy

1 The Reverend Alexander Webster's *Analysis of Population*, was published in 1755.

2 Devine, T. M., *The Scottish Nation 1700–2000* (London, 1999), p. 49.

3 Ibid., p. 196.

4 Shaw, J. S., *The Management of Scottish Society 1707–1764* (Edinburgh, 1983), p. 86.

5 Devine, *The Scottish Nation, p. 22.*

6 He went on to serve no fewer than four terms of office.

7 The Philosophical Society of Edinburgh later became the Royal Society of Edinburgh.

8 *Medicina Curiosa* was published at The George in Fleet Street in London in 1684. However, only two numbers were produced, the first on 17 June and the second (and final) on 23 October.

9 *Medical Essays and Observations*, 1737, vol. 1, p. 17.

10 *Pharmacopoeia Collegii Regii Medicorum Edinburgensis*, 1756.

11 Minutes of the Royal College of Physicians of Edinburgh.

12 Ibid.

13 *Edinburgh Medical and Surgical Journal* 1805, vol. 1, pp. 486–7.

14 *Edinburgh Review*, 1803–4, vol. 3, p. 458.

15 *The British Pharmacopoeia* was published by the General Medical Council as ordered in the Medical Act of 1858.

16 In 1682 Fellows were fined 12 shillings Scots for each failure to attend a meeting of the College.

17 Ritchie, A., *The Early Years of the Royal College of Physicians of Edinburgh* (Edinburgh, 1899), p. 87.

18 Emerson, R. L., *Academic Patronage in the Scottish Enlightenment* (Edinburgh, 2008), p. 336.

19 At that time there were very few 'fixed' professors appointed to teach only one subject. Each newly enrolled class of students was taught all the subjects on the syllabus for that year by a regent. The same regent would then guide the same class through the remaining

years of their course.

20 Emerson, *Academic Patronage*, p. 383.

21 Ibid., p. 340.

22 Ibid., p. 5.

23 Grant, Sir A., *The Story of the University of Edinburgh*, vol. II (London, 1884), p. 337.

24 Grant, Sir A., *The Story of the University of Edinburgh*, vol. I (London, 1884), p. 237.

25 'Jupiter' Carlyle in his autobiography, edited by Hill Burton and published in 1860, 55 years after his death.

26 Von Pufendorf, S., *The Whole Duty of Man According to the Law of Nature* (1637).

27 Grant, *The Story of the University of Edinburgh*, I, p. 237; Passmore, R., *Fellows of Edinburgh's Royal College of Physicians during the Scottish Enlightenment* (Edinburgh, 2001), p. 20.

Chapter 4 A Commission in the Army

1 Browning, R., *The War of the Austrian Succession* (New York, 1995), p. 375.

2 Whatley, C. A., *Scottish Society 1707–1830* (Manchester, 2000), p. 54.

3 Broadie, A., *The Scottish Enlightenment* (Edinburgh, 2001), p. 7.

4 An estimate based on the figures listed in Emerson, R. L., *Academic Patronage in the Scottish Enlightenment* (Edinburgh, 2008), p. 615.

5 James Bruce Pringle, personal communication, 2012.

6 His own phrase in his letters to Andrew Mitchell.

7 Discussed in Chapter 5.

8 Hamilton, D., 'Sir John Pringle', *Journal of the Royal Army Medical Corps*, 1964, vol. 110, p. 139.

9 In 1742, the Physician-General was Dr Charles Peters; the Surgeon-General was Mr John Pawlett.

10 James Bruce Pringle, personal communication.

11 At the age of nine, John Dalrymple unfortunately killed his older brother by accidentally discharging a loaded pistol. John Dalrymple, later the first Lord Stair, had always intended that his eldest son should follow him in making a career in the law. Having taken his brother's place, the young John Dalrymple was enrolled to study law at Leiden University. After two years at Leiden he was sent home to Edinburgh to complete his legal training in Scotland but by then, perhaps inspired by William of Orange's heroic struggle to defend the Dutch Republic's independence against the territorial ambitions of Louis XIV of France, he had become determined to become a soldier.

12 He was made the Earl of Stair in 1703.

13 Churchill, W. S., *Marlborough: His Life and Times* (London, 1947), pp. 381, 760–1.

14 Letter, Pringle to Andrew Mitchell, 27 April 1742.

15 Letter, Pringle to Andrew Mitchell, 18 September 1742.

16 Beale, N. and Beale, E., *Echoes of Ingen Housz* (Salisbury, 2011), p. 20.

17 Pringle, J., *John Pringle's Correspondence with Albrecht van Haller* (Basel, 1999).

18 Letters, Pringle to Andrew Mitchell, 24 September and 6 October 1742.

19 Gabriel, R. and Metz, K., *A History of Military Medicine* (New York, 1992), p. 122.

20 Ibid., p. 123.

21 Keegan, L. and Durracot, J., *The Nature of War* (Austin, 1981), p. 206; Howard, H. A. L, 'Army Surgeons and the Care of the Sick and Wounded in the British Campaigns during the Tudor and Stuart Periods', *Journal of the Royal Army Medical Corps*, 1904, vol. 2, p. 733; Atkinson, C. T., 'Gleanings from the Cathcart MSS', *Journal of the Society for Army*

Historical Research, 1952, vol. 30, p. 97.

22 Porter, R., *English Society in the Eighteenth Century* (London, 1999), p. 12.

23 Pringle, J., *Observations on the Diseases of the Army*, 7th edition (London, 1775), p. 15.

Chapter 5 Dettingen: Victory and Catastrophe

 1 Smith, G. B., *Illustrated British Ballads Old and New* (London, 1881), p. 5.

 2 Browning, R., *The War of the Austrian Succession* (New York, 1995), p. 18.

 3 Aix-la-Chapelle is used in English to refer to Aachen, the westernmost city in Germany, located along its border with Belgium and the Netherlands.

 4 Letter, Pringle to Andrew Mitchell, 2 February 1743.

 5 Ibid.

 6 His observations were later to form the substance of his most famous work, *Observations on the Diseases of the Army.*

 7 Letter, Pringle to Andrew Mitchell, 21 April 1743.

 8 In some campaigns in the eighteenth century death by disease made up between 80 per cent and 90 per cent of the total deaths. Gabriel, R. and Metz, K. *A., History of Military Medicine* (New York,1992), p. 107.

 9 Browning, *The War of the Austrian Succession*, p. 6.

10 David. S., *All The King's Men* (London, 2012), pp. 107–8.

11 Pringle, J., *Observations on the Diseases of the Army*, 7th edition (London, 1775), p. 17.

12 A Flying Hospital was a mobile hospital of up to 200 beds opened close to Regimental Infirmaries that were overburdened with sick and likely to be soon moved on. The staff and equipment were provided by the General Hospital. The policy was to keep cases until the General Hospital had moved to a sizeable town in the vicinity. The objective was to prevent the many deaths suffered when very sick patients were carried long distances back to the General Hospital at the army's base.

13 Cantlie, N., *A History of the Army Medical Department*, vol. I (Edinburgh, 1973), p. 84.

14 Ibid., p. 85.

15 Ibid., p. 85.

16 Pringle's comments on the battle and its aftermath were made in letters to Andrew Mitchell.

17 Langford, P., *The New Oxford History of England*, vol. II: *A Polite and Commercial People* (Oxford, 1998), p. 192.

18 Coxe, W., *Memoirs of the Administration of Henry Pelham*, vol. II (London, 2012), p. 470.

19 Boswell, J., *A Journey to the Western Isles of Scotland and the Journal of a Tour of the Hebrides* (London, 1984), p. 393.

20 Cantlie, *A History of the Army Medical Department*, vol. I, p. 85.

Chapter 6 Fontenoy: Defeat and Triumph

 1 War of the League of Augsburg.

 2 Callow, J., *King in Exile: James II: Warrior, King and Saint* (London, 2004), p. 292.

 3 France had been opposed by Great Britain, the Dutch Republic, Savoy and Portugal.

 4 Wilkinson, S., *The Defence of Piedmont* (Oxford, 1958), p. 100.

 5 Douglas, H., *Jacobite Spy Wars* (Stroud, 1999), p. 52.

 6 The name is used here for convenience. The anti-Bourbon alliance had been reformed by the Treaty of Worms in September 1743 and its objective was to contain the power of

France rather than to uphold the Pragmatic Sanction.

7 Howell, H., 'The Story of the Army Surgeon and the Care of the Sick and Wounded in the British Army', *Journal of the Royal Army Medical Corps*, 1914, vol. 22, p. 456.

8 Ibid., p. 108.

9 Pringle, J., *Observations on the Diseases of the Army*, 7th edition (London, 1775), p. 33.

10 Browning, R., *The War of the Austrian Succession* (New York, 1995), p. 181.

11 *Scots Magazine*, July 1745.

12 Cantlie, N., *A History of the Army Medical Department*, vol. I (Edinburgh, 1973), p. 89.

13 Pringle, *Observations*, 7th edition, p. 38.

14 Cantlie, *A History of the Army Medical Department*, I, pp. 81–98.

Chapter 7   Rebellion: A Very Different Campaign

1 Duncan Forbes was also Lord President of the Court of Session, the senior law officer in Scotland.

2 James II's son who hoped to return to his father's throne was commonly referred to as the 'Pretender'. His son Prince Charles Edward Stuart was the 'Young Pretender'.

3 *The Culloden Papers*, New York Public Library.

4 Douglas, H., *Jacobite Spy Wars* (Stroud, 1999), p. 123.

5 Devine, T. M., *The Scottish Nation* (London, 1999), p. 42.

6 Reid, S., *Culloden 1746* (Barnsley, 2005), p. 16.

7 David, S., *All the King's Men* (London, 2012), p. 115.

8 Sir John Cope was later court martialled at Berwick but was exonerated. It was decided that under the circumstances his decision was fully justified.

9 Duffy, C., *The '45* (London, 2003), p. 213.

10 Pringle, J., *Observations on the Diseases of the Army*, 7th edition (London, 1755), p. 39.

11 Ibid.

12 Pringle, *Observations*, 7th edition, p. 40.

13 Duffy, *The '45*, p. 300; Douglas, H., *Jacobite Spy Wars*, p. 92.

14 Browning, R., *The War of the Austrian Succession* (New York, 1995), p. 244.

15 Duffy, *The '45*, p. 126. Hawley was widely believed to be the illegitimate son of George ll. General James Wolfe said of him that his 'own troops dread his severity, hate the man and hold his military knowledge in contempt'.

16 Tomasson, K. and Buist, F., *Battles of the '45* (New York, 1962), p. 105.

17 Duffy, *The '45*, p. 410.

18 Browning, *War of the Austrian Succession*, p. 264.

19 Pringle, *Observations*, 7th edition, p. 41

20 Browning, R., *War of the Austrian Succession*, p. 265.

21 Ibid.

22 Pringle, *Observations*, 7th edition, p. 44.

23 *Account of Lady Robertson*, quoted by Duffy, *The '45*, p. 524.

24 At this time pus formed in wounds was often called 'laudable pus'.

25 Pringle, *Observations*, 7th edition, p. 45.

26 Ibid., p. 52.

Chapter 8   Fever in Flanders: the End of the War

1 Browning, R., *The War of the Austrian Succession* (New York, 1995), p. 285.

2 Pringle, J., *Observations on the Diseases of the Army*, 7th edition (London, 1775), p. 53.
3 Browning, *War of the Austrian Succession*, p. 286.
4 Ibid., p. 303.
5 Ibid., p. 304.
6 David, S., *All the King's Men* (London, 2012), p. 129.
7 Pringle, *Observations, 7th edition*, pp. 52–9.
8 Ibid., p. 55.
9 The troops were encamped at Bergen op Zoom and nearby on the Island of Walcheren.
10 The governing body of the Province of Holland, one of the seven provinces of the Dutch Republic.
11 Browning, *War of the Austrian Succession*, p. 358.
12 Cantlie, N., *A History of the Army Medical Department*, vol. I (London, 1973), p. 92.
13 Ibid., p. 95.
14 The identity of Miss N. is unknown even to the Pringle family.

Chapter 9   Observations on the Diseases of the Army

1 Bank of England Inflation Calculator.
2 Letter from Ghent to Andrew Mitchell, 3 December 1743.
3 Langford, P., *The New Oxford History of England*, vol. II: *A Polite and Commercial People* (Oxford, 1998), p. 71.
4 Darnton, R., 'The Unity of Europe: Culture and Politeness', in Darnton, R., *George Washington's False Teeth: An Unconventional Guide to the Eighteenth Century* (New York, 2003), p. 86.
5 All the houses on the south side of Pall Mall belonged to the Crown.
6 He had given his name to the Bath Oliver biscuit.
7 Hamilton, D.,' Sir John Pringle', *Journal of the Royal Army Medical Corps*, 1964, vol. 110, p. 142.
8 Ibid.

Chapter 10   On Treating the Diseases of Armies

1 Vickers, B. (ed.), *Francis Bacon: Major Works* (Oxford, 2008), p. 213.
2 Boerhaave had used a thermometer designed by Gabriel Fahrenheit in 1724, but thermometers did not come into more general use until the late nineteenth century.
3 The tubercles in the lungs in cases of *phthisis pulmonale* were first described by Sylvius (Franz de le Boe) in 1679.
4 Setons were soft cotton tapes inserted under the skin at the site of the pain. They were usually inserted to allow accumulating pus to escape. They were described by Hippocrates.
5 Pringle, J., *Observations on the Diseases of the Army*, 7th edition (London, 1775), pp. 226, 254.
6 Ibid., p. 252.
7 Vickers (ed.), *Francis Bacon*, p. 147
8 Cantlie, N., *A History of the Army Medical Department*, vol. I (Edinburgh, 1974), p. 502.

Chapter 11   Studies on Putrefaction and Digestio

1 As he commented, this was 'not to be wondered at considering how offensive such operations are'. Pringle, J., 'Some Experiments on Substances Resisting Putrefaction', *Philosoph-*

ical Transactions, 1752, vol. 46, p. 480.

2 Giovanni Morgagni (1682–1771), Professor of Anatomy at Padua, is recognised as the first of the great morbid anatomists.

3 It was only in 1864 that Pasteur was able to show the part played by bacteria in fermentation and putrefaction.

4 Pringle, 'Some Experiments on Substances Resisting Putrefaction', p. 483.

5 Ibid., p. 482.

6 Ibid., p. 527

7 Ibid., p. 529.

8 Ibid., p. 527.

9 Ibid., p. 529.

10 Ibid., p. 530.

11 Ibid., p. 485.

12 Ibid., pp. 480–8, 525–34, 550–8.

13 Bacon, F., *Major Works* (ed. B. Vickers) (Oxford, 2002), p. 151.

14 Pringle, J., *Observations on the Diseases of the Army*, 7th edition (London, 1775), p. xxxii.

15 Bacon, *Major Works*, p. 154.

16 Pringle, *Observations*, 7th edition, p. li.

17 Ibid., p. xliv.

18 Ibid., p. xlvii.

Chapter 12 The Raids on Rochefort and St Malo

1 In her will she left £1,000 (£180,700 at today's values) to her father and £500 to each of her two sisters.

2 In 1761, Pringle moved from the south side to a new house in the north side of Pall Mall.

3 Fraser, D., *Frederick the Great* (London, 2000), p. 287.

4 Ibid., p. 92.

5 First Treaty of Versailles, 1 May 1756; Second Treaty of Versailles, 1 May 1757.

6 This alliance of Hapsburg and Bourbon was denounced as 'unnatural' by King George II in his Speech from the Throne in Parliament in 1756.

7 Fraser, *Frederick the Great*, p. 361.

8 Pringle, J., Medical Annotations, vol. III (unpublished, Library of the Royal College of Physicians of Edinburgh), pp. 35–43.

9 Ibid., pp. 41–2, 180–1.

10 An edition edited by Benjamin Rush was published in Philadelphia in 1810.

Chapter 13 The Health of the Army in North America, the Caribbean and Britain

1 Darwin, J., *Unfinished Empire* (London, 2012), p. 68.

2 Cantlie, N., A *History of the Army Medical Department*, vol. I (Edinburgh, 1974), p. 112.

3 Speech from the Throne, 1 December 1756.

4 Churchill, W. S., *A History of the English Speaking People*, vol. III (London, 1957), p. 123.

5 Large numbers of the provincial troops had deserted or had become sick.

6 La Roche, R., *Yellow Fever* (Philadelphia, 1855).

7 Richard Brocklesby , FRS FRCP (1722–1792). Retired as Physician-General to the Ordinance in 1790.

8 Donald Monro, FRS FRSE, FRCP (1728–1802). A son of Alexander Monro primus,

the first of the dynasty of three Alexander Monros who held the Chair of Anatomy at Edinburgh University from 1722 until 1846. He retired from being Physician-General to the Army in Germany in 1763.

9 Brocklesby, R., *Oeconomical and Medical Observations* (London, 1764).

10 Monro, D., *Observations on the Means of Preserving the Health of Soldiers* (London, 1780).

11 Cantlie, *A History of the Army Medical Department*, I, p. 106.

Chapter 14 Life in London

1 Pringle, J., *Six Discourses as President of the Royal Society* (London, 1783), pp. 2–41.

2 Isaacson, W., *Benjamin Franklin: An American Life* (London, 2008), p. 169.

3 Both had been disappointed when Hume was not appointed to the Chair of Philosophy when Pringle resigned from it in 1749.

4 Lenman, B., 'From the Union of 1707 to the Franchise Reform of 1832', in Houston R. A. and Knox, W. W. J. (eds), *The New Penguin History of Scotland* (London, 2001), pp. 276–354.

5 Pringle's enemy Dr Samuel Johnson denounced Macpherson as 'a liar and a fraud' and the poems as forgeries.

6 Letter, Pringle to David Hume, 9 May 1765. Hume Papers, Library of the Royal Society of Edinburgh.

7 Van Doren, C., *Benjamin Franklin*, vol. I (New York, 2002), p. 271.

8 Morgan, E., *Benjamin Franklin* (Yale, 2002), p. 124.

9 Ibid., p. 182.

10 Ibid., p. 126. Bute became Prime Minister and was later to play his part in determining the future American colonies.

11 Ibid., p. 280.

12 Van Doren, *Benjamin Franklin*, p. 281.

13 Isaacson, *Benjamin Franklin*, p. 184.

14 Morgan, *Benjamin Franklin*, p. 152.

15 Van Doren, *Benjamin Franklin*, p. 356.

16 Isaacson, *Benjamin Franklin*, p. 215.

17 Spencer, M., *David Hume and Eighteenth Century America* (Rochester, New York, 2005), p. 54.

18 Ibid., p 17.

19 Letter, Pringle to Hume, 26 January 1774, Hume Papers, Library of the Royal Society of Edinburgh.

20 Isaacson, *Benjamin Franklin*, p. 259.

21 Langford, P., *The New Oxford History of England*, vol. II: *A Polite and Commercial People* (Oxford, 1998).

22 Ibid., p. 68.

23 Porter, R., *Health for Sale* (London, 1989).

24 Ibid., pp. 8–9.

25 Ibid. pp. 6–7.

26 They met during Graham's visit to North America.

27 Quoted by Porter, *Health for Sale*, p. 158

28 Ibid., p. 166.

29 It is now known that the most common cause was poor circulation of the blood due to incipient heart failure.

30 Whytt, R., *Observations on the Dropsy in the Brain* (Edinburgh, 1768), pp. 3–4.

31 Osler, W., *The Principles and Practice of Medicine* (New York, 1892), p. 922.

Chapter 15   Triumph and Frustration

1 Singer, D., 'Sir John Pringle and His Circle', *Annals of Science*, 1949–50, p, 180.
2 Sir Alexander Dick, a President of the Royal College of Physicians of Edinburgh, carefully preserved 47 letters that he had received from Pringle.
3 Singer, 'Sir John Pringle and His Circle', pp. 127–80, 229–324.
4 They were later published in book form by his friend Andrew Kippis. Kippis, A., *Six Discourses Delivered by Sir John Pringle, Bart.* (London, 1778).
5 Singer, 'Sir John Pringle and His Circle', p. 168.
6 Ibid., p. 173.

Bibliography

Books

Bacon, F., *The Advancement of Learning* (1605).

Beale, N. and Beale, E., *Echoes of Ingen Housz* (Salisbury, 2011).

Boswell, J., *A Journey to the Western Isles of Scotland and the Journal of a Tour of the Hebrides* (London, 1984).

Broadie, A., *The Scottish Enlightenment* (Edinburgh, 2001).

Brocklesby, R., *Oeconomical and Medical Observations* (London, 1764).

Browning, R., *The War of the Austrian Succession* (New York, 1995).

Callow, J., *King in Exile: James II: Warrior, King and Saint* (London, 2004).

Cantlie, N., *A History of the Army Medical Department*, vol. I (Edinburgh, 1973).

Churchill, W. S., *Marlborough: His Life and Times* (London, 1947).

Churchill, W. S., *A History of the English Speaking People*, vol. III (London, 1957).

Coxe, W., *Memoirs of the Administration of Henry Pelham*, vol. II (London, 2012).

Darnton, R., *George Washington's False Teeth* (New York, 2003), p. 86.

Darwin, J., *Unfinished Empire* (London, 2012).

David. S., *All The King's Men* (London, 2012).

Devine, T. M., *The Scottish Nation 1700–2000* (London, 1999).

Dingwall, H., *A Famous and Flourishing Society: The History of the Royal College of Surgeons of Edinburgh* (Edinburgh 2005).

Douglas, H., *Jacobite Spy Wars* (Stroud, 1999).

Duffy, C., *The '45* (London, 2003).

Emerson, R. L., *Academic Patronage in the Scottish Enlightenment* (Edinburgh, 2008).

Fraser, D., *Frederick the Great* (London, 2000).

Fry, M., *The Union* (Edinburgh, 2006).

Gabriel , R. and Metz, K. *A History of Military Medicine* (New York, 1992).

Galileo, G., *Discoveries and Opinions*, trans. Stillman Drake (New York, 1957).

Gleick, J., *Isaac Newton* (London, 2003).

Grabiner, J., 'Newton, Maclaurin and the Authority of Mathematics', in Cohen, I. B. and Westfall, R. S. (eds) *Newton: Texts, Backgrounds, Commentaries* (New York, 1995), pp. 841–852.

Grant, R., *The University of St Andrews* (Edinburgh, 1970).

Grant, Sir A., *The Story of the University of Edinburgh*, 2 vols (London, 1884).

Gribbin, J., *The Fellowship: The Story of a Revolution* (London, 2005).

Harris, T., *Restoration: Charles II and his Kingdoms* (London, 2005).

Innes Smith, R. W., *English Speaking Students of Medicine at the University of Leiden* (Edinburgh, 1931).

Isaacson, W., *Benjamin Franklin: An American Life* (London, 2008).

Keegan, L. and Durracot, J., *The Nature of War* (Austin, 1981).

Kippis, A., 'Preface', in Pringle, J., *Six Discourses delivered by Sir John Pringle when President of the Royal Society; on Occasion of Six Annual Assignments of Sir Godfrey Copley's Medal* (London, 1783).

La Roche, R., *Yellow Fever* (Philadelphia, 1855).

Landes, D. S., *The Wealth and Poverty of Nations* (New York, 1999).

Langford, P., *The New Oxford History of England*, vol. II: *A Polite and Commercial People* (Oxford, 1998).

Lenman, B., 'From the Union of 1707 to the Franchise Reform of 1832', in Houston R. A. and Knox, W. W. J. (eds), *The Penguin New History of Scotland: From the Earliest Times to the Present Day* (London, 2001), pp. 276–354.

Lindeboom, G., *Boerhaave* (Methuen, 1968).

Lockhart, G., *Memoirs Concerning the Affairs in Scotland* (London, 1714).

Monro, D., *Observations on the Means of Preserving the Health of Soldiers* (London, 1780).

Morgan, E., *Benjamin Franklin* (Yale, 2002).

Osler, W., *The Principles and Practice of Medicine* (New York, 1892).

Passmore, R., *Fellows of Edinburgh's Royal College of Physicians during the Scottish Enlightenment* (Edinburgh, 2001).

Porter, R., *Health for Sale* (London, 1989).

Porter, R., *English Society in the Eighteenth Century* (London, 1999).

Porter, R., *The Greatest Benefit to Mankind* (London, 1999).

Prebble, J., *The Darien Disaster* (London, 1968).

Principe, L., *The Scientific Revolution* (Oxford, 2011).

Pringle, J., *Observations of the Diseases of the Army*, 7th edition (London, 1775).

Pringle, J., *Six Discourses as President of the Royal Society* (London, 1783).

Pringle, J., Medical Annotations, vol. III (unpublished, Library of the Royal College of Physicians of Edinburgh).

Pringle, J., *John Pringle's Correspondence with Albrecht van Haller* (Basel, 1999).

Reid, S., *Culloden 1746* (Barnsley, 2005).

Ritchie, A., *The Early Years of the Royal College of Physicians of Edinburgh* (Edinburgh, 1899).

Shaw, J. S., *The Management of Scottish Society 1707–1764* (Edinburgh, 1983).

Smith, G. B., *Illustrated British Ballads Old and New* (London, 1881).

Spencer, M., *David Hume and Eighteenth Century America* (Rochester, New York, 2005).

The Culloden Papers, New York Public Library.

Tomasson, K. and Buist, F., *Battles of the '45* (New York, 1962).

Van Doren, C., *Benjamin Franklin*, vol. I (New York, 2002).

Van Swieten, G., *Boerhaave's Aphorisms Concerning the Knowledge and Cure of Diseases* (London, 1724).

Van Swieten, G., *Commentaries upon Boerhaave's Aphorisms Concerning the Knowledge and Cure of Diseases* (Edinburgh, 1776).

Vickers, B. (ed.) *Francis Bacon: Major Works* (Oxford, 2008).

Von Pufendorf, S., *The Whole Duty of Man According to the Law of Nature* (1637).

Watson P., *Ideas: A History*, vol. II (London, 2005).

Whatley, C. A., *Scottish Society 1707–1830* (Manchester, 2000).

Whytt, R., *Observations on the Dropsy in the Brain* (Edinburgh, 1768).
Wilkinson, S., *The Defence of Piedmont* (Oxford, 1958).
Williams, R., *The Lords of the Isles* (London, 1997).
Ziegler, P., *The Black Death* (London, 1997).

Journals

Annals of Science, 1949.
Edinburgh Medical and Surgical Journal, 1850.
Edinburgh Review, 1803–4.
Journal of the Royal Army Medical Corps, 1904, 1914 and 1964.
Journal of the Society for Army Historical Research, 1952.
Medical Essays and Observations, 1737.
Medical History, 1987.
Philosophical Transactions of the Royal Society, 1745–1778.
Proceedings of the Royal College of Physicians of Edinburgh, 1900 and 1995.
Scots Magazine, July 1745.

Index

Notes: British monarchs are listed simply by their name and regnal number e.g. 'Charles II, King'. Monarchs of other nations have the country appended e.g. 'Charles II, King of Spain'. References to the endnotes have 'n' after the page number, e.g. '203n'.

Abercrombie, General James 153
Adair, John 55
Adair, Robert 55
ageratina (snake-root) 128
ague 33
Aikman, William 44
Aix-la-Chapelle (Aachen) 61, 63, 198n
Aix-la-Chapelle, Treaty of 108, 111, 142, 143
Albany, New York 152–156
Albinus, Professor Bernhard 18
Alexander III, King 1
Alsace 77, 78, 81
Alston, Charles 15
Alva, Duke of 17
American Declaration of
        Independence 169
Amherst, Major General 153–155
Angers, University of 14, 17
angina 125
Anjou, Duke of 8
Anne, Queen 9, 10
Anson, Admiral 159, 160
Antigua 160
antimony, use of 171
antiseptics 134–137, 184
    first use of term 134
Antwerp 84, 85
apoplexy 176
Argatherian Party 48
Argyll, Duke of 47
Argyll, Marquess of 5, 49
Aristotle 20, 21, 23, 25, 28, 29, 38, 43, 122
Army Medical Board 85, 131
Army of Observation 144, 145

arthritis 125
Aschaffenburg 63, 65–67, 70, 71
Auchinleck, Lord 72
Austria, Archduke of 8
Austria, Empress of see Maria Theresa
Austrian Succession, War of 46, 142
Avicenna 22

Bacon, Sir Francis 12, 23, 29, 43, 131, 132,
        137–139, 169, 174
Baker, Sir George 192
Ballonius (Guillaume de Ballou) 123
Bank of Scotland 32
Banks, Sir Joseph 191
Bannockburn, Battle of 1
Barrier Treaty, 1713 77
Barrington, Colonel John 158
Basel, University of 23
bastard smallpox (chickenpox) 33
Bellini, Lorenzo 29
Bergen op Zoom 104–106
black bile 20, 21
Black Death 22
Black Watch 157
Blair, Professor Hugh 164, 165
bleeding (blood letting) 21, 33–35, 37, 68, 96,
        110, 123–129, 147, 148, 173, 175, 178, 179
Blenheim, Battle of 49, 53
blood, circulation of 24, 25, 28, 29
bloody flux see dysentery
Board of Ordnance 188, 189
Board of Trustees for Fisheries, Manufactures
        and Improvements in Scotland 32, 44
bodily humours 20

bodily temperaments 21
Boerhaave, Professor Herman 16, 18, 19, 28, 29, 41, 42, 116, 137
Bohemia, invasions of 61, 81, 144
Bologna, University of 14
Borelli, Giovani 29
Boston Tea Party 168
Boswell, Alexander 45
Boswell, James 72, 195n
Bothwell Bridge, Battle of 4, 5
Boyle, Robert 133, 185
Brabant 106
Braddock, General 152
Breda 84, 104, 108
Breda, Treaty of 151
British Pharmacopoeia 41, 197n
broadsword wounds 98
Brocklesby, Richard 161, 162, 203n
Bruges 57, 84
Brussels 77, 80, 84, 85
Buck's Club, Edinburgh 89
Bute, Earl of 164, 166, 203n
Byng, Admiral 143, 144

calculus, discovery of 25, 27
Cambridge University 28, 122
camphire 136
Canton, John 188
Cape Breton Island 153
Carlisle, siege of 91, 94
Carlyle, Rev Alexander 'Jupiter' 164, 166, 197n
Carteret, Lord 46, 52, 55, 58, 61, 66, 67, 70, 71, 81
Cathcart, Lord 160
Cavendish, Lord Charles 192
Cavendish, Henry 189
Celestial Magnetico-Electrico Bed 172
Cessford Castle 2
Chamberlain, Dr Paul 171
Charleroi, fortress of 101, 102
Charles I, King 3, 4
Charles II, King 3, 4
Charles II, King of Spain 8
Charles VI, Holy Roman Emperor 59
Charles VII, Holy Roman Emperor 81
Charles, Prince of Lorraine 52, 102
Charles Albert, King of Bavaria 60, 61, 73, 101
Chatham Barracks 161

chickenpox 33
cholera 36
Church of England 3
Church of Scotland 3
Clan Cameron 88
Clan Campbell 88
Clerk, Sir James 45, 192
Collinson, Peter 187, 188
Commonwealth, The 3
Company of Scotland 8
conjunctivitis 33
Connecticut Regiment 154, 156
continuous fever *see* typhus
Cook, Captain James 142, 164, 186
Cookson, Dr 187
Cooper, J. Fenimore 152
Cope, Sir John 89, 200n
Copernicus (Nicolaus Kopernikus) 25
Copley Medal 137, 165, 184–188
Country Party 11, 12
Court Party 11, 12
Covenanters 3, 4, 49
Cromwell, Oliver 161
Cullen, William 41, 42, 45, 137, 166
Culloden, Battle of 97–100, 184
Cumberland, Duke of 66, 81–87, 90–100, 102–104, 113, 114, 144, 145, 191

Dalrymple, James 49
Dalrymple, John *see* Stair, Earl of
Darien Scheme 8–11
de Haller, Albert 123
de Montcalm, General 154
de Saxe, Marshal 64, 76–78, 81–85, 98, 101–104
Delaval, Edward 188, 189
Derby, Jacobite retreat from 92
Dettingen, Battle of 66–74, 77, 80, 85, 87, 103, 110, 128
Devonshire, Duchess of 171
diarrhoea 58, 128
Dick, Sir Alexander 45, 166, 204n
digestion, studies of 140, 141
distemper 57, 100, 105, 160
Douglas, Charles 36
Douglas, Earl of 1, 2
dropsy, treatment of 177
Drummond, George 32
Drummond, John (physician) 36
Drummond, Lord John 94–96

Du Teillay (ship) 88
Dundas, Dr Thomas 160
Dutch War of Independence 17
Duval, Edward 188
dysentery (bloody flux) 68, 73, 80, 84,
 104–106, 109, 111, 117, 127, 128, 146,
 155, 158, 169

East India Company 31, 143
Edinburgh Castle 4
Edinburgh Pharmacopoeia 38–41, 45, 112
Edinburgh Royal Infirmary 45
Edinburgh University 14, 26, 42, 51, 113,
 122, 164, 171
Edward I, King 1
electorate, small number of 31
electricity, therapeutic uses of 171, 172, 186
Elizabeth (ship) 88
Elizabeth Farnese, Queen of Spain 60, 101
Ellis, John 55, 80
Eriskay 88
erysepilas 33
Eyre, William 55

Fahrenheit, Gabriel 201n
Falkirk, Battle of 95, 96
famine in Scotland 8, 30
Ferdinand, Prince of Brunswick 145, 146,
 148
55th Regiment 156
Flodden, Battle of 1
Flying Hospitals 65, 79, 152, 155, 199n
Fontenoy, Battle of 82–86, 98, 99
Forbes, Brigadier General 153
Forbes, Captain 159
Forbes, Duncan 87, 200n
Fordun, John of 22
Fort Augustus 78, 100
Fort Duquesne 152, 153
Fort George 78
Fort Louis (Guadeloupe) 157, 158
Fort Oswego 152, 153, 155, 156
Fort Stanwix 154
Fort Ticonderoga 153, 154
Fort William Henry 152
Frankfurt, Cartel of 72, 73, 84, 98
Franklin, Benjamin 142, 165–169, 171,
 187–190
Frascatorius 130
Frazer, J.A. (pseudonym of Sir John

Pringle) 62
Frederick II of Prussia 60, 61, 64, 81, 101,
 142, 144, 145
French Academy of Sciences 28
French and Indian War 153
Furnes, fortress of 77

Galen 13, 18, 19, 21, 23–25, 28, 29, 38, 105,
 122, 130, 170
Galilei, Galileo 25, 185, 187
gangrene 108
Garleis, Andrew 13
General Hospitals 78, 79, 93, 102, 120, 146,
 149
 Aberdeen 97, 100, 128
 Albany (USA) 152, 155
 Antwerp 84, 85
 Bechtheim 69
 Brussels 80, 84, 85, 107
 Fechenheim 69, 110
 Ghent 80, 81
 Halifax, Nova Scotia 152
 Ipswich 108, 110
 Lichfield 93
 Mons 83–85
 Nairn 98, 100, 109
 Neuwied 70, 110
 New York (USA) 152
 Oosterhout 108
 Osthofen 69
 Ravenstein 105
 Tournai 80, 81
Geneva Convention 73
George II, King 19, 32, 38, 44, 46, 48, 50,
 60, 61, 63, 65–68, 70, 71, 74, 75, 90,
 114, 143–146, 200n, 202n
 commanding army at Dettingen 66–68,
 70, 71
George III, King 7, 166
Ghent 57, 58, 62, 77, 80, 81, 111
Gibraltar 143
Glaubius, Professor David 18
Glasgow University 13
Glenfinnan 88, 89
Glorious Revolution, 1688 5, 14, 27, 49
Godolphin, Sidney 50
gonorrhoea 110, 115, 126
Gordon, Captain 159
Göttingen, University of 19, 51, 167, 190,
 192

gout 97, 125, 170, 171, 178, 179, 191
Gowan, Rev Thomas 18
Graham, James 171, 172
grain trade, growth of 44
Grammont (Flanders) 58
Grammont, Duke of 66, 67, 70
Great Plague (Black Death) 22
Gregory, David 26, 27, 196n
Gregory, James 26
Guadeloupe 157–160

haemorrhoids, treatment of 175
Hales, Sir Edward 177–179
Halidon Hill, Battle of 1
Halket, James 14
Hall, Sir James of Dunglass 12
Hamilton, William of Bangour 12
Handel, Georg Frederick 70, 142
Harderwyck, University of 14, 17
hartshorn, salts of 134–136
hartshorn, spirit of 124–126, 129, 134, 173
Harvey, William 24, 25
Hawke, Admiral Sir Edward 145, 146
Hawley, General Henry 94–96, 200n
heartburn 140, 141
Heberden, William 188, 192
Henry VIII, King 2
Hippocrates 13, 18–23, 28, 116, 122, 170, 195n
    theory of bodily humours 20, 21, 132
Hoechst 65
Holyroodhouse, Palace of 89
Home, Earls of 7, 11
Hope, Dr 40
Hope, Isaac 52
Hoppryngill family 1, 2
Hoppryngill, John de, of that Ilk 7, 12
Hopson, Major General 157
hospital fever 93, 97, 99, 105–110, 129, 130, 184
Houghton's Regiment 99, 100
Housz, Jan Ingen 51, 163
How, John 55
Howe, Commodore Richard 148
Huck, Richard 152, 154, 156, 158, 159, 192
Hume, David 45, 164, 167–169, 189, 192
Hume, John 164
Hunter, John 180
Hutton, Charles 187
Huxham, John 130

hydrocephalus 181

Incorporation of Surgeons and Barbers of
    Edinburgh 12, 13
influenza 191
Innes, Dr John 14, 15
inoculation, introduction of 171
intermittent fever 104–107, 110, 111, 116, 127, 136, 158
invasion of Britain 76, 87, 88, 143
ipecacuanha 127, 155, 180
Irish Brigade 75
Islay, Lord 31, 44, 48
Italian Renaissance 23

Jacobite Risings 31, 75, 85–100, 152, 161, 192
Jacobite students 17
Jacobites 16, 27, 31
jail fever (typhus) 91, 93, 99, 100, 114, 129, 130, 148, 184
James II, King 1
James IV, King 1, 14
James V, King 1
James VI and I, King 2, 3
James VII and II, King 9, 14, 31, 49, 74, 75
James VIII and III (the Old Pretender) 9, 10, 74, 75, 87, 89
Jefferson, Thomas 169
Jenkins' Ear, War of 46
Jenner, Edward 171
Johnson, Dr Samuel 72, 203n

Kames, Lord 45, 166
Kelly, Fr George 89
Ker, Patrick 37
Kerr, Robert 55
Kers of Cessford 2, 7, 11
Ketling, George 55
Khevenhöller, Count 53
Killing Times, The 5
King's College, Aberdeen 13, 14
King's Troops 154, 155
kink cough (whooping cough) 33
Knight, Gowin 187
Knocke, fortress of 77
Kopernikus, Nicolaus *see* Copernicus

Laffeld, Battle of 105, 108
Lake Champlain 153, 154
Lake George 152, 153

Lake Ontario 152, 153
laudanum (morphine), use of 128
Lauderdale, Earl of (James Maitland) 45
Law, William 42
leeches, use of 110, 123–126, 129, 179
Leiden, University of 14–18, 26–30, 41, 51,
    166, 198n
Lichfield 90–93
lightning conductors 187–189
Ligonier, Sir John (later Viscount) 63, 81,
    83, 90, 91, 102, 147
linen trade, growth of 44
Lion, HMS 88
Lobositz, Battle of 144
Locke, John 43
London Pharmacopoeia 38
Lords of the Isles 22
Loudoun, Dowager Countess of 50
Loudoun, Earl of 50, 51, 152, 153
Louis XIV, King of France 8, 9, 75
Louis XV, King of France 60, 61, 73, 75–78,
    81, 82, 87, 88, 94, 101, 103, 104, 146,
    167
    attempted invasion of Britain 76, 87, 88,
        143
    declaring war on Britain 76
    ill with smallpox 81
Louisburg, Cape Breton Island 153, 157
Louvain, University of 17
lumbago 33
lymph glands 130

Maastricht, fortress of 103–106
Maclaurin, Colin 26, 32, 45, 51, 52, 192
Macpherson, James 44, 164, 165, 203n
Mainz 66
Maison du Roi 149
Maitland, James *see* Lauderdale, Earl of
malaria 33, 57, 104, 158, 169
Malplaquet, Battle of 49
malt tax, 1713 10, 30
Maria Theresa, Empress of Austria 19, 51,
    59, 60, 101, 102, 143, 144
Marischal College, Aberdeen 14
Marlborough, Duke of 49, 50, 53, 148,
    149
Martinique 157
Mary Queen of Scots 2
Maskelyne, Nevil 186
Massachusetts Company 151

Massachusetts Regiment 154
Maurepas, Count 74
Maurice of Nassau, Prince 77
Maxwell, Dr 80
Mead, Richard 142, 171, 184
measles 99, 115
Medical Act, 1858 197n
Medical Essays and Observations 32–37, 45
Menin, fortress of 76
Mercator, Gerardus 53, 54
mercury, use of 171
Michaelis, John David 190
migraine, treatment of 175, 186
Miller, Dr William 160
Minorca 143, 144, 157
'Miss N' 111, 112, 201n
Mitchell, Sir Andrew 49–51, 56, 61–64, 71,
    111, 115, 121, 142, 184, 192
Mitchell, James 45
Monboddo, Lord 166
Monro, Alexander 15, 37, 203n
Monro, Donald 161, 203n
Mons, fortress of 101, 102
Montpellier, University of 14
Montreal 153–156
Moore, Admiral 157, 158
Mordaunt, General Sir John 145, 146
Morgagni, Giovanni 123, 202n
morphine (laudanum), use of 128
Morton, Earl of 179, 180, 191
mosquitoes 116
Mozart, Wolfgang Amadeus 142
Mudge, John 186
mumps 33
Murray, C. (matron) 55
Murray, Lord George 92, 94–96
musket bullet wounds 98

Namur, fortress of 102
National Covenant 3, 4
Neville's Cross, Battle of 1
New York Regiment 154, 156
Newcastle, Duke of 81, 86
Newgate Prison 114, 184
Newton, Sir Isaac 11, 25–28, 43, 45, 186,
    187, 196n
Newtonian Style 26, 196n
Nine Years' War 75
Noailles, Duke of 63, 65–68, 72, 77, 81
Northwest Passage, search for 52

Observations on the Diseases of the Army 115–132, 142, 150, 151, 161–163, 183, 184, 191–193
Old Bailey assizes 114
Oliver, Charlotte (wife of Sir John) 114
Oliver, Dr William 114, 201n
ophthalmia 33, 124
opium, use of 171
Orange, University of 14, 17
Ores, William 55
Osler, Sir William 181
Ossian, poetry of 164, 165
Oudenarde, Battle of 49, 84
Oxford University 27, 122

Padua, University of 14, 17, 24
Paracelsus (Theophrastus Bombast von Hohenheim) 23
Paris, University of 14
Pawlett, John 54
Pelham, Henry 87
Penn, William 165
Pennsylvanian Assembly 165, 166
peptic ulcers 180, 191
Perth, Duke of 92, 94
Peruvian Bark (quinine) 110, 124, 127, 128, 136, 137
Peters, Dr Charles 48, 54
Philip V, King of Spain 76
phlegm 20
phrenitis 124
Pitcairn, Archibald 14, 26–29
Pitt, William 153, 157
Plains of Abraham, Battle of 154
pleurisy 123
Pliny 53
Plummer, Professor Andrew 14–16, 37
Plutarch 53
Plymouth Company 151
pneuma (life breath) 21
pneumonia 33, 123, 126, 147
poppy, syrup of 126
Portsmouth Barracks 161
Pragmatic Army 60, 61, 63, 66, 67, 70, 77, 78, 83, 101–104
Pragmatic Sanction 59, 60, 73, 199n
Prestonpans, Battle of 89, 97
Priestley, Joseph 142, 163, 185
Pringle, David 2
Pringle, Francis (cousin of Sir John) 12, 13, 42
Pringle, Gilbert (brother of Sir John) 12
Pringle, James (great-uncle of Sir John) 12, 13
Pringle, Sir James (nephew of Sir John) 192
Pringle, Katherine (sister of Sir John) 12
Pringle, Sir John
    appointed Assistant Professor of Ethics 42, 43
    appointed Physician-General to the Army 55
    awarded Copley Medal 137
    awarded many honours 183
    at Battle of Culloden 98–100
    at Battle of Dettingen 67–73
    at Battle of Fontenoy 83–85
    birth and childhood 7, 10, 12
    criticisms of Dettingen campaign 71
    death 192
    in Edinburgh 32, 37
    elected FRCP 39, 163
    elected FRS 111, 163
    end of Army career 111, 150
    first experience of battle 67
    in Flanders 56–58, 61, 64, 104–108
    gift for languages 18
    inventing terms 'antiseptic' and 'septic' 134
    at Leiden University 16, 18, 19, 29
    at Lichfield 91–93
    made a baronet 163
    marriage 114, 142
    Medical Annotations 174, 178–182, 191
    mention of 'Miss N' 111, 112, 201n
    musical talent 142
    personal physician to Lord Stair 61
    Physician-in-Ordinary to King George III 183
    popular and generous host 113, 142, 163
    President of the Royal Society 184–190
    proposing Cartel of Frankfurt 72
    proposing neutrality for military hospitals 63
    publishing *Observations* 115–121, 183
    reforming Army hygiene 110, 118–121
    reforming Army medical services 78, 79, 110
    seeking commission in the Army 46, 48–54
    settling in London 113

at siege of Rochefort 145–147
at siege of St Malo 148–150
at St Andrews University 12
studies of digestion 141, 142
studies of putrefaction 126–140
use of pseudonym J.A. Frazer 62
wide circle of influential friends 45, 51, 142
with Hawley's army 95–97
working on *Edinburgh Pharmacopoeia* 38–40
Pringle, Sir John, 3rd Baron Stichill (father of above) 7, 10–12
Pringle, Margaret (sister of Sir John) 12
Pringle, Robert (brother of Sir John) 12, 192
Pringle, Robert (uncle of Sir John) 5
Pringle, Robert (great-great-grandfather of Sir John) 2, 3, 7
Pringle, Walter of Craigcrook (great-uncle of Sir John) 4, 49
Pringle, Walter of Greenknowe 4
Pringle, Wilfred (brother of Sir John) 12
Pringle family branches 7
Privy Council (England) 10, 11, 166
Privy Council (Scotland) 3
Ptolemy 25
pulmonary tuberculosis 126
purging 34, 37, 159, 160
putrefaction, study of 126–140

quack doctors 170–172
Quebec 142, 154, 168
quinine, use of 110, 124, 136
quinsy 33, 125

Ragman Roll 1
Ramillies, Battle of 49
Ramsay, Allan 44
Ranby, John 142
Rankenian Club, Edinburgh 45
Reformation, The 3
Regimental Infirmaries 79, 149, 155, 161, 162
remitting fever 84, 91, 96, 116, 147
Rheims, University of 14, 17
rheumatism 33, 110, 123, 125, 169, 171
River Hudson 153
River Jaar 102
River Maas 106
River Main 65, 66

River Meuse 102
River Rhine 65
River Scheldt 76, 82, 104
Robert the Bruce, King 1
Robertson, John 189
Robertson, William 45, 166
Rochefort 145–147, 149
Roxburghe, Dukes and Earls of 7, 11, 42, 48
Royal Bank of Scotland 44
Royal College of Physicians of Edinburgh 14, 15, 32, 36, 38, 39, 45, 112, 166, 192
Royal College of Physicians of London 38, 39, 47, 48, 163, 170
Royal Ecossais regiment 94
Royal Navy 44, 95, 106
Royal Society 11, 27, 28, 45, 112–114, 132, 135, 137, 141, 142, 163, 165, 166, 169, 184–188
Copley Medal 137, 165, 185–188
Rush, Benjamin 115, 131
Rutherford, Dr John 14, 15
Ruthven Barracks 78
Ryswick, Treaty of 75

Sackville, Lord George 148, 149
sagapenum resin 136
St Andrews University 12, 13, 26, 43, 194n
St Cecilia Hospital, Leiden 18
Saint-Germain-en-Laye, Château of 75
St Giles Cathedral, Edinburgh 45
St Lawrence River 154
St Leonards' College, St Andrews 12
St Malo 148–150
St Paul's Cathedral, London 188
Sandilands, Dr Alexander 55, 56, 62, 80
scabies 57, 110, 119, 150
Scheldt estuary 76, 82
Scotch Fusiliers 107
Scots Greys 107
Scots Magazine 45
Scott, William 42
Scottish Ministers' Widows Fund 26
scurvy 154, 159, 162, 186
Senegal 159
septic (first use of term) 134
setons, use of 126, 177, 201n
Sheridan, Sir Thomas 89
Sibbald,. Sir Robert 14, 38
Silesia, attacks on 60, 61, 81, 108, 144

Sinclair (or St Clair), Dr Andrew 14, 15
slow fever 34, 35
smallpox 57, 81, 99, 115, 147, 155
Smith, Adam 45, 166
Smollett, Tobias 44
Snake-root (ageratina) 128
Society for the Improvement of Medical
    Knowledge 32
Society of Antiquaries of Scotland 192
Sophia, Electress of Hanover 9
Spanish Succession, War of 49, 75
Squadrone Volante 11, 12, 42, 48, 52
Stair, Earl of (John Dalrymple) 48–54, 56,
    58, 61, 63, 65–67, 70, 71, 78, 198n
Stamp Act, 1765 167
Stanhope, Lord 166
Stevenson, Sir Archibald 38
Stevenson, John 45
Stichill, Baron of *see* Pringle, Sir John
Stichill House 7, 12
Stirling Bridge, Battle of 1
Stirling Castle 95
Stuart, Prince Charles Edward (the Young
    Pretender) 75, 76, 85, 87–100
    defeated at Culloden 97–100
    landing on Eriskay 88
    marching on Edinburgh 89
    retreating from Derby 92
Sullivan, John 89
Sydenham, Thomas 123, 127, 130
syphilis 110, 115, 126

tartar emetic, use of 127, 129
tertian ague 33, 34
theriaca 129
Thomson, James 44
Thunderer, HMS 178
tobacco trade, growth of 44
toothache 33
Tournai, fortress of 82
Turnbull, George 45
Tweeddale.Marquis of 11, 48
typhus (continuous or jail fever) 58, 68, 73,
    91, 93, 107, 109, 114, 148, 155, 169

Union of the Parliaments, 1707 5, 10, 11, 16,
    30, 31, 44
USA, campaigns in 151–156
Utrecht, University of 17

van Calcar, Jan Stephan 24
van Royen, Professor Adrian 18
van Swieten, Gerhard 19, 51, 123, 192
van Wesele, Andries (Vesalius) 24, 28
Vernon, Admiral 93
vinegar–whey, use of 124
violets, syrup of 133, 134
vitriol, elixir of 124
Voltaire 84
von Haller, Albrecht 19, 51, 192
von Hohenheim, Theophrastus
    Bombast *see* Paracelsus
von Pufendorf 43

Wade, Field Marshal George 71, 77, 78, 81,
    90–92
Wallace, William 1
Walpole. Robert 31, 46, 48, 60, 161
Walsh, John 185, 186
Walters, George 88
War Office 147
Wardens of the Marches 2
Washington, George 151, 152
Watson, William 188, 189
Watt, James 41, 166
West Indies, campaigns in 157–160
Westminster Convention 143, 144
Wharton, Mr 183, 192
whooping cough 181
Whytt, Dr Robert 179, 181
William III, King 5, 8, 11, 14, 17, 27, 49
William the Silent, Prince of Orange 17
Wilson, Benjamin 188, 189
Wintringham, Dr 80
Wishart, William 45
Wolfe, General James 142, 145, 153, 154,
    200n
worms, treatment of 174
Worms, Treaty of 73, 199n
wormwood, salt of 135, 136, 173
Wynn, Robert 55

Xenophon 53

yellow bile 20, 21
yellow fever 159, 160, 162, 191
York, James Duke of 5
Young, Dr 174
Ypres, fortress of 77